# HIGHER LEVEL
# GCSE MATHEMATICS

*By the same author (with Martin Amor)*

A Complete GCSE Computer Studies (Stanley Thornes 1987)

# HIGHER LEVEL GCSE MATHEMATICS

**John Fairhurst, B.Sc.**
Head of Mathematics
Farnborough Sixth Form College, Hampshire

**Stanley Thornes (Publishers) Ltd**

First published in 1987 by
Stanley Thornes (Publishers) Ltd
Educa House
Old Station Drive
Leckhampton
CHELTENHAM GL53 0DN

Reprinted 1988

British Library Cataloguing in Publication Data

Fairhurst, J.S.
    Higher level GCSE mathematics
    1. Mathematics—1961—
    I. Title
    510      QA 39.2

ISBN 0–85950–653–3

Typeset by Tech-Set, Gateshead, Tyne & Wear.
Printed and bound in Great Britain at The Bath Press, Avon.

# CONTENTS

# PREFACE

This book is written for those preparing for the higher level papers of the GCSE examination in Mathematics who expect to qualify with one of the four higher grades, A, B, C or D.

The author strongly sympathises with the main aims of the new exam — in particular, it is crucially important for youngsters to be presented with mathematics at a level appropriate to their abilities. Only then can they be expected to understand the underlying ideas and answer successfully most (if not all) of the questions subsequently asked of them. (The higher level GCSE 'target group' — those who will be graded 'B' — must show success in at least two-thirds of the examination.)

Equally, it is important that young people should see the relevance of what they are learning at school to the world in which we live. Though, having said that, much abstraction is unavoidable as the complexity of the mathematical theory increases. And abstraction is *desirable* if a young person's thinking skills are to develop and mature: at its highest level GCSE must in part act as a preparation for a possible further study in the Sixth Form and beyond.

Classroom practice must also keep abreast of modern developments such as the electronic calculator. Throughout this text, the use of calculators is not only presumed but is also actively encouraged — a number of exercises would be inappropriate without one.

Furthermore, as the Cockcroft committee noted, although routine practice of basic techniques and exposition from the teacher must always remain important components of good mathematics teaching, on their own they are not enough. Students need to be encouraged to discuss and think through problems for themselves and apply their knowledge to new situations. Accordingly, there are, embedded within the text, a number of problems and investigative type questions which I hope will give students opportunities for thinking more deeply about the mathematics they have learned.

All the main topics included by the five Examining Groups on their higher level syllabuses (first published in May 1986) are covered in detail. Little previous knowledge (except some facility with basic arithmetic) is assumed.

Each topic is broken down into manageable sections. Key definitions and mathematical methods are explained simply and illustrated by a large number of worked examples and carefully graded exercises. There is plenty of material to keep the most able busy, but at all times ideas and concepts are built up slowly and logically so that any student capable enough to be entered for GCSE at this level should be able to follow them.

The book is also intended to be a ready-made notebook from which students, working individually at home in the run up to the examination, may consolidate the key terms and techniques that were introduced to them throughout the course.

Often young people have been confused by the mathematics presented to them, not because the ideas themselves were too difficult, but because the concepts were developed too quickly. GCSE has addressed this problem by shortening the syllabuses. However, it is more than likely that the work on practical projects and open ended investigations will fully absorb the time saved.

It follows that classtime will remain as valuable as ever. It is hoped that this book will provide not just a classroom working text but also a concise set of explanations and examples that will save both students and teachers the need to use precious classtime copying notes from the board.

I would like to thank my former colleagues and pupils at George Abbot Comprehensive School, Guildford, for many helpful comments and suggested improvements on the initial draft of this book where most of the material was tested.

In particular, I would like to thank Janette Barstow and Stephen Lugg for their detailed criticisms of the typescript, Mark Berezicki, then of George Abbot Comprehensive School and Simon Evans, of Farnborough Sixth Form College, for working through the exercises, Richard Day for proof-reading, and Subhi Al-Zuhairi for encouragement and ideas.

Also I am indebted to the following Examining Boards for permission to use previous GCE and CSE examination questions:

**London and East Anglian Group**   (LEAG)
University of London Schools Examinations Department   (LU)
East Anglian Examinations Board   (EAEB)
London Regional Examinations Board   (LREB)

**Midland Examining Group**   (MEG)
University of Cambridge Local Examinations Syndicate   (CU)
Oxford and Cambridge Schools Examination Board   (O & C)
Southern Universities Joint Board   (SUJB)
East Midland Regional Examinations Board   (EMREB)
West Midlands Examination Board   (WMEB)

**Northern Examining Association**   (NEA)
Joint Matriculation Board   (JMB)
Associated Lancashire Schools Examining Board   (ALSEB)
North Regional Examinations Board   (NREB)
North West Regional Examinations Board   (NWREB)
Yorkshire and Humberside Regional Examinations
   Board   (YHREB)

**Southern Examining Group**   (SEG)
Oxford Delegacy of Local Examinations   (Ox)
Associated Examining Board   (AEB)
Southern Regional Examinations Board   (SREB)
South East Regional Examinations Board (SEREB)
South Western Examinations Board   (SWEB)

**Welsh Joint Education Committee**   (WJEC)

Responsibility for errors in the answers to these and other questions is mine alone.

John Fairhurst
January 1987

# 1 NUMBERS

## TYPES OF NUMBERS

Numbers that are used in the normal, simple process of counting, i.e. $1, 2, 3, 4, 5, 6, 7$, etc., are called *natural numbers*. Natural numbers are necessarily whole numbers, or *integers*. However, the set of integers includes zero and negative whole numbers as well. Thus, of the set of numbers $\{-4, -3, -2, -1, 0, +1, +2\}$ only $+1$ and $+2$ are natural numbers although *all* are examples of integers.

Numbers that are not integers may be *fractions* (e.g. $\frac{3}{4}$ or $-2\frac{1}{4}$) or *decimal fractions* (e.g. $0.38$ or $-1.1$).

Any integer or fraction is a *rational number*. So, too, are decimal numbers that terminate (such as $0.38$ or $1.1$) and decimal numbers that recur (e.g. $0.333\,333\ldots$ or $2.182\,182\,182\ldots$). Decimals that go on for ever, with *no* recurring pattern, are called *irrational numbers*. Two examples of irrational numbers are $\pi$ and $\sqrt{2}$.

All these types of numbers — natural numbers, integers, fractions, decimals, rational numbers, irrational numbers — are *real numbers* that may be shown as points on a *number line* (see Fig. 1.1).

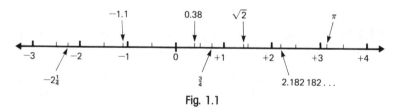

**Fig. 1.1**

Remember that 0 is an integer and is therefore both a real and a rational number.

## RELATING NUMBERS

The *sum* of two numbers is found by *adding* them together. Thus the sum of 3 and 2 is $3 + 2 = 5$.

The *difference* between two numbers is found by *subtracting* the smaller number from the larger one. Thus the difference between 3 and 2 is $3 - 2 = 1$.

The *product* of two numbers is found by *multiplying* them. The product of 3 and 2 is $3 \times 2 = 6$.

Take great care when combining negative numbers. Remember in particular the following points:

(*i*) Adding a negative number is like subtracting a positive one:
$$6 + (-2) = 6 - (+2) = +4$$

(*ii*) Subtracting a negative number is like adding a positive one:
$$6 - (-2) = 6 + (+2) = +8$$

(*iii*) Multiplying a negative number by a positive number gives a negative number:
$$6 \times (-2) = -12$$

(*iv*) But multiplying two negative numbers together gives a positive result:
$$-6 \times (-2) = +12$$

(*v*) Division behaves exactly like multiplication:
$$6 \div (-2) = -3$$
$$-6 \div (-2) = +3.$$

**EXERCISE 1a**

1. What is an *integer*? Which of the following numbers are integers: $7, 7.7, -2, \frac{2}{7}, 0.18, \sqrt{2}$?

2. What is a *real* number? Which of the following numbers are real: $3, 5.23, 0.555\,555\ldots, \frac{5}{9}, -3, 0.000\,01$?

3. Is zero
   (a) a natural number
   (b) an integer
   (c) a real number
   (d) a rational number?

4. What is an *irrational* number? Which of these are irrational: $0.151\,151\ldots, 0, -1\frac{1}{2}, \frac{3}{4}, \sqrt{2}, \pi, \sqrt{4}$?

5. Work out (without a calculator):
   (a) $12 + (-3)$
   (b) $2 - 5$
   (c) $6 - (-8)$
   (d) $9 + (-3)$
   (e) $9 - (-3)$
   (f) $-12 + (-4)$
   (g) $-11 - (-2)$
   (h) $8 \times (-6)$
   (i) $10 \div (-5)$
   (j) $-3 \times (-7)$
   (k) $-16 \div (-8)$
   (l) $36 \div (-6)$.

2

6. Find the sum of 15 and 5. What is their product? What is their difference?

7. Find
   (a) the product of 10 and −11    (b) the sum of 10 and −11.
   What is the difference between your answers to (a) and (b)?

8. The product of two numbers is 24. The difference between them is 10. Can you find the two numbers?

9. $\sqrt{3}$ is an irrational number but $\sqrt{4}$ is not. Explain.
   Use a calculator to find the following:
   (a) $\sqrt{121}$        (b) $\sqrt{12.1}$        (c) $\sqrt{1.21}$
   (d) $\sqrt{0.121}$      (e) $\sqrt{14.4}$        (f) $\sqrt{1.44}$
   Which of your answers are irrational?

10. Use the $\pi$ button on your calculator to write down the value of $\pi$ to as many decimal places as possible.

    Is the value you write down a rational or irrational number? Explain.

    Now use your calculator to find the value of 22/7. Does $\pi = 22/7$? Find the difference between $\pi$ and 22/7. Which of the following is the best approximation to $\pi$, and which is the worst:
    (a)  223/71        (b)  333/106        (c)  355/113

11. Write any number you choose into your calculator. Then keep taking the square root of the square root of the square root of the square root ... What happens?

    Does the same thing happen for any number? Does it matter whether the number you start with is more or less than one?

    What happens if the number you start with is negative?

12. Write any number you choose into your calculator (and store it in memory if your machine has one). Either by repeated multiplication or by using the power button find your number squared, cubed, to the power of four, five ...

    What happens this time? Does it matter whether the number you start with is more or less than one?

    What happens if the number is negative?

13. (a) What temperature is indicated by the thermometer in Fig. 1.2?

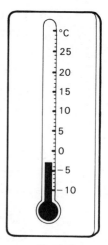

Fig. 1.2

(b) If the temperature falls 6 degrees before it reaches its overnight low, what will the temperature be then?

By mid-afternoon the following day the temperature has risen 9 degrees above the reading shown.

(c) What is the temperature that afternoon?

(d) What is the difference between the afternoon temperature and the overnight low?

14. On the 29th March I had £85.50 in my account with the bank. On the 30th I withdraw £100 and on the same day my mortgage repayment of £192.30 is paid automatically. By how much have I overdrawn?

On the 31st March my salary of £730 is paid directly into the account. How much do I now have in the bank?

15. Nick likes to go pot-holing and hill-walking in his spare time. He keeps a record of his achievements over one Easter holiday. His entries in his log book show

| Day | Set Out | Return | Destination | Height Reached |
|---|---|---|---|---|
| Easter Holidays | ~ | ~ | The Peaks | (metres) |
| Good Friday | 0830 | 2045 | Derwent | −38 |
| Saturday | 0730 | 1700 | Kinder Scout | 727 |
| Easter Sunday | 1200 | 1730 | Alport | −41 |
| Easter Monday | 0900 | 1500 | Bleaklow | 705 |

Fig. 1.3

(a)  Was he hill-walking or pot-holing on Easter Monday?

(b)  How much higher was he on Saturday than Friday?

(c)  How much lower was he on Sunday than Monday?

# FACTORS

A *factor* of a number divides exactly into it to give a whole number. For example, 5 is a factor of 40 since $40 \div 5 = 8$. Similarly, 2 is a factor of 40 since $40 \div 2 = 20$. On the other hand, 7 is *not* a factor of 40 since $40 \div 7$ does *not* give a whole number. 40 has eight factors {1, 2, 4, 5, 8, 10, 20, 40}.

A *prime* number is one that has exactly two factors: itself and one. For example, 13 is a prime number since it has only two factors: 13 and 1.

2 is also prime — the only even prime number, since all other even numbers have 2 as a factor.

1 is a special case. It is *not* regarded as a prime number since it has just *one* factor: itself.

The *highest common factor*, or HCF, of two numbers is the highest number that is a factor of both. For example, the factors of 40 are

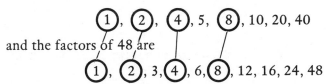

and the factors of 48 are

The factors common to both 40 and 48 are 1, 2, 4 and 8. The *highest* common factor is 8.

## Prime Factors

A number can also be broken down into a set of *prime factors*, i.e. the set of prime numbers which multiplied together give the number in question. Often it will be necessary to repeat the same prime factor several times; prime factors repeated can be shown as a power.

**Example**   $40 = 2 \times 20$.

Now 2 is a prime factor, but 20 is not; it has factors $2 \times 10$, so continuing:

$$40 = 2 \times 2 \times 10$$

But 10 is still not prime, though its
factors, $2 \times 5$ are. We get:

$$40 = 2 \times 2 \times 2 \times 5$$

Using powers, or *index notation*:

$$40 = 2^3 \times 5$$

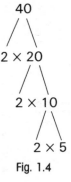

Fig. 1.4

**Example**  90 has factors 2 and 45

i.e. $\qquad\qquad 90 = 2 \times 45$

2 is a prime, but 45 has factors 3 and 15.

Hence $\qquad\qquad 90 = 2 \times 3 \times 15$

3 is also prime but 15 has prime factors 3 and 5

Hence $\qquad\qquad 90 = 2 \times 3 \times 3 \times 5$

or $\qquad\qquad 90 = 2 \times 3^2 \times 5$

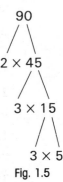

Fig. 1.5

Note that any natural number (except 1) is either itself a prime
number or can be written as a product of prime numbers.

## MULTIPLES

If one number is a factor of a second number, then the second is
said to be a *multiple* of the first.

You might like to think of factors and multiples as opposites.

So, 4 is a multiple of 2 as 2 is a factor of 4. Similarly, 6, 8, 10,
12 ... are all multiples of 2 since they all have 2 as a factor.

The number 12 is also a multiple of 1, 3, 4, 6 and of itself, 12.

The *lowest common multiple*, or LCM, of two numbers is the
lowest number that is a multiple of *both*. For example, multiples
of 6 are

$$6, 12, 18, \textcircled{24}, 30, 36, 42, \textcircled{48}, 54, 60, 66, \textcircled{72}, 78, \ldots$$

and multiples of 8 are

$$8, 16, \textcircled{24}, 32, 40, \textcircled{48}, 56, 64, \textcircled{72}, 80, 88, 96, 104, \ldots$$

The multiples common to both 6 and 8 are 24, 48, 72, ... The
*lowest* common multiple is 24.

1. Complete this list of factors of 36:
   1, 2, 3, −, −, −, −, −, 36.

2. Complete this list of factors of 108:
   1, −, −, −, −, −, 12, −, 27, −, −, 108.

3. What is the HCF of 36 and 108?

4. List all the factors of
   (a) 16      (b) 24.

5. What is the HCF of 16 and 24?

6. List the factors of
   (a) 13      (b) 17.
   What sort of numbers are these?

7. Which of the following are prime numbers:
   1, 2, 3, 4, 5, 7, 9, 11, 15, 27?

8. Can an even number be prime?

9. List all the prime numbers less than 50.

10. Which of the following are factors of 84:
    1, 2, 4, 5, 7, 8, 9, 11, 21?

11. What do the numbers 2, 5, 29, 31 and 47 have in common?

12. Find all the prime numbers between 120 and 140.

13. Show that $2^4 \times 3 = 48$. Find the prime factors of the following numbers:
    (a) 18      (b) 66      (c) 84      (d) 144

14. What is the smallest number to have 2, 3, 5 and 7 as prime factors?

15. What is the largest prime factor of 2178? What is the largest odd factor?

16. What are the prime factors of
    (a) 12      (b) 24      (c) 36.
    Can you work out how to use prime factors to find the HCF?
    Try your method on several sets of numbers of your own choosing.

17. (a) Find the prime factors of 102. By separating the factors into two groups in as many ways as possible, find the complete set of factors of 102.
    (b) Find in the same way the complete set of factors of
    (i) 30   (ii) 12   (iii) 75.

18. Complete this list of multiples of 5:
    5, 10, −, −, −, −, 35, −, −−, 50.

19. List six multiples of
    (a) 6         (b) 15.

20. What is the LCM of
    (a) 5 and 6       (b) 6 and 15.

21. Find the LCM of
    (a) 3 and 4     (b) 6 and 8     (c) 6 and 12.

22. Find the LCM and the HCF of 3, 5 and 15.

23. Find the LCM and the HCF of 10, 25 and 60.

24. List the prime factors of
    (a) 10     (b) 25     (c) 60.

    Can you work out a way of using prime factors to find the
    LCM of several numbers? Try your method on several sets of
    numbers of your own choosing.

## NUMBER PATTERNS

Much of the usefulness of mathematics depends upon our being
able to find an underlying pattern from which we can make some
generalisation. Once proven and tested, that generalisation can save
a lot of subsequent work!

Some number patterns are very simple. For example, the series
2, 4, 6, 8, ...

Others are less so, for example 1, 3, 6, 10, 15, ... These are called
the *triangle numbers*, from the pattern of dots that can be made
up with them:

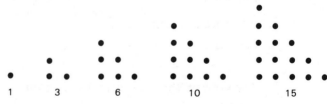

Fig. 1.6   The Triangle Numbers

Notice that the difference between two neighbouring terms follows
a simple pattern:

$$
\begin{array}{cccccc}
1 & & 3 & & 6 & & 10 & & 15 \ldots \\
 & +2 & & +3 & & +4 & & +5 & & +6 \ldots
\end{array}
$$

8

The numbers  1, 4, 9, 16, 25, 36, 49, ...  are known as the *square numbers* or *perfect squares* being simply,  $1^2, 2^2, 3^2, 4^2, 5^2, 6^2, 7^2 ...$

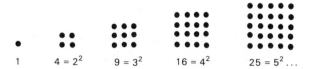

Fig. 1.7    The Square Numbers

In the same way the numbers 1, 8, 27, 64, 125, 216, ... are known as the *cube numbers* or *perfect cubes* being  $1^3, 2^3, 3^3, 4^3, 5^3, 6^3, ...$

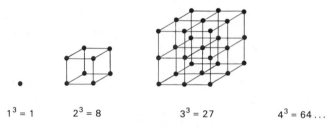

Fig. 1.8    The Cube Numbers

One important pattern of numbers is the *Fibbonacci sequence* in which, after the first two 1s, each number in the sequence is the sum of the previous two. Thus the third term is  $1 + 1 = 2$; the fourth is  $1 + 2 = 3$; the fifth is  $2 + 3 = 5$  and so on to give the sequence:  1, 1, 2, 3, 5, 8, 13, 21, ...

Another important pattern is *Pascal's triangle*. Each row of numbers in the triangle begins and ends with a 1. The numbers that make up the row are found by adding two numbers in the row above, as shown.

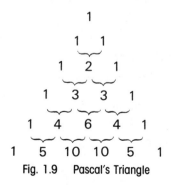

Fig. 1.9    Pascal's Triangle

1. Continue the sequences given in the text for a further five terms:
    (a)  the triangle numbers:  1, 3, 6, 10, 15, —, —, —, —, —.
    (b)  the square numbers:  1, 4, 9, 16, 25, —, —, —, —, —.
    (c)  The Fibbonacci sequence:  1, 1, 2, 3, 5, 8, 13, —, —, —, —.

2. Copy the numbers in Pascal's triangle (Fig. 1.9) and write in the next four rows. Check that your fourth additional row would lead correctly to the next row which is:

    1   10   45   120   210   252   210   120   45   10   1

    Now check the diagonals of the triangle. What patterns can you find?

3. Add up the numbers in each row of Pascal's triangle. What is the pattern?

4. Find $11^2$, $11^3$, $11^4$. How are your answers related to Pascal's triangle? Try for higher powers and explain why the relationship breaks down.

5. Write down the next five numbers in each of the following sequences.
    (a)  1, 4, 7, 10, 13, 16, —, —, —, —, —, . . .
    (b)  19, 15, 11, 7, 3, −1, —, —, —, —, —, . . .
    (c)  −31, −27, −23, −19, −15, −11, —, —, —, —, —, . . .
    (d)  3, 4, 6, 9, 13, 18, —, —, —, —, —, . . .
    (e)  2, 6, 12, 20, 30, —, —, —, —, —, . . .
    (f)  1, 8, 27, 64, —, —, —, —, —, —, —, . . .
    (g)  2, 8, 18, 32, 50, 72, —, —, —, —, —, . . .
    (h)  −2, 1, 6, 13, 22, 33, —, —, —, —, —, . . .
    (i)  2, 3, 5, 7, 11, 13, —, —, —, —, —, . . .
    (j)  16, 19, 14, 21, 12, 23, —, —, —, —, —, . . .
    (k)  11, 9, 15, 5, 19, 1, —, —, —, —, —, . . .
    (l)  −3, 4, 1, 8, 5, 12, —, —, —, —, —, . . .

6. Find as many mathematical rules as you can for continuing the sequence  2, 4, 8, . . .

7. Draw the next two of these patterns.

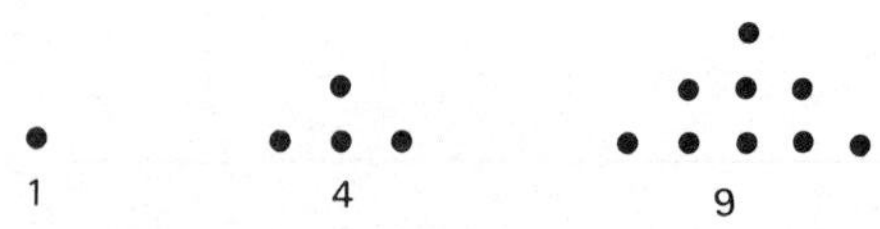

Fig. 1.10

8. Draw the next two of these patterns.

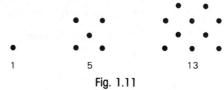

1    5    13

Fig. 1.11

9. Draw the next two of these patterns.

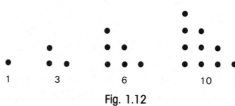

1    3    6    10

Fig. 1.12

Use the patterns of Fig. 1.12 to show that the sum of two consecutive triangle numbers is a square number.

10. Fig. 1.13 illustrates a relationship between odd numbers and square numbers.

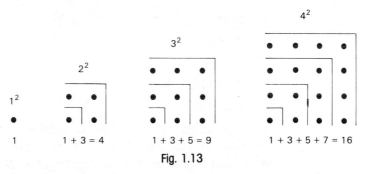

1    1 + 3 = 4    1 + 3 + 5 = 9    1 + 3 + 5 + 7 = 16

Fig. 1.13

Show that the pattern continues for 5, 6, 7, ... Describe this relationship in your own words.

Use it to work out the following, avoiding long-winded additions:

(a) $1 + 3 + 5 + \ldots + 23$    (b) $1 + 3 + 5 + \ldots + 11$

(c) $13 + 15 + \ldots + 23$    (d) $25 + 27 + \ldots + 39$.

11. Fig. 1.14 illustrates another pattern leading to the square numbers.

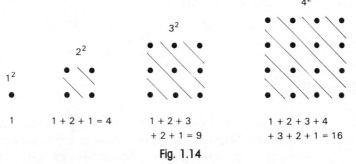

1    1 + 2 + 1 = 4    1 + 2 + 3 + 2 + 1 = 9    1 + 2 + 3 + 4 + 3 + 2 + 1 = 16

Fig. 1.14

Show that the pattern continues for 5, 6, 7, ... Describe the pattern in your own words.

Use the result to find $1 + 2 + 3 + ... + 19 + 20 + 19 + ... + 3 + 2 + 1$.

12. $1 + 2 + 3 = \dfrac{3 \times 4}{2}$

$1 + 2 + 3 + 4 = \dfrac{4 \times 5}{2}$

$1 + 2 + 3 + 4 + 5 = \dfrac{5 \times 6}{2}$

Investigating this pattern for longer chains of numbers. Does it still hold? Use your result to find, without long-winded addition, the following

(a) $1 + 2 + 3 + 4 + ... + 99 + 100$

(b) $50 + 51 + 52 + ... + 99 + 100$.

13. $1^5 - 1 = 0 = 30 \times 0$

$2^5 - 2 = 30 = 30 \times 1$

$3^5 - 3 = 240 = 30 \times 8$

$4^5 - 4 = ?$

Investigate this pattern for larger numbers. (You will need a calculator to find the powers.) Is the result always a multiple of 30? Can you predict *which* multiple of 30?

14. $1^2 + 1 + 41 = 43$

$2^2 + 2 + 41 = 47$

$3^2 + 3 + 41 = 53$

Check that 43, 47 and 53 are all prime numbers.

Does $4^2 + 4 + 41$ also give a prime number?

Does $5^2 + 5 + 41$?

Does $6^2 + 6 + 41$?

Investigate further.

Can you think of a number for which the pattern *could not* work?

## PLACE VALUE

The number 7 6 7 3 means 'seven thousand six hundred and seventy-three'. Each digit in the number has a *place value*, i.e. it is recognised to mean thousands or hundreds or tens or units according to its place in the number. Thus, in the number 7 6 7 3 the digit '7' means seven thousands in the first position and seven tens in the other.

Notice especially how the number 7 6 7 3 0 differs from 7 6 7 3; the value of every digit is changed by the extra zero at the end of the number.

| Place value | Ten thousands 10 000 | Thousands 1000 | Hundreds 100 | Tens 10 | Units 1 |
|---|---|---|---|---|---|
| Digit | — | 7 | 6 | 7 | 3 |
| | 7 | 6 | 7 | 3 | 0 |

If a zero is placed at the right of 7 6 7 3, each digit moves one place to the left and takes a new place value of ten times the previous value. Thus 7 6 7 3 0 is ten times larger than 7 6 7 3.

A decimal point is used to locate the units column (immediately to its left). The place values of the digits to the right of the decimal point are then fractions: tenths, hundredths, thousandths, ... So 7 6 . 7 3 means seven tens, six units, seven tenths and three hundredths.

| Place value | Hundreds 100 | Tens 10 | Units 1 | • | Tenths $\frac{1}{10}$ | Hundredths $\frac{1}{100}$ |
|---|---|---|---|---|---|---|
| Digit | | 7 | 6 | • | 7 | 3 |
| | 7 | 6 | 7 | • | 3 | |

Again, notice that shifting the digits to the left, so that the number reads 7 6 7 . 3, increases the place value of each digit ten times. Thus

$$7 6 . 7 3 \times 10 = 7 6 7 . 3$$

You will probably prefer to think of moving the decimal point of the number, rather than the digits; multiplying by ten is therefore equivalent to moving the point one place to the right.

$$7 6 \cdot 7 3 \times 10 = 7 6 7 \cdot 3$$

Your calculator will also use a *floating decimal point*:

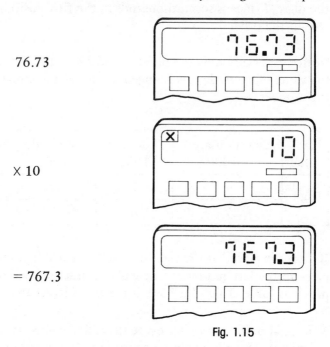

76.73

× 10

= 767.3

Fig. 1.15

Moving the decimal point to the left is equivalent to division, since the place value of every digit is decreased

$$76 \cdot 73 \div 10 = 7 \cdot 673$$

Moving the decimal point *two* places right or left effectively multiplies or divides the number by 100 (i.e. 10 × 10); moving *three* places effectively multiplies or divides the number by 1000 (10 × 10 × 10), and so on.

$$7673 \div 100 = 76.73$$

$$123 \div 1000 = 0.123$$

Understanding place value is crucial to many everyday uses of number. For example, reading a scale:

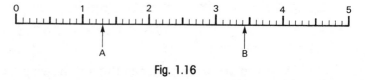

Fig. 1.16

Pointer A indicates a mark on the scale; it is not too hard to read: 1.3.

Pointer B lies between two marks on the scale, between 3.4 and 3.5. Since the pointer lies slightly to the left of the mid-point we shall estimate the reading to be 3.44. That is, the distance representing the 0.1 difference between 3.4 and 3.5 is further subdivided (into hundredths) and a value given 'by eye'.

Similarly, many meters use dials to indicate numbers. (Check your electricity or gas meters at home.) Sometimes the dials turn anti-clockwise. This meter is showing

$5 \times 10\,000,$    $8 \times 1000,$    $3 \times 100,$    $2 \times 10,$

$9 \times 1$   and   5 tenths

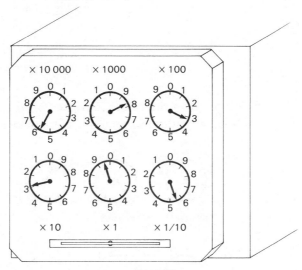

Fig. 1.17

Thus the reading is:   58 329.5.

**EXERCISE 1d**   1. Write down the following numbers in figures:

(a) eight hundred and nine

(b) four thousand and forty

(c) fifty-five thousand and fifty

(d) seven hundred and one thousand, one hundred and seven.

2. Write down the values indicated on the scale by the pointers A, B, C, D. (A and B are exact; you will need to estimate C, and D.)

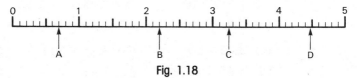

Fig. 1.18

3. Write down the values indicated on this scale by the pointers A, B, C, D. (Beware: this is an awkward scale!)

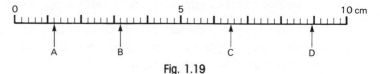

Fig. 1.19

4. What is the reading on this micrometer?

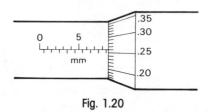

Fig. 1.20

5. Write down the values indicated on the following dials. (Again, beware, some move anticlockwise!)

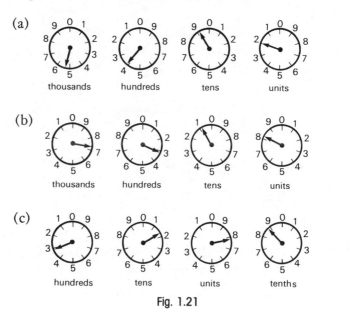

Fig. 1.21

Work out with*out* a calculator:

6. (a) 23 × 10          (b) 23 × 100          (c) 23 × 10 000

   (d) 2.3 × 100        (e) 2.3 × 1000        (f) 2.3 × 10 000

7. (a) 2300 ÷ 10        (b) 2300 ÷ 100        (c) 2300 ÷ 1000

   (d) 2300 ÷ 10³       (e) 2300 ÷ 10⁴        (f) 2300 ÷ 10⁷

8. (a) 3.45 × 10        (b) 3.45 × 100        (c) 3.45 × 10 000

   (d) 3.45 × 10³       (e) 3.45 × 10⁵        (f) 3.45 × 10⁸

9. (a) $345 \div 10$      (b) $345 \div 100$      (c) $345 \div 10\,000$

   (d) $345 \div 10^3$      (e) $345 \div 10^5$      (f) $345 \div 10^6$

10. (a) $0.002 \times 10$      (b) $0.002 \times 100$      (c) $0.002 \times 1000$

    (d) $0.002 \div 10$      (e) $0.002 \div 100$      (f) $0.002 \div 1000$

## WORKING WITH DECIMALS

### Addition and Subtraction

Decimal points must be placed underneath each other.

**Example** $3.56 - 0.0503$.

Rewrite 3.56 as 3.5600 then:

$$
\begin{array}{r}
^{5\ 9\ 10}\\
3.5\,6\,0\,0\\
-0.0\,5\,0\,3\\
\hline
3.5\,0\,9\,7
\end{array}
$$

### Multiplication

To multiply two decimals:

(*i*)   multiply the numbers, disregarding the decimal points;

(*ii*)  count the total number of decimal places;

(*iii*) place the decimal point in your answer to (*i*) so that it has the same number of decimal places that you counted in (*ii*).

**Example** $0.0003 \times 0.02$.

(*i*)   $3 \times 2 = 6$

(*ii*)  0.0003 has 4 decimal places

     0.02   has 2 decimal places

     Total:     6 decimal places

(*iii*) Place a decimal point in (*i*) so that there are 6 decimal places: $0.000\,006$

### Division

To divide two decimals:

(*i*)   move the decimal point of the dividing number to the right, to make it a whole number;

17

(ii) compensate for (i) by moving the decimal point of the other (divided) number in *exactly* the same way;

(iii) divide.

**Example** $5.49 \div 0.9$.

(i) $0.9 \to 9$      by moving the decimal point one place to the right

(ii) $5.49 \to 54.9$      by moving the decimal point one place to the right, as in (i)

(iii) $54.9 \div 9$      $= 6.1$

**EXERCISE 1e**    *Without* using a calculator, work out:

1. (a) $5.41 + 0.39$          (b) $4.51 - 3.78$
   (c) $2.1 + 0.009$          (d) $2.1 - 0.009$

2. (a) $2.3 \times 0.02$          (b) $0.023 \times 0.02$
   (c) $5.4 \div 0.002$          (d) $0.054 \div 0.002$

3. (a) $7.11 - 6.031$          (b) $102.1 + 0.0002$
   (c) $121 \times 0.0011$          (d) $121 \div 0.0011$

4. (a) $0.001\,44 \div 1.2$          (b) $2 \div 0.0005$
   (c) $10.8 \div 0.009$          (d) $1080 \div 0.036$

5. (a) $(0.003)^2$          (b) $(0.01)^2$
   (c) $0.013 \times 90$          (d) $1001 \times 10.01$

6. (a) $\dfrac{0.04 \times 0.12}{0.24}$          (b) $\dfrac{3.0 \times 6.3}{0.009}$
   (c) $\dfrac{5.6 \times 0.2}{0.08}$          (d) $\dfrac{2.7 \times 0.1}{0.03}$

7. (a) $\dfrac{0.03 - 0.003}{0.3}$          (b) $\dfrac{1.12 + 0.09}{1.1}$
   (c) $\dfrac{2.02 + 0.18}{0.0022}$          (d) $\dfrac{3.12 + 1.08}{0.007}$

8. (a) $\dfrac{(0.04)^2}{0.016}$          (b) $\dfrac{0.288}{(1.2)^2}$
   (c) $\dfrac{(0.05)^2}{0.125}$          (d) $\dfrac{(0.03)^2}{0.9}$

9. (a) $\dfrac{0.003 \times 0.4}{0.2 \times 1.2}$  (b) $\dfrac{0.6 \times 1.08}{0.9 \times 0.4}$

   (c) $\dfrac{0.8 \times 0.9}{0.72}$  (d) $\dfrac{0.08 \times 0.006}{9.6 \times 0.2}$

10. (a) $\dfrac{1.5 - 0.06}{0.36}$  (b) $\dfrac{1.1 - 0.02}{0.09}$

   (c) $\dfrac{0.8 - 0.08}{0.3 - 0.18}$  (d) $\dfrac{0.68 + 0.07}{(0.5)^2}$

## APPROXIMATING DECIMALS

Sometimes, a number is given to more decimal places (d.p.) than is desirable, in which case it may be *rounded off* provided that some indication of the rounding off process is given.

How a number rounds off in the *first* decimal place depends only upon the digit in the *second*; rounding off in the *second* place depends only upon the digit in the *third*; and so on. The digits 0, 1, 2, 3, 4 round off leaving the digit in the preceding place unaltered. The digits 5, 6, 7, 8, 9 round *up* increasing the digit in the preceding place by 1.

**Examples**
$$0.1465 \approx 0.147 \quad \text{(3 d.p.)}$$
$$0.1465 \approx 0.15 \quad \text{(2 d.p.)}$$
$$0.1465 \approx 0.1 \quad \text{(1 d.p.)}$$

Alternatively, we may wish to round off to a given number of *significant figures* (s.f.). The digits 1, 2, 3, 4, 5, 6, 7, 8, 9 are *always* significant. Zero is significant when it is part of the number; it is *not* significant when it is a 'spacer', locating the decimal point, and maintaining the place value of the other digits.

**Examples** 234.7    has *four* significant figures

203.85    has *five* significant figures

0.000 234    has *three* significant figures (the zeros are 'spacers' only)

0.0560    also has *three* significant figures since the last digit, 0, is part of the number, indicating that it is neither 0.0561 nor 0.0559.

Always declare an approximation whenever you make one, otherwise people will assume your numbers are exact.

**Example**

$$2342 \approx 2340 \quad (3 \text{ s.f.})$$
$$\approx 2300 \quad (2 \text{ s.f.})$$
$$\approx 2000 \quad (1 \text{ s.f.})$$

## ESTIMATION

Rounding off numbers to one significant figure is useful when a rough estimate of some calculation is required.

Many practical situations require such estimates: perhaps you do not have a calculator to hand, perhaps you just want a 'quick' answer — or perhaps it is simply not possible to take accurate measurements.

**Example** Without using a calculator, estimate, to one significant figure, the answer to $219.3 \times 587.14$.

Very roughly

$$219.3 \approx 200$$

and

$$587.14 \approx 600$$

So

$$219 \times 587.14 \quad \approx 200 \times 600 = 120\,000$$

So to *one* significant figure, the answer to $219.3 \times 587.14$ is 100 000.

## CALCULATORS

It is good practice to make this sort of estimate whenever you use a calculator — after all, it is very easy to push a wrong button! For example, the decimal point may not register when I enter 219.3 (or so I think) into my calculator. It says

$$219.3 \times 587.14 = 1\,287\,598$$

But, because we made an estimate (and so are expecting an answer of around 100 000) we know that this answer is ten times too large and the error in the use of the calculator is apparent. Double checking, we find

$$219.3 \times 587.14 = 128\,759.8$$

which *is* about what we expected.

Most calculators display numbers to eight or ten figures. This is too many for GCSE, so your calculations will usually need to be rounded off. A good rule is work to *five* significant figures throughout a problem and give *answers* to *three* significant figures.

**Example** An eight-digit calculator shows $\sqrt{3}$ to be 1.732 050 8. So write down in your working $\sqrt{3} = 1.7321$ (rounding up the fifth digit because of the 5 in the next place).

Give as your answer

$$\sqrt{3} = 1.73 \quad (3 \text{ s.f.})$$

**EXERCISE 1f**

1. Round off to 2 d.p.:
   (a) 7.767    (b) 9.785    (c) 10.005    (d) 10.004
   (e) 6.666    (f) 7.294    (g) 7.295    (h) 7.2945.

2. Round off to 3 s.f.:
   (a) 5.0467    (b) 12.123    (c) 121.5    (d) 10.06
   (e) 10.03    (f) 12.08    (g) 12.02    (h) 100.5.

3. Round off the following, (a) to 3 d.p. and (b) to 3 s.f.:
   (i) 0.1234    (ii) 0.001 234    (iii) 123.4567.

4. How many significant figures are there in the numbers
   (a) 123    (b) 1203    (c) 1230    (d) 123.0
   (e) 0.001 002 3    (f) 0.001 00    (g) 3.00    (h) 3
   (i) 6    (j) 6.0    (k) 10.0    (l) 10.00?

5. Without using a calculator, estimate to *one* significant figure only the results of the following calculations:
   (a) $231 \times 170$    (b) $0.9157 \times 6017$    (c) $975.7 \times 1109$
   (d) $53.97 \times 62.98$    (e) $0.198 \times 0.054$    (f) $0.869 \div 0.032$
   (g) $0.0098 \div 0.119$    (h) $0.12 \div 0.011$
   (i) $2.32 \div 0.012$.

6. Without using a calculator, place the decimal point in the following calculations:
   (a) $237.1 \times 56.2 = 1\,332\,502$
   (b) $23.54 \times 11.45 = 269\,533$
   (c) $36\,543 \div 243.1 = 150\,321$
   (d) $41.67 \div 0.003 = 138\,900$
   (e) $23.56 \times 0.0245 = 57\,722$
   (f) $0.004\,56 \times 1123 = 512\,088$.

7. An eight-digit calculator shows $\sqrt{7}$ to be 2.645 751 3; how would you record this in your working, and what would your answer be to $\sqrt{7} = \ldots$?

8. An eight-digit calculator shows the following:
$$\cos 45° = 0.707\ 106\ 7 \qquad \tan 30° = 0.577\ 350\ 2.$$

Copy these down rounding off to 5 s.f. (as you would from the calculator). Find to 3 s.f.

(a) $2 \cos 45° - \tan 30°$       (b) $\cos 45° - 2 \tan 30°$.

9. Use your calculator to find the values of the following to 5 s.f.:

(a) $\sin 61.1°$      (b) $\cos 72.2°$      (c) $\tan 32.33°$

(d) $\sqrt{42}$      (e) $(3.241)^2$      (f) $\pi$.

10. State the largest and the smallest four-digit number that would round off to

(a) 1.11      (b) 1.24      (c) 1.42      (d) 1.54

(e) 1.55      (f) 2.24      (g) 2.25      (h) 1.00.

11. (a) A number is given as 1.24 (3 s.f.). What is the smallest five-digit number that could round up to this value? What is the largest five-digit number that would round down?

   (b) Elsewhere, a number is given as 1.240 (4 s.f.). What is the smallest five-digit number that would round up to this and what is the largest that would round down?

12. A boy and a girl are arguing over their maths. The girl says there is a technical difference between the numbers 12.30 and 12.3. The boy says they are the same.

Who is right, and why?

## METRIC MEASUREMENT

The metric system of measurement is based upon ten, just like the number system. The common prefixes and their meanings are as follows:

| | | | |
|---|---|---|---|
| *kilo-* | 1000 times | e.g. 1 kilogram (kg) | $= 1000$ grams (g) |
| | | 1 kilometre (km) | $= 1000$ metres (m) |
| *milli-* | $\frac{1}{1000}$ | e.g. 1 milligram (mg) | $= \frac{1}{1000}$ g |
| | | 1 millimetre (mm) | $= \frac{1}{1000}$ m |
| *centi-* | $\frac{1}{100}$ | e.g. 1 centimetre (cm) | $= \frac{1}{100}$ m |

Note that

$$1 \text{ metric tonne (t)} = 1000 \text{ kg}$$
$$1 \text{ cubic metre (m}^3\text{)} = 1000 \text{ litres}$$
$$1 \text{ cubic centimetre (cm}^3\text{)} = 1 \text{ millilitre (ml)}$$
$$1 \text{ litre} = 1000 \text{ cm}^3$$

1 litre of water has a mass of 1 kg

## Care with Units

In any calculation it is essential to ensure that your units are correct — always double check.

Be particularly careful when dealing with areas and volumes. For although there are, for example, ten millimetres to a centimetre, there are one hundred square millimetres in a square centimetre and a thousand cubic millimetres in a cubic centimetre:

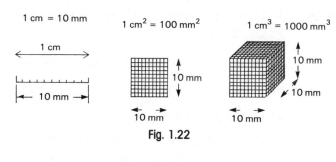

Fig. 1.22

$$10 \text{ mm} = 1 \text{ cm}$$
$$10 \text{ mm} \times 10 \text{ mm} = 100 \text{ mm}^2 = 1 \text{ cm}^2$$
$$10 \text{ mm} \times 10 \text{ mm} \times 10 \text{ mm} = 1000 \text{ mm}^3 = 1 \text{ cm}^3$$

## IMPERIAL UNITS

Britain has not yet fully converted to the metric system and many of the old imperial units are still in widespread use. You should know that:

*Length* is measured in inches, feet, yards and miles:

$$12 \text{ inches (in)} = 1 \text{ foot (ft)}$$
$$3 \text{ feet} = 1 \text{ yard (yd)}$$
$$1760 \text{ yards} = 1 \text{ mile}$$

Sometimes the symbol ' is used to denote feet and " to denote inches. Thus 6 feet 4 inches might be written *6 ft 4 in* or *6'4"*.

An inch is about 2.5 cms; a foot is about 30 cm; a metre is slightly more than a yard and a kilometre is about $\frac{5}{8}$th of a mile.

*Weight* is measured in ounces, pounds and stones:

$$16 \text{ ounces (oz)} = 1 \text{ pound (lb)}$$
$$14 \text{ pounds} = 1 \text{ stone}$$
$$8 \text{ stones} = 1 \text{ hundredweight (cwt)}$$

A kilogram is rather more than two pounds.

*Volume* is measured in pints and gallons.

$$8 \text{ pints (pt)} = 1 \text{ gallon}$$

A litre is rather less than two pints.

**EXERCISE 1g**

1. How many watts are there in a kilowatt? How many amps in a milliamp?

2. How many grams are there in 2.534 tonnes?

3. How many centimetres are there in 2.25 kilometres?

4. How many seconds are there in
   (a) one minute      (b) one hour?
   How many milliseconds are there in 1 h 15 min?

5. 100 centimetres are equal to 1 metre.
   (a) How many square centimetres are there in one square metre?
   (b) How many cubic centimetres are there in one cubic metre?

6. One inch is approximately 2.5 cm. How many square centimetres are equal to one square inch?

7. Twelve inches are equal to one foot.
   (a) How many square inches are equal to a square foot?
   (b) How many square centimetres are equal to a square foot?

8. A kilometre is about $\frac{5}{8}$ of a mile.
   (a) How many miles is a distance of 40 kilometres?
   (b) How many kilometres is a distance of 50 miles?
   (c) How many square kilometres are equivalent to one square mile?

9. One pound (lb) weight is equivalent to 454 grams.

   (a) How many kilograms is one stone?

   (b) How many pounds in a kilogram?

10. Find the volume of the tank illustrated in Fig. 1.23

    (a) in cubic metres    (b) in cubic centimetres

    (c) in litres.

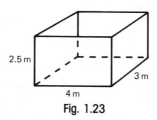

2.5 m

3 m

4 m

**Fig. 1.23**

11. A rectangular bath is 2 m long and 80 cm wide; it holds 960 litres of water when full. How high is it?

12. An empty rectangular fish-tank, measuring 1 m by 75 cm at the base and 60 cm high is filled with water to a depth of 345 mm.

    Find the volume of water poured in (answer in litres).

    A further 100 litres is added. How much higher does the water rise?

13. Find the length, in metres, of a roll of wallpaper 11 yards long, given that 1 yard is 1.1 m. Now give your answer to the nearest centimetre.

    The same roll of wallpaper is 21 inches wide. Given that 1 inch = 2.54 cm, how wide is the wallpaper, to the nearest millimetre?

14. If £1 can be exchanged for $1.40, how many dollars will I receive for:

    (a) £50        (b) £125        (c) £180?

    How many pounds will I receive for

    (d) $77        (e) $560?

15. If £1 can be exchanged for 250 Japanese yen, how much is one yen worth?

    What would be the cost in yen of a hi-fi system costing £360?

    What would be the cost in pounds of a car priced at 1 125 000 yen?

16. The density of a substance is given by the ratio weight/volume. Gold has a density of 19.3 g per $cm^3$. Convert this to kilograms per $m^3$.

    What volume of gold would weigh 1 kg?

17. The density of copper is $8.8\,g/cm^3$. Find, in kilograms, the mass of $2\,m^3$ of copper.

18. At a particular pressure, 11.4 litres of hydrogen have a mass of 1 g. What is the density of hydrogen in $g/cm^3$? What is the mass of 39.9 litres of hydrogen?

19. One pint is equivalent to 583 ml. If I order 2 pints of milk per day from the milkman, how many litres is this? Correct your answer to one decimal place.

    Later the same day, I buy 1 gallon (8 pints) of motor oil, only to find later that the can actually contains 5 litres. Is this more or less than I intended to buy, and by how much?

20. Convert 54 km/h to m/s. How long would it take to travel 67.5 cm at this speed (give your answer in milliseconds)?

21. A particle travels 32 mm in 4 milliseconds. How far would it travel in 3 h at this speed?

## MISCELLANEOUS EXERCISE 1

1. Which of the following are (a) real numbers   (b) natural numbers   (c) integers   (d) rational numbers?

    $$-101, -96.1, 0, \tfrac{1}{2}, 1, \sqrt{11}, 11, 12.7, 101$$

2.

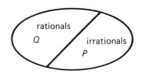

Fig. 1.24

The Venn diagram (Fig. 1.24) shows the set of all real numbers, which are either rational or irrational.

   (a) Copy the diagram and put into it both the set of integers, $I$, and the set of natural numbers, $N$.

   (b) For each of the following numbers, state *all* of the sets, using the letters $I, N, P, Q$, to which each belongs:
   (i) $\pi$,   (ii) $3\tfrac{1}{7}$,   (iii) 4,   (iv) $-4$.                (LU)

3. Arrange these numbers in order, smallest first, illustrating your answer with a number line:

$$2.1 \quad -4 \quad -3.2 \quad \sqrt{3} \quad 0.2 \quad 0.18$$

4. Which of the following numbers:
   $1, 3, 7, 27, 64, 87, 232, 256$
   (a) are prime?
   (b) are factors of 21?
   (c) are multiples of 21?
   (d) are cube numbers (i.e. one of the series $1^3, 2^3, 3^3 \ldots$)?

5. Members of the series $1, 3, 6, 10, 15, 21, \ldots$ are called triangle numbers.
   (a) Why are the numbers called triangle (or triangular) numbers?
   (b) Which of the numbers given is prime?
   (c) Find the next prime triangle number.
   (d) Find the complete set of triangle numbers that are also factors of 84.

6. The Ancient Greeks described a number as *perfect* if its factors (including 1 but excluding itself) add up to that number. For example 6 has factors 1, 2, and 3 (excluding 6 itself) and $1 + 2 + 3 = 6$.

   Show that 28 is a 'perfect number' but 24 is not.

   Show that 496 and 8128 are also perfect numbers.

7. From the given numbers $1, 2, 3, 4, 5, 6, 7, 8, 9, 10$ find
   (a) three multiples of 3,
   (b) three square numbers,
   (c) three factors of 434.
   (d) three different numbers such that the product of two of them added to the third gives 62.

   Find three different ways of answering (d). Are there more than three ways?

8. Find the number under 1000 which has the largest number of factors.

9. What whole number
   (a) has only one factor
   (b) is a factor of every number
   (c) is a factor of an infinite number of numbers
   (d) is not a factor of any other number?

10. $7, 37, 337$ are all prime numbers. Is $3337$? Is $33337$?
    Investigate further.

11. $153 = 1^3 + 5^3 + 3^3$

    $407 = 4^3 + 0^3 + 7^3$

    There are two more numbers like this between $153$ and $407$.
    Can you find them?

12. Pentagonal numbers can be built up as shown.

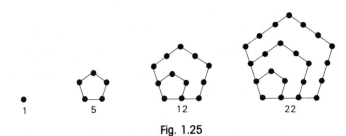

Fig. 1.25

Find two more pentagonal numbers. Can you work out how to find the ninth pentagonal number without drawing out the pattern?

13. Adding together the digits of a number gives its *digit sum.* For example, the digit sum of 7398 is $7 + 3 + 9 + 8 = 27$.

    It is said that if the digit sum of a number is divisible by 9 then so is the number itself. Investigate with numbers of your own choosing. Can you prove the result is always true?

    Does it work for other divisors — say, 6 or 2? Investigate further.

14. By taking the digit sum of the digit sum . . . any number can be *reduced* to a single digit.

    For example, the digit sum of 7398 is $7 + 3 + 9 + 8 = 27$, and the digit sum of 27 is $2 + 7 = 9$.

    Thus 7398 reduces to 9: $7398 \rightarrow 27 \rightarrow 9$.

    It is said that any number reduces to its remainder when divided by 9. Investigate.

It is also said that if two numbers are reduced, then the result of adding the two reduced numbers is the same as reducing the sum of the two original numbers. Investigate further.

Would this work if the original numbers were multiplied together, subtracted or divided? Investigate.

15. A gardener plants clusters of white and red tulip bulbs in a pre-set pattern, as shown.

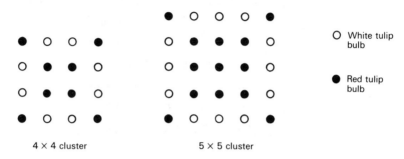

Fig. 1.26

(a) Illustrate the pattern for a $6 \times 6$ cluster.

(b) How many white and red tulip bulbs does he use in each case?

(c) Calculate the number of bulbs of each colour tulip he will need to plant a
(i) $7 \times 7$ cluster    (ii) $8 \times 8$ cluster    (iii) $n \times n$ cluster.

(d) If the bulbs are to be planted about 9 cm apart, what is the largest cluster the gardener could plant in a flower bed 1 metre square? How many bulbs of each colour will he need?

16. Use your calculator to find the values of
(a) $1 \times 2 \times 3 \times 4 + 1$
(b) $2 \times 3 \times 4 \times 5 + 1$
(c) $3 \times 4 \times 5 \times 6 + 1$
(d) $4 \times 5 \times 6 \times 7 + 1$

Can you find the pattern? Predict a value for $5 \times 6 \times 7 \times 8 + 1$ *before* you work it out!

17. Given that $26.389 \times 97.23 = 2565.8025$, *write down* the values of

(a) $26\,389 \times 9723$  (b) $0.002\,638\,9 \times 0.097\,23$.

(c) $2565.8025 \div 97.23$  (d) $2565.8025 \div 0.9723$

29

18. Given that $23.31 \div 3.15 = 7.4$, *write down* the answers to the following:

(a) $23.31 \div 7.4$     (b) $3.15 \times 74$     (c) $2.331 \div 315$

(d) $0.315 \times 0.74$     (e) $23.31 \div 0.74$     (f) $0.2331 \div 0.74$.

19. Suppose that your calculator lets you down so that the decimal point fails to show. Place the decimal point in the following calculations by first estimating the approximate answers:

(a) $45.6 \times 97.82 = 4\,460\,592$

(b) $12\,310.2 \div 42 = 2931$

(c) $134.342 \div 2.02 = 6\,650\,594$

(d) $110.164 \times 21.32 = 23\,486\,965$

(e) $45.63 \div 0.0021 = 21\,728\,571$.

20. Write down the number $0.050\,506$ correct to

(a) 4 d.p.     (b) 4 s.f.     (c) 1 d.p.     (d) 1 s.f.

21. A car travels a distance of 32.7 miles per gallon of petrol.

(a) Round this to one significant figure.

(b) Estimate the number of gallons of petrol the same car would use travelling from Lincoln to Carlisle — a distance of 177 miles.

(c) If petrol costs £1.72 per gallon, will £10 cover the cost of the petrol for the journey?

22. A piece of wire is 4.76 m long.

(a) What is its length

(i) to the nearest whole number of metres,
(ii) to two significant figures,
(iii) to one place of decimals.

(b) The wire is bent to form a rectangle whose length is 1.3 m. Using your answer to (a) part (iii) find

(i) the breadth of the rectangle in metres,
(ii) the area of the rectangle in square metres. (NWREB)

**23.** Fig. 1.27 shows a sketch of my house.

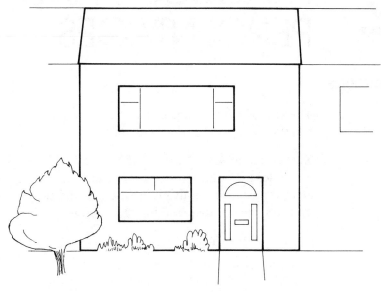

Fig. 1.27

If the front door is 2 m high, estimate to one significant figure

(a) the width of the front door.

(b) the length and breadth of each of the windows.

(c) the height of the house.

(d) the width of the house.

(e) the area of wall I would need to paint, should I decide to redecorate the front of the house.

# 2 FRACTIONS AND PERCENTAGES

## FRACTIONS

The top of a fraction is called the *numerator*; the bottom of a fraction is called the *denominator*.

Two fractions are *equivalent* if they are of the same value. For example, $\frac{1}{2}$ is equivalent to $\frac{2}{4}$. We can find any number of equivalent fractions by multiplying the top and the bottom of a fraction by the same number (see Fig. 2.1). Thus

$$\frac{1}{2} = \frac{1 \times 2}{2 \times 2} = \frac{2}{4} \qquad \text{and} \qquad \frac{1}{2} = \frac{1 \times 3}{2 \times 3} = \frac{3}{6}$$

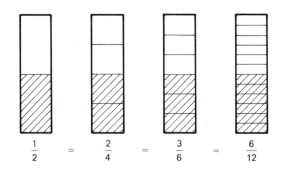

$$\frac{1}{2} = \frac{2}{4} = \frac{3}{6} = \frac{6}{12}$$

Fig. 2.1

Similarly, we can show that $\frac{3}{6}$ is the fraction $\frac{1}{2}$ by dividing the top and bottom by the same number:

$$\frac{3}{6} = \frac{3 \div 3}{6 \div 3} = \frac{1}{2}$$

This process is called *cancelling down* into *lowest terms*.

**Example** Write $\frac{12}{156}$ in its lowest terms.

Cancelling down in stages:

$$\frac{12}{156} = \frac{12 \div 2}{156 \div 2} = \frac{6}{78} = \frac{6 \div 2}{78 \div 2} = \frac{3}{39} = \frac{3 \div 3}{39 \div 3} = \frac{1}{13}$$

32

*Mixed numbers*, such as $7\frac{1}{2}$ and $5\frac{3}{4}$, may also be written as *top-heavy* or *improper fractions*. For example

$$7 = \frac{7}{1} = \frac{14}{2}$$

so

$$7\frac{1}{2} = \frac{14}{2} + \frac{1}{2} = \frac{15}{2}$$

$$5 = \frac{5}{1} = \frac{20}{4}$$

so

$$5\frac{3}{4} = \frac{20}{4} + \frac{3}{4} = \frac{23}{4}$$

## WORKING WITH FRACTIONS

### Addition and Subtraction

**Example**

$$\frac{1}{2} + \frac{1}{3}$$

These two fractions must be written in equivalent form, that is with the *same* denominator. The lowest common multiple of 2 and 3 is 6, and it follows that both $\frac{1}{2}$ and $\frac{1}{3}$ can be written as sixths (Fig. 2.2).

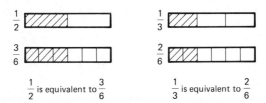

$\frac{1}{2}$ is equivalent to $\frac{3}{6}$          $\frac{1}{3}$ is equivalent to $\frac{2}{6}$

**Fig. 2.2**

Then:

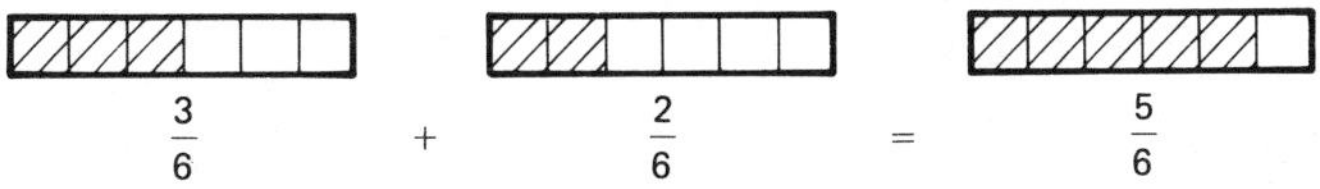

$$\frac{3}{6} \quad + \quad \frac{2}{6} \quad = \quad \frac{5}{6}$$

**Fig. 2.3**

So

$$\frac{1}{2} + \frac{1}{3} = \frac{3}{6} + \frac{2}{6} = \frac{5}{6}$$

**Example** $2\frac{3}{4} - \frac{5}{6}$.

First, write $2\frac{3}{4}$ as a top-heavy fraction: $2\frac{3}{4} = \frac{11}{4}$.

Now, the LCM of 4 and 6 is 12, so

$$\frac{11}{4} = \frac{11 \times 3}{4 \times 3} = \frac{33}{12}$$

$$\frac{5}{6} = \frac{5 \times 2}{6 \times 2} = \frac{10}{12}$$

Hence

$$\frac{11}{4} - \frac{5}{6} = \frac{33}{12} - \frac{10}{12} = \frac{23}{12} = 1\frac{11}{12}$$

## Multiplication

**Example**
$$\frac{3}{4} \times \frac{1}{2} = \frac{3 \times 1}{4 \times 2} = \frac{3}{8}$$

Sometimes it is possible to cancel out a factor that appears on the top and on the bottom *before* multiplying.

**Example**
$$\frac{6}{7} \times \frac{1}{9} = \frac{\overset{2}{\cancel{6}} \times 1}{7 \times \underset{3}{\cancel{9}}} = \frac{2 \times 1}{7 \times 3} = \frac{2}{21}$$

If a fraction is to be multiplied by a whole number, then the whole number should first be changed into a fraction.

**Example**
$$\frac{3}{4} \times 5 = \frac{3}{4} \times \frac{5}{1} = \frac{3 \times 5}{4 \times 1} = \frac{15}{4} = 3\frac{3}{4}$$

Mixed numbers (such as $7\frac{1}{2}$ and $5\frac{3}{4}$) should be changed to top-heavy fractions.

**Example**
$$\frac{4}{9} \times 5\frac{3}{4} = \frac{4}{9} \times \frac{23}{4} = \frac{\overset{1}{\cancel{4}} \times 23}{9 \times \underset{1}{\cancel{4}}} = \frac{23}{9} = 2\frac{5}{9}$$

## Division

To divide one fraction by another, turn the second fraction upside down and multiply.

**Example**
$$\frac{3}{5} \div \frac{7}{8} = \frac{3}{5} \times \frac{8}{7} = \frac{3 \times 8}{5 \times 7} = \frac{24}{35}$$

## CONVERTING FRACTIONS TO DECIMALS

A fraction can be converted into a decimal by rewriting the top as a decimal (so 1 becomes 1.0000, 3 becomes 3.0000, and so on) and then dividing it by the denominator.

**Example**

$$\frac{1}{8} = \frac{1.000}{8}$$

then

$$\frac{^01.{}^10{}^20{}^40}{8} = 0.125$$

Thus $\frac{1}{8} = 0.125$.

You will probably prefer to use a calculator to work out the division. If the division is not exact or continues for more than the required number of decimal places, then round off.

Sometimes, the division leads to the same number or group of numbers repeating. The decimal is said to be *recurring*, and the recurring digits are denoted by dots placed above them.

**Examples**

$$\frac{1}{3} = 0.333\,33\ldots = 0.\dot{3}$$

$$\frac{60}{111} = 0.540\,540\,540\ldots = 0.\dot{5}4\dot{0}$$

## CONVERTING DECIMALS TO FRACTIONS

**Examples**

$$0.25 = \frac{25}{100} = \frac{25 \div 25}{100 \div 25} = \frac{1}{4}$$

$$0.108 = \frac{108}{1000} = \frac{108 \div 4}{1000 \div 4} = \frac{27}{250}$$

There are two steps:

(*i*)  write the decimal as a whole number, divided by the appropriate power of ten;

(*ii*)  cancel down if possible.

**EXERCISE 2a**  Work out the following as fractions:

1. (a) $\frac{1}{3} + \frac{1}{4}$  (b) $\frac{1}{4} + \frac{1}{5}$  (c) $\frac{3}{4} + \frac{2}{3}$  (d) $\frac{3}{4} + \frac{3}{5}$

2. (a) $\frac{1}{2} - \frac{1}{5}$  (b) $\frac{2}{3} - \frac{2}{5}$  (c) $\frac{3}{4} - \frac{2}{7}$  (d) $\frac{5}{8} - \frac{1}{2}$

3. (a) $\frac{3}{16} + \frac{1}{2}$    (b) $\frac{9}{16} + \frac{1}{4}$    (c) $\frac{1}{2} + \frac{2}{3}$    (d) $\frac{7}{8} + \frac{2}{5}$

4. (a) $\frac{1}{2} - \frac{3}{16}$    (b) $\frac{3}{4} - \frac{5}{12}$    (c) $\frac{5}{8} - \frac{3}{10}$    (d) $\frac{7}{8} - \frac{5}{12}$

5. (a) $\frac{1}{8} \times \frac{4}{7}$    (b) $\frac{4}{5} \times \frac{3}{4}$    (c) $\frac{8}{11} \times \frac{3}{8}$    (d) $\frac{7}{8} \times \frac{6}{7}$

6. (a) $\frac{2}{9} \times \frac{3}{4}$    (b) $\frac{5}{18} \times \frac{2}{15}$    (c) $\frac{9}{16} \times \frac{2}{3}$    (d) $\frac{3}{4} \times \frac{5}{12}$

7. (a) $\frac{3}{8} \div \frac{3}{10}$    (b) $\frac{4}{11} \div \frac{3}{22}$    (c) $\frac{3}{4} \div \frac{1}{12}$    (d) $\frac{4}{7} \div \frac{16}{21}$

8. (a) $\frac{1}{2} \div \frac{7}{10}$    (b) $\frac{2}{3} \div \frac{8}{15}$    (c) $\frac{6}{7} \div \frac{3}{14}$    (d) $\frac{5}{9} \div \frac{1}{18}$

9. (a) $\frac{5}{7} \times 2$    (b) $\frac{8}{11} \div 2$    (c) $\frac{2}{5} \times 3$    (d) $\frac{6}{13} \div 3$

10. (a) $3\frac{1}{4} - 1\frac{1}{2}$    (b) $\frac{11}{13} \times 1\frac{6}{7}$    (c) $1\frac{4}{5} \div 2\frac{1}{4}$    (d) $1\frac{3}{4} - 3\frac{1}{3}$

11. (a) $2\frac{1}{8} + 1\frac{3}{4}$    (b) $2\frac{1}{8} - 1\frac{3}{4}$    (c) $2\frac{1}{8} \times 1\frac{3}{4}$    (d) $2\frac{1}{8} \div 1\frac{3}{4}$

12. (a) $3\frac{2}{9} + 1\frac{1}{3}$    (b) $3\frac{2}{9} - 1\frac{1}{3}$    (c) $3\frac{2}{9} \times 1\frac{1}{3}$    (d) $3\frac{2}{9} \div 1\frac{1}{3}$.

13. Convert these decimals to fractions, written in their lowest terms:

     (a) 0.2    (b) 0.75    (c) 1.6    (d) 0.16    (e) 0.55

     (f) 0.6    (g) 0.06    (h) 0.006    (i) 0.45    (j) 0.72

     (k) 0.05    (l) 0.48    (m) 0.125    (n) 0.375    (o) 0.004.

14. Without using a calculator convert these fractions to decimals showing your working clearly:

     (a) $\frac{5}{8}$    (b) $\frac{7}{20}$    (c) $\frac{3}{16}$    (d) $\frac{6}{25}$.

15. Now convert these, again without a calculator. Be sure to show your working and mark accurately the digit or block of digits that recur.

     (a) $\frac{1}{3}$    (b) $\frac{5}{6}$    (c) $\frac{3}{11}$    (d) $\frac{2}{7}$.

     Write down in your own words what happens when a fraction converts to a recurring decimal.

16. Use your calculator to convert these fractions to decimals. Give your answers to 3 significant figures.

     (a) $\frac{11}{13}$    (b) $\frac{7}{15}$    (c) $\frac{9}{17}$    (d) $\frac{1}{19}$

     (e) $\frac{1}{13}$    (f) $\frac{23}{29}$    (g) $\frac{16}{21}$    (h) $\frac{25}{37}$ .

17. Use your calculator to find the following fractions as decimals

     (a) $\frac{1}{11}$    (b) $\frac{2}{11}$    (c) $\frac{3}{11}$    (d) $\frac{4}{11}$ .

     Can you see the pattern? Predict the decimal equivalents to $\frac{5}{11}$, and $\frac{8}{11}$ and use the calculator to check your rule is valid. What is the decimal equivalent to $\frac{11}{11}$? What prediction does your rule lead to for $\frac{11}{11}$?

**18.** Can you find a simple rule for the decimal equivalents to $\frac{1}{9}$, $\frac{2}{9}, \frac{3}{9} \ldots$ What does this rule suggest would be the equivalent to $\frac{9}{9}$?

**19.** Use your calculator to find the decimal equivalents to $\frac{1}{7}$ and $\frac{2}{7}$. What do you notice? Estimate to one significant figure the decimal value of $\frac{3}{7}$ and so predict its full recurring-decimal equivalent. Check your prediction with the calculator. Can you similarly predict the decimal equivalents of $\frac{4}{7}, \frac{5}{7}$ and $\frac{6}{7}$?

**20.** Investigate the pattern of recurring digits for $\frac{1}{13}, \frac{2}{13}, \frac{3}{13}, \frac{4}{13} \ldots$ The pattern is not as simple this time. Try to predict the decimal equivalents to $\frac{8}{13}, \frac{9}{13}, \frac{10}{13}, \frac{11}{13}, \frac{12}{13}$ *before* you find them on your calculator.

## PERCENTAGES

One part per hundred, i.e. the fraction $\frac{1}{100}$, is called *one per cent* and is written 1%. 25% represents twenty-five parts per hundred, i.e. the fraction $\frac{25}{100}$; 40% represents $\frac{40}{100}$, and so on.

One whole unit is represented by $\frac{100}{100}$ or 100%. Amounts greater than one are represented by percentages greater than 100%. For example, if a quantity is doubled, it is 200% of its old value; if a wage is increased by, say, 6% then the new wage is 106% of the old.

Decimals and fractions are converted to percentages by multiplying by 100%. Thus

$$0.45 = 0.45 \times 100\% = 45\%$$

$$1.67 = 1.67 \times 100\% = 167\%$$

and similarly with fractions

$$\frac{1}{8} = \frac{1}{8} \times 100\% = \frac{1}{\overset{}{\underset{2}{8}}} \times \frac{\overset{25}{100}}{1} = \frac{25}{2} = 12\tfrac{1}{2}\%$$

$$1\frac{1}{2} = \frac{3}{2} \times 100\% = \frac{3}{\underset{}{2}} \times \frac{\overset{50}{100}}{1} = 150\%$$

Conversely, a percentage may be converted to a decimal by dividing it by 100:

$$31\% = 0.31$$

$$16.7\% = 0.167$$

$$121\% = 1.21$$

$$8\tfrac{1}{2}\% = 8.5\% = 0.085$$

Percentages can be rewritten as fractions by writing the denominator as 100 instead of % and cancelling down if possible:

$$32\% = \frac{32}{100} = \frac{32 \div 4}{100 \div 4} = \frac{8}{25}$$

$$125\% = \frac{125}{100} = \frac{125 \div 25}{100 \div 25} = \frac{5}{4} = 1\frac{1}{4}$$

$$5\frac{1}{2}\% = \frac{5\frac{1}{2}}{100} = \frac{5\frac{1}{2} \times 2}{100 \times 2} = \frac{11}{200}$$

To find a percentage of a given quantity, you need to remember how to convert the percentage into a decimal. Then use a calculator to multiply the numbers together.

**Example** Find 15% of £22.

As 15% = 0.15,

$$15\% \text{ of } £22 = 0.15 \times £22 = £3.30$$

Some calculators have a percentage key — but there is little need for one. Just write the percentage as an ordinary decimal!

**Example** Find $8\frac{1}{4}$% of £203.59.

Firstly, convert the fraction to a decimal, i.e.

$$8\frac{1}{4} = 8.25$$

Then convert the percentage to a decimal, i.e.

$$8.25\% = 0.0825$$

Use the calculator

$$0.0825 \times £203.59 = £16.796$$

Finally round off to the nearest penny:

$$= £16.80$$

**Example** A girl scores 49 out of a possible 60 marks in a maths test. Convert her score to a percentage, rounded to the nearest whole number.

The girl has scored a fraction of the available marks, namely $\frac{49}{60}$.

Convert this to a decimal, using a calculator:

$$49 \div 60 = 0.816\,67$$

Convert to a percentage by multiplying by 100:

$$= 81.667\%$$

Round off to the nearest whole number:

$$= 82\%$$

**EXERCISE 2b** Write the following decimals and fractions as percentages:

1. (a) 0.31    (b) 0.05    (c) 1.5    (d) 0.005    (e) 0.001

2. (a) $\frac{3}{5}$    (b) $\frac{2}{3}$    (c) $\frac{1}{25}$    (d) $\frac{3}{8}$    (e) $\frac{21}{200}$

3. (a) $1\frac{3}{4}$    (b) $1\frac{2}{3}$    (c) $2\frac{4}{5}$    (d) $3\frac{5}{8}$    (e) $2\frac{37}{200}$.

4. Write these percentages as decimals:
   (a) 32%    (b) 89%    (c) 10%    (d) 67%    (e) 88%
   (f) 43.1%    (g) 83.4%    (h) 32.2%    (i) 110%    (j) 108.4%
   (k) $58\frac{1}{2}\%$    (l) $83\frac{1}{2}\%$    (m) $51\frac{1}{4}\%$    (n) $85\frac{3}{4}\%$    (o) $74\frac{2}{5}\%$
   (p) 8%    (q) 3%    (r) 6.9%    (s) $8\frac{1}{2}\%$    (t) $1\frac{1}{4}\%$.

5. Write these percentages as fractions in their lowest terms:
   (a) 75%    (b) 60%    (c) 32%    (d) 30%    (e) 45%
   (f) 24%    (g) 85%    (h) 18%    (i) 11%    (j) 47%
   (k) $15\frac{1}{2}\%$    (l) $12\frac{1}{2}\%$    (m) $3\frac{1}{3}\%$    (n) $5\frac{1}{4}\%$    (o) $16\frac{2}{3}\%$.

6. Find, using a calculator where necessary,
   (a) 10% of 85            (b) 15% of £60
   (c) 30% of 250          (d) 20% of £6.50
   (e) 12% of £6.50        (f) 12% of £24
   (g) 6.8% of 47          (h) 32.5% of £11.30
   (i) 15% of £12.80      (j) $12\frac{1}{2}\%$ of 125
   (k) $\cdot 37\frac{1}{2}\%$ of £54.67     (l) $8\frac{1}{2}\%$ of £630.

7. A boy scores 36 out of 60 for his maths and 63 out of 90 in English. Convert these marks to percentages. Is he better at maths or English?

8. In a school of 350, 105 are boys. What percentage are girls? If 14 boys are absent, what percentage is this of
   (a) the whole school      (b) the boys?

9. I fit an attachment to my car that the advertisers claim will improve my petrol consumption by 'up to 5%'. I normally get 40 miles per gallon. What should I get now, if the advertisers' claim is valid? In fact I get 41 miles per gallon, with the attachment fitted. What is the percentage improvement?

10. In an exam, 10.5% of the candidates are awarded grade 'A'. If there are 20 000 candidates, how many will receive a grade A? 5200 candidates were awarded grade B. What percentage is this?

11. A candidate in this examination scored 37 out of 50 on the first paper and $66\frac{1}{2}$ out of a possible 80 marks on the second. Find his percentage score on each of the papers.

12. An enterprising estate agent charges $1\frac{1}{2}$% commission on the sale price of a house. All the other estate agents in the area charge 2%. I am hoping to sell my house for £57 500. How much would I save by asking the cheaper estate agent to handle the sale?

   Altogether, the estate agent's fees, legal costs and other moving expenses cost me £1825. What percentage of my selling price (£57 500) is this?

## TAXES

Taxes are usually expressed as percentages. For example, value added tax (VAT) has been fixed at 15% for a number of years. Income tax has been changed more often, but is usually around 30%. Everyone has a 'tax allowance', that is, some part of their income upon which no income tax is charged.

**Example** A man earns £148 per week. He has a tax allowance of £28 per week. If income tax is 30%, how much tax is deducted and what is his 'take-home' pay?

The man earns £148. He pays tax on £148 − £28 = £120 (i.e. his weekly earnings less £28 weekly tax allowance).

$$30\% \text{ of } £120 = 0.30 \times £120 = £36$$

He pays £36 tax and takes home £148 − £36 = £112 per week.

**EXERCISE 2c** 1. How much VAT at 15% is due on goods worth:
   (a) £5.00  (b) £8.50  (c) £10.29  (d) £13.85
   (e) £12.93  (f) £84.53  (g) £21.74  (h) £32.85?
   Give your answers to the nearest penny.

2. In the State of New York, a local sales tax of $1\frac{1}{2}$% is charged on all goods, rather like VAT in this country. There is also an 8% Federal tax.

   (a) What is the total percentage tax charged on any sale?

(b) What, to the nearest cent, will be the tax charged on items costing before tax   (i) $3.20   (ii) $34.80   (iii) $110.56?

3. VAT in France is charged at 22%. Find the tax due on items costing, before tax:

(a) FF5.83   (b) FF55.42   (c) FF163.96.

4. A girl earns £125 per week, but has a tax allowance of £55.
   (a) What is her 'taxable pay' i.e. the amount upon which she must pay tax?
   (b) If income tax is set at 30%, how much tax does she pay?

5. If a woman earns £150 per week and has a tax allowance of £50 per week, how much income tax, charged at 29%, does she have to pay?

6. A man earns £132 per week and has a tax allowance of £48. How much income tax, at 30%, does he have to pay? How much does he save if the tax rate drops to 27%?

7. A successful salesman earns £22 000 in one year. He is allowed £4500 free of tax, and pays income tax at 29% on the first £10 000 of taxable pay and at 40% on the rest. What is his tax bill that year?

8. A boy earns £44 per week in his first job. He has a tax allowance of £28 per week, but must pay income tax at 29% on the rest; he also must pay 9% National Insurance on *all* of the £44.

   How much will he have when he opens his pay packet? What percentage, to the nearest whole number, is this of his weekly earnings before deductions?

# SIMPLE INTEREST

When someone invests a sum of money, the *principal*, he receives *interest* at a *rate* quoted as a percentage.

If a principal of £$P$ is invested for $T$ years at an interest rate of $R$% per year, then the investor will receive interest, £$I$, given by the formula

$$I = \frac{P \times R \times T}{100}$$

41

**Example** My grandmother leaves me £10 000 to be kept in trust for 8 years at 12% interest. What will the money be worth after that time?

$$P = £10\,000; \qquad R = 12\%; \qquad T = 8\,\text{years}$$

$$I = \frac{£10\,000 \times 12 \times 8}{100} = £9600$$

Thus the total amount will be £10 000 + £9600 = £19 600.

## COMPOUND INTEREST

The calculations are harder, but your money will earn more if interest is paid compound — so it is worth having!

If you invest money and leave the first year's interest untouched, in the second year you will be paid interest not only on your original investment *but also on last year's interest.*

In the third year you will be paid interest on the second year's interest, on the first year's interest and on the original sum ... and so on.

**Example** Suppose the £10 000 trust set up by my grandmother pays 12% compound interest.

If an amount rises by 12% in one year, it will end the year 112% of its original value. Converting 112% to its decimal equivalent, i.e. 1.12, leads to:

*Year 1*     112% of £10 000 = 1.12 × £10 000 = £11 200

This larger amount will rise by a further 12% the following year:

*Year 2*     112% of £11 200 = 1.12 × £11 200 = £12 544

Then

*Year 3*     112% of £12 544 = 1.12 × £12 544 = £14 049.28

*Year 4*     112% of £14 049.28 ...

and so on.

All we are doing is repeatedly multiplying by 1.12, the decimal equivalent of 112%. If you have a 'constant' function on your calculator, you could complete the calculation very quickly.

However, if your calculator has a power button, $\boxed{y^n}$, you could simplify the arithmetic still further. For 1.12 × 1.12 × 1.12 × ... × 1.12 eight times is $(1.12)^8$.

$$(1.12)^8 \times £10\,000 = £24\,759.63$$

## WAGE AND PRICE INCREASES

Wage and price increases work in a similar way to compound interest.

**Example**  A girl earns £12 per week for helping in a shop on Saturdays. She is promised an increase of 15% each year for the next four years. How much will she be earning then?

Each year the girl's Saturday wage will increase by 15%, i.e. to 115% of its old value.  115% = 1.15.

After one year she will be paid  1.15 × £12.

After four years she will be paid  $(1.15)^4 \times £12 = £20.98$.

## DEPRECIATION

As machinery gets older, it *depreciates* in value, that is it is worth less and less with each year that passes. Calculations involving depreciation are similar to those involving compound interest.

**Example**  Machinery in a factor is depreciated by 20% each year. What will be the value in five years time of a machine now worth £234 000?

If machinery is depreciated by 20% per year, then after one year it will be worth just 80% of its original value.  80% = 0.80.

So after 5 years it will only be worth

$$(0.80)^5 \times £234\,000 \ = \ £76\,677.12$$
$$= \ £76\,680 \quad \text{(to nearest £10)}$$

**EXERCISE 2d**

1. A man invests £2400. What would be his simple interest in one year at
   (a) 6%      (b) 8%      (c) $12\frac{1}{2}$%      (d) $9\frac{1}{4}$%?

2. A man invests £5600 at 9%. What will be his simple interest after
   (a) 1 year      (b) 2 years      (c) 5 years      (d) 10 years?

3. £5000 is kept in a trust for 5 years, during which time it earns $12\frac{1}{2}$% simple interest per year. What will the trust be worth at the end of the 5 years?

4. A woman invests £2230 at 11% simple interest per year. How much would the investment be worth after

(a) 1 year  (b) 3 years  (c) 6 years?

How long before her investment is worth more than £3000?

5. If the lady in question 4 was able to invest her money at 11% compound interest, what would her investment be worth after

(a) 1 year  (b) 3 years  (c) 6 years?

How long would she have to wait for the investment to be worth more than £3000?

6. I have £1000 to invest for five years. Which would be the better return, 9% compound interest per year or $10\frac{1}{2}$% simple interest per year?

7. I have £439 in my building society account paying me 9% compound interest. If I leave the account untouched, how much will I have there after

(a) 8 years  (b) 12 years  (c) 17 years  (d) 21 years?

How many years will it take for this investment to grow to more than £1000?

8. In 1987 a newsagent pays local teenagers 60p per day, i.e. £4.20 per week, for delivering newspapers. If prices rise at 10% per year, and the £4.20 is increased each year to keep pace, what will paper boys and girls earn in the year 2000?

How much should your grandchildren, delivering newspapers in the year 2050 earn? How much will they pay for a chocolate bar that cost 18p in 1987?

9. A motor car bought for £6950 depreciates by 25% of its value each year for three years and then by £500 each year for the next five years. Rounding to the nearest £10 at each stage, find the worth of the car after

(a) 1 year  (b) 2 years  (c) 3 years  (d) 5 years

How many years would it take for the car's value to fall below its scrap value of £300?

10. The table shows the repayments due, per month, on mortgages of various size at three different rates of interest, payable over 25 years.

| Mortgage | Rate of interest | | |
|---|---|---|---|
| | $10\frac{1}{2}\%$ | $11\frac{1}{2}\%$ | $12\frac{1}{2}\%$ |
| £1 000 | £9.54 | £10.26 | £11.00 |
| £5 000 | £47.70 | £51.30 | £55.00 |
| £10 000 | £95.40 | £102.60 | £110.00 |
| £20 000 | £190.80 | £205.20 | £220.00 |
| £40 000 | £381.60 | £410.40 | £440.00 |

The repayments for mortgages of any amount can be found 'pro rata'. For example, a mortgage of £23 000 at $10\frac{1}{2}\%$ would cost £190.80 + 3 × £9.54 = £219.42 per month.

Find the repayments per month for mortgages of

(a) £15 000 at $10\frac{1}{2}\%$  (b) £17 000 at $11\frac{1}{2}\%$

(c) £22 000 at $10\frac{1}{2}\%$  (d) £29 500 at $12\frac{1}{2}\%$.

A young couple are hoping to buy their first house. It will cost them £32 000. They can raise a deposit of 10% and are looking for a 25 year mortgage.

(e) How much will they have to borrow?

(f) How much will this mortgage cost them per month if they borrow at $11\frac{1}{2}\%$?

(g) If, after a year, the rate of interest falls to $10\frac{1}{2}\%$ how much will they save per month?

(h) What is the highest mortgage they could afford (at $10\frac{1}{2}\%$) if they can repay a maximum of £340 per month?

## COSTS, PROFITS AND DISCOUNTS

A trader buys stock at *cost price* and sells it to his customers at a *selling price*. Normally, the selling price is higher than the cost price, so the trader makes a *profit*:

$$\text{profit} = \text{selling price} - \text{cost price}$$

45

Sometimes, however, the trader makes a *loss* — that is, the selling price is lower than the cost price:

$$\text{loss} = \text{cost price} - \text{selling price}$$

On other occasions, a trader may offer a *discount* on the old price of an article:

$$\text{new price} = \text{old price} - \text{discount}$$

Profits, losses, costs and discounts are often expressed as percentages.

**Example** A shopkeeper buys bars of chocolate of a certain size at £5.60 for a box of 35 bars. He sells them at 25% profit. What is the selling price of each bar?

The chocolate bars cost £5.60 for 35, i.e. £5.60 ÷ 35 = 16 p each.

The profit is 25% of 16 p, i.e.

$$0.25 \times 16 = 4\text{p}$$

$$\text{selling price} = \text{cost} + \text{profit} = 16\text{p} + 4\text{p} = 20\text{p per bar}$$

## REVERSE PERCENTAGES

If we know the selling price of an article, and the percentage profit that is made on the sale or the discount offered, it is possible to work out the original cost of the item.

**Example** A trader makes a profit of 30% on an article for sale in his shop at £26. What is the cost price?

If the trader is selling at 30% profit, then the selling price is 100% + 30% = 130% of cost price. Thus

$$130\% \text{ of cost} = £26$$

so $\qquad$ 1% of cost $= £26 \div 130 \quad \text{or} \quad \dfrac{2600}{130} \text{ pence}$

$$= 20\text{p}$$

Therefore

$$100\% \text{ of cost} = 20\text{p} \times 100 = £20$$

That is, the cost price of the article is £20.

*Check* $\quad$ 130% of £20 = 1.30 × £20 = £26. ✓

**Example** Everything in a sale is reduced by 10% of its normal price. If I buy something in this sale for £4.86, what is the normal price and how much is the discount?

$$\text{Sale price} = 90\% \text{ of normal price} = £4.86 = 486\text{p}$$

so $$1\% \text{ of normal price} = 486 \div 90$$

$$= 5.4\text{p}$$

$$100\% \text{ of normal price} = 5.4 \times 100 = 540\text{p}$$

$$= £5.40$$

$$\text{Discount} = £5.40 - £4.86 = 54\text{p}$$

**EXERCISE 2e**

1. A shopkeeper buys tins of baked beans in boxes of 144 for £30.24.
   (a) What is his cost price per tin?
   (b) If he sells each tin for 28p, how much profit does he make per tin?
   (c) What percentage of his costs is this?

2. A trader buys 144 packets of soap powder for £57.60. If he makes a profit of 40% on this, what is the shop price of an individual packet of soap powder?

   They do not sell well at this price, so the trader makes a 'special offer' of 6p off the shop price of each packet. What, now, is his percentage profit on the cost price of each packet?

3. An electric car is for sale with '70% off the maker's originally recommended price'. The asking price for the car is now £120.
   (a) What percentage of 'the maker's originally recommended price' is £120?
   (b) Find *one* per cent of the maker's originally recommended price.
   (c) What price did the maker originally recommend?

4. In a sale, everything is reduced by 15%. If I buy something for £4.25, what was its original price?

5. I buy a book for £3.60. The bookseller is making a profit of 25% on his cost price. What did he pay for the book?

6. A company offers a discount of 4% if I pay my bills within 7 days.
   (a) My first bill is for £130. What is the discount worth?
   (b) I pay my second bill the day it arrives. If I actually pay £144.00, what was the original amount on the bill?

7. A man is given a mortgage of £25 500, which is 85% of the cost of a house which he hopes to buy. What is the cost of the house and how much must the man raise himself?

8. A hi-fi shop is offering a music centre at £280 which it advertises as '30% off the original price'. What was the original price?

## MISCELLANEOUS EXERCISE 2

1. Consider four numbers: $0.5, 0.4, \frac{1}{5}, \frac{1}{4}$.
   (a) Explain, in your own words, the meaning of 0.4.
   (b) Why is 0.4 *not* equal to $\frac{1}{4}$?
   (c) Which is larger, 0.5 or $\frac{1}{5}$?
   (d) Find the sum of the two fractions, $\frac{1}{5}$ and $\frac{1}{4}$.
   (e) Find the product of the two decimals.

2. Which of the following numbers is closest to 1?
   
   $1.01$      $99\%$      $\frac{9}{10}$      $\frac{999}{1000}$      $0.99$

3. A trader makes 25% profit on his costs for articles which he sells at £400. What do these articles cost him?

4. A girl scores 33 points out of a possible 60 in her maths test. What is her percentage? Is this better or worse than $38\frac{1}{2}$ out of 70 in English and 45 out of 81 in French?

5. Two-thirds of a fence has been painted. If there are still 15 m to paint, how long is the fence?

6. After a wage increase of 8% a man's weekly earnings rise to £162. How much did he earn before the increase?

   If, at the same time, he must pay tax at 30% on all his earnings, by what percentage will his tax bill rise?

7. Two friends plan a three-day hike. They plan to walk $\frac{1}{3}$ of the whole journey on the first day and $\frac{3}{8}$ of the whole journey on the second day.
   (a) What fraction of the whole journey do they plan to walk on the first two days?
   (b) What fraction of the whole journey would be left for the third day?
   (c) The third day's journey is planned to be 14 miles. How long is the whole journey? (WMEB)

8. A 'do it yourself' tax manual gives the following instructions:
   1. take £2000 from gross pay to find taxable pay;
   2. calculate 30% of taxable pay to find tax paid;
   3. take tax paid away from gross pay to find net pay.

   (a) Use these instructions to find the tax paid and the net pay when the gross pay is £8000.

   (b) If $G$ is the gross pay, $T$ is the taxable pay, and $X$ is the tax paid, express
       (i) $T$ in terms of $G$, and
       (ii) $X$ in terms of $T$.                    (NREB)

9. A wine trader buys Italian wine at a cost to him of 1800 lire per bottle. What is this in pence if £1 = 2400 lire? The trader sells the wine in the United Kingdom at £2.25 per bottle, but 40% of this is tax. What is the tax per bottle and how much profit does the trader enjoy on each bottle sold? What are the trader's profits as a percentage of his costs?

10. I have £1000 worth of stocks and shares. Their value falls by 10% one week, but rises the following week by 20% of their new lower value. Show that the rise over the fortnight is 8% of the original value.

11. The menu lists the price of a meal as £8.00 before the service charge of 10% and VAT at 15% are added. Show that the final cost of the meal is £10.12, and that this is $26\frac{1}{2}$% more than the menu price. Why is the increase *not* simply $10\% + 15\% = 25\%$?

12. Universal Record Distributors supply gramophone records and tapes to local shops. They offer 10% discount on orders of 25 or more copies of the same record. What numbers of copies of one record is it *never* worth ordering?

13. The cash price of a video recorder is £450.

   Under a Hire Purchase agreement a customer pays a deposit of 20 per cent of the cash price, and interest is charged at 8 per cent per annum simple interest on the balance.

   The payments are to be spread over 36 monthly instalments.

   Calculate:
   (a) the deposit paid
   (b) the balance to be paid
   (c) the interest to be paid
   (d) the total amount to be repaid by instalments over three years
   (e) the amount repaid each month.                    (EAEB)

49

14. A shopkeeper made a profit of £20 by selling a suit of clothes for £92.

Write down the cost price to the shopkeeper, and calculate the percentage profit which he made on this cost price.

At a later date, the cost price to the shopkeeper was increased, but the shopkeeper still sold similar suits for £92, although his profit was reduced to 15%. Calculate the new cost price to the shopkeeper.

Later still, the cost price to the shopkeeper was increased to £90, and the shopkeeper raised his selling price so that he still made 15% profit. Calculate
(i)  the new selling price to the customer
(ii) the percentage increase in the price paid by the customer.
(C)

15. A trader buys 300 kg of strawberries for £210. He begins to sell them at the rate of £1.20 per kilogram. When 180 kg have been sold, the strawberries begin to go soft and he reduces the price to 60 p per kilogram. He sells another 60 kg at this price, but the rest go bad and have to be thrown away. Calculate the percentage profit on his outlay.

Next day he buys another 300 kg for £210 and begins to sell them at £1 per kilogram. When 200 kg have been sold at this price, he decides to reduce the price. Find the price per kilogram that he must charge in order to make a profit of 25% on this day's outlay, assuming that all the strawberries are sold and none are thrown away.          (O & C)

16. Three children, $A$, $B$ and $C$, are sharing a bowl of food. When the bowl is passed to $A$, he always takes one-sixth of whatever is in it, whereas $B$ and $C$ always take one-fifth and one-quarter respectively, of whatever is in the bowl when it is passed to them. If the bowl, which is full at the start, is passed round in the order $A$, $B$, $C$,

(a) show that all the children receive equal amounts

(b) find what fraction of the food is left when each child has taken (i) one helping  (ii) two helpings.

If, on the other hand, the bowl is passed round in the order $C$, $B$, $A$,

(c) show that the sizes of the helpings taken by $C$, $B$ and $A$ are in the ratio $5 : 3 : 2$,

(d) find what fraction of the bowlful each child has eaten, and what fraction is left, after each child has taken two helpings.          (LU)

17. Work out the value of these continuous fractions.

(a) $1 + \dfrac{1}{1 + 1}$

(b) $1 + \dfrac{1}{1 + \dfrac{1}{1 + 1}}$

(c) $1 + \dfrac{1}{1 + \dfrac{1}{1 + \dfrac{1}{1 + 1}}}$

Continue the sequence. You should recognise the pattern of numerators and denominators. What is the sequence called?

What do you notice about the decimal value of these fractions.

# 3 RATIO AND PROPORTION

## RATIO

Fractions are sometimes written as *ratios*. For example, the ratio $1:10$ is equivalent to the fraction $\frac{1}{10}$.

Ratios may be cancelled down to lower terms, just like fractions. Thus the ratio $2:8$ would normally be cancelled down to $1:4$ just as the fraction $\frac{2}{8}$ would normally be cancelled down to $\frac{1}{4}$.

The scales of maps and models are often given as ratios. Ordnance Survey maps, for example, are scaled $1:50\,000$. Thus a distance of 1 cm on the map represents a distance of 50 000 cm or 500 m on the ground.

**Example** A model aircraft is built to the scale $1:120$. If the wing-span of the model is 20 cm, what is the wing-span of the aircraft?

As the scale of the model is $1:120$, the wing-span of the actual aircraft will be $120 \times 20$ cm $= 2400$ cm $= 24$ m.

If the aircraft is 42 m long, how long is the model?

The aircraft is $42$ m $= 4200$ cm long. The model is $\frac{1}{120}$ of this size:

$$4200 \times \frac{1}{120} = 35 \text{ cm}$$

Unlike a fraction, however, a ratio may show the relationship between more than two amounts.

**Example** Martin, Alan and Patrick share £60 between them in the ratio $3:4:5$. How much does each receive?

The ratio apportions $3 + 4 + 5 = 12$ equal parts. Thus each part is worth $£\frac{60}{12} = £5$. Martin receives three parts, i.e. $3 \times £5 = £15$; Alan receives four parts, i.e. $4 \times £5 = £20$; and Patrick receives five parts, i.e. $5 \times £5 = £25$.

**Example** If $a:b = 4:5$ and $b:c = 6:7$ find $a:b:c$.

Multiplying both parts of the ratio $a:b$ by 6 gives $4 \times 6 : 5 \times 6 = 24:30$ and similarly multiplying $b:c$ by 5 gives $6 \times 5 : 7 \times 5 = 30:35$. Now, as $b$ in both ratios is the same, i.e. 30, we can say

$$a:b:c = 24:30:35$$

**EXERCISE 3a**

1. Express in lowest terms the ratios
   (a) $2:4$        (b) $3:9$        (c) $12:8$
   (d) $10:20:40$    (e) $15:25:30$    (f) $16:24:32:48$.

2. Express in lowest terms the ratios
   (a) $1\,cm:1\,m$      (b) $1\,m:1\,km$      (c) $1\,cm:1\,km$
   (d) $1\,cm:4\,km$.     (e) $1\,mm:5\,cm$    (f) $15\,mm:1\,m$.

3. A model bridge is 30 cm long and represents a real bridge which is 120 m long. What is the scale of the model?

   If the model is 3 cm wide, what is the width of the actual bridge?

   The bridge supports are 20 m high; what is the height of the supports of the model bridge?

4. I draw a map for a friend so that his journey of 5 km to my house is represented by a road of 20 cm. What is the scale of this map?

   If my friend misses a turning, and his actual journey is represented on the map by a road 34 cm long, how far has he come?

5. Divide 12 in the ratio
   (a) $1:2$        (b) $1:2:3$       (c) $1:4:7$.

6. Divide 54 in the ratio
   (a) $3:2:1$      (b) $3:3:2:1$     (c) $3:5:4:6$.

7. Divide 108 in the ratio
   (a) $7:5$        (b) $2:3:4$      (c) $2:3:3:4$.

8. Divide 144 in the ratio
   (a) $2:1$        (b) $3:4:5$      (c) $7:8:9$.

9. Divide 242 in the ratio
   (a) $1:1$        (b) $4:7:11$     (c) $1:2:3:5$.

10. Sharon and Darren share £3.57 in the ratio $4:3$. What fraction of the money does Sharon get? How much is this?

11. Three girls share a sum of money in the ratio $9:2:5$. If the smallest share is £1.20, what are the other two shares?

12. Three boys share a sum of money in the ratio $4:2:9$. If the boy with the largest share gets £1.80, what was the sum of money?

13. The firm of ABC Plastics is started up by three partners with a total investment of £50 000. Mr. Abbott, Mr. Bamford and Mr. Cross invest money in the ratio $5:8:12$.
    (a) Calculate how much money each of the three partners invests.
    (b) At the end of a year's trading, a profit of £4000 is declared. The profit is shared by the three partners in the same ratio as their original investments.

    Calculate how much of the profit Mr. Bamford should receive.                                        (EMREB)

14. A mixture contains calcium, carbon and oxygen in the ratio $10:3:12$ respectively.
    (a) What fraction of the mixture is calcium? Give your answer in its lowest terms.
    (b) What percentage of the mixture is calcium?
    (c) In a jar of the mixture there are 432 grams of oxygen. How many grams of carbon are there?          (WMREB)

15. Jonathan divides £56 between himself and Janette, so that he keeps three times as much as he gives her. How much does Janette get?

16. In a game of Scrabble, Harry scores twice as many as Dick but half as many as Tom. Write down a ratio representing Tom, Dick and Harry's scores. If the three together score a total of 567, what are their three scores?

17. A photograph has sides in the ratio $3:2$. If a standard print is $7\frac{1}{2}$ cm long, find the length of the shorter side. If the photograph is enlarged so that the longer side is $10\frac{1}{2}$ cm, what is the width?

18. The angles of a triangle are in the ratio $2:2:5$. What are its angles in degrees?

19. The angles of another triangle are in the ratio $4:5:6$. Find the size of its smallest angle.

20. If $x:y:1 = 3:1:4$ find $x$ and $y$ as decimal fractions.

21. $x, y$ and $z$ are three quantities such that $x : y = 5 : 7$ and $y : z = 4 : 3$. Find the ratio $x : y : z$.

22. If $x : y = 3 : 5$ and $y : z = 6 : 7$, find $x : y : z$.

23. If $a : b = 2 : 3$ and $b : c = 5 : 4$, find $a : b : c$.

24. If $l : m = 8 : 5$ and $m : n = 8 : 3$, find $l : m : n$.

25. If $a : b = 2 : 1$ and $b : c = 4 : 1$, find $a : c$.

26. If $m : n = 2 : 7$ and $n : p = 2 : 9$, find $m : p$.

27. If $x : y = 7 : 2$ and $y : z = 3 : 1$, find $x : z$.

28. An ordnance survey map has a scale of $1 : 25\,000$.
    (a) How far, in kilometres, is a journey shown as 21 cm on the map?
    (b) What distance on the map would represent an actual distance of 10 km?
    (c) A rectangular field is shown to be 0.8 cm by 1.2 cm on the map. What are the actual length and breadth of the field?
    (d) What is the actual area of the field (in m²)?

29. An ordnance survey map has a scale of $1 : 50\,000$.
    (a) How far is a journey shown as 9 cm on the map?
    (b) On the map, a reservoir is represented by a rectangle 0.2 cm by 0.5 cm. What are the length and breadth of the reservoir, and what is its area?
    (c) On another map a journey of 15 km was shown as 50 cm. What is the scale of this map?

30. A map is drawn to a scale of $1 : 50\,000$.
    (a) Calculate the actual distance, in kilometres, represented by 1 cm on the map.
    (b) Two towns are 24 km apart. Calculate, in centimetres, their distance apart on the map.
    (c) On the map, a farm has an area of 20 cm². Calculate, in square kilometres, the actual area of the farm.           (C)

## DIRECT PROPORTION

Two quantities that increase or decrease together, always staying in the same ratio to each other (i.e. if one is doubled then so is the other; if one is halved, then so is the other; and so on), are said to be in *direct proportion* or to *vary directly*.

55

If $y$ is proportional to $x$ we write

$$y \propto x$$

which is taken to mean that the ratio $y:x$ is fixed.

$$y:x = k:1$$

where $k$ is a constant, called the *constant of proportionality*.

We can solve problems involving proportions using ratios.

**Example** The height, $y$, of an image on a screen is in direct proportion to the distance, $x$, of the screen from the projector. If the image is 30 cm high when the screen is 150 cm from the projector, how far from the screen should the projector be if the image is to be reduced to 24 cm?

$$y \propto x$$

$$y:x = k:1 \qquad \text{(where } k \text{ is a constant)}$$

We wish to find $x$ when $y = 24$ given that $y = 30$ when $x = 150$.

Hence

$$24:x = 30:150$$

or

$$\frac{x}{24} = \frac{150}{30}$$

Leading to

$$x = \frac{150}{30} \times 24 = 120$$

The projector must be placed 120 cm from the screen.

## INVERSE PROPORTION

Two quantities that vary in such a way that one increases in the same proportion as the other decreases are said to be *inversely proportional* or to *vary inversely*.

$$y \propto \frac{1}{x}$$

It follows that

$$y:1/x = k:1$$

But this is a rather clumsy expression to work from. However $y:1/x$ can be written as $xy:1$.

Thus $xy:1 = k:1$ and $xy = k$.

So, $y \propto 1/x$ gives $xy = k$ (where $k$ is constant)

56

**Example** The pressure, $P$, of a quantity of gas varies inversely with the volume, $V$, of its container. If the gas pressure is $10 \, \text{N/m}^2$ in a container of $25 \, \text{m}^3$, what will be the pressure of the same quantity of gas in a container of $20 \, \text{m}^3$ volume?

Since $P$ varies inversely with $V$,

$$P \propto 1/V$$

Hence $\qquad PV = k \qquad$ (where $k$ is a constant)

We require $P$ when $V = 20$ given that $P = 10$ when $V = 25$, so

$$P \times 20 = 10 \times 25$$

$$P = \frac{250}{20} = 12.5 \, \text{N/m}^2$$

**Example** If $y$ is inversely proportional to the square of $x$ and $y = 3$ when $x = 4$, find the value of $y$ when $x = 6$.

$$y \propto 1/x^2$$

Hence $\qquad x^2 y = k \qquad$ (where $k$ is a constant)

We require $y$ when $x = 6$, given that $y = 3$ when $x = 4$

$$36 \times y = 16 \times 3$$

$$y = \frac{16 \times 3}{36} = 1\tfrac{1}{3}$$

**EXERCISE 3b**

1. If $y \propto x$, and $y = 4$ when $x = 10$, find
   (a) $y$ when $x = 15$ $\qquad$ (b) $x$ when $y = 16$.

2. If $y \propto x$ and $y = 7$ when $x = 10.5$, find
   (a) $y$ when $x = 17.5$ $\qquad$ (b) $x$ when $y = 3.5$.

3. If $y \propto x$ and $y = 8$ when $x = 5$, find
   (a) $y$ when $x = 12.5$ $\qquad$ (b) $x$ when $y = 10$.

4. If $y \propto x$ and $y = 12$ when $x = 16$, find
   (a) $y$ when $x = 20$ $\qquad$ (b) $x$ when $y = 21$.

5. If $y \propto x^2$ and $y = 36$ when $x = 3$, find
   (a) $y$ when $x = 1.5$ $\qquad$ (b) $x$ when $y = 25$.

6. If $y \propto x^2$, and $y = 3$ when $x = 2$, find
   (a) $y$ when $x = 4$ $\qquad$ (b) $x$ when $y = 48$.

7. If $y \propto \dfrac{1}{x}$, and $y = 4$ when $x = 6$, find

   (a) $y$ when $x = 8$  (b) $x$ when $y = 2$.

8. If $y \propto \dfrac{1}{x}$ and $y = 3$ when $x = 12$, find

   (a) $y$ when $x = 4$  (b) $x$ when $y = 6$.

9. If $y \propto \dfrac{1}{x}$ and $y = 2$ when $x = 27$, find

   (a) $y$ when $x = 18$  (b) $x$ when $y = 6$.

10. If $y \propto \dfrac{1}{x}$ and $y = 3.6$ when $x = 4$, find

    (a) $y$ when $x = 1.2$  (b) $x$ when $y = 0.9$.

11. If $y \propto \dfrac{1}{x}$ and $y = 0.5$ when $x = 3$, find

    (a) $y$ when $x = 0.6$  (b) $x$ when $y = 15$.

12. If $y \propto \dfrac{1}{x^2}$, and $y = 4$ when $x = 6$, find

    (a) $y$ when $x = 4$  (b) $x$ when $y = 1$.

13. If $p \propto q^3$, and $p = 12$ when $q = 2$, find
    (a) $p$ when $q = 3$  (b) $q$ when $p = 324$.

14. If $r \propto \dfrac{1}{\sqrt{s}}$, and $r = 7$ when $s = 36$, find

    (a) $r$ when $s = 49$  (b) $s$ when $r = 10\frac{1}{2}$.

15. The thickness of a wooden barrier is directly proportional to the number of planks used to build it. If four planks make a 9 cm barrier, how thick would a barrier of six planks be?

16. The number of neighbours who complain about the noise of my record player is in direct proportion to the volume setting. If two neighbours complain when I have it set on '3', how many will complain when I turn it up to '9'?

17. The number, $n$, of people in the queue in the post office seems to vary inversely with the time, $t$, I have to spare, i.e.

    $n \propto \dfrac{1}{t}$. When I have 6 minutes, two people are queuing. How

    long is the queue likely to be when I have only 1 minute to complete my business?

18. The time it takes me to get to work in the mornings is inversely proportional to the speed at which I drive. At 40 m.p.h. it takes me 12 minutes. How long will it take me at

    (a) 30 m.p.h.  (b) 48 m.p.h.  (c) 64 m.p.h.?

19. The pressure of a gas in a container varies directly with the temperature. If it is at a pressure of $50 \, \text{N/m}^2$ at $75°$ what will the pressure be at $135°$?

20. The commission earned by the Worseforware perfume sales-man varies directly with his sales. If he is paid £22 in one week, having sold £143 worth of goods, what commission can he expect in a week when he sells £208 worth? How much would he need to sell to earn £40?

21. The length of time taken to complete a job varies inversely with the number of men working on it. If 10 men take 10 days, how long will eight men take?

22. Corresponding sides of similar triangles are directly pro-portional to each other. The three triangles in Fig. 3.1 are similar. Find the lengths $x, y$ and $z$.

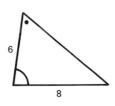  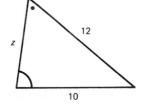

Fig. 3.1

23. The heat, $H$, produced in a wire is directly proportional to the square of the current, $I$, that flows through it. Given that a current of 4 amps produces 448 joules per minute find

    (a) an equation relating $H$ and $I$,

    (b) the heat per minute produced by a current of 11 amps.

    What current would produce heat at the rate of 600 joules per minute?

24. The resistance, $R$, in a given length of copper wire is inversely proportional to the square of the diameter, $d$, of the wire. Given that the resistance in a wire with diameter 2 mm is 12 ohms, find

    (a) an equation relating $R$ and $d$,

    (b) the resistance in a similar piece of wire of identical length but of diameter 2.8 mm,

    (c) the diameter of a third wire which has resistance of 15.2 ohms.

# 4 POWERS

$$5 \times 5 \text{ is written } 5^2$$

Five is said to be *raised to the power two* (or *squared*) as there are *two* fives multiplied together. Similarly,

$$5 \times 5 \times 5 \text{ is written } 5^3$$

Five is said to be *raised to the power three* (or *cubed*) as there are *three* fives multiplied together.

$$5 \times 5 \times 5 \times 5 \text{ is written } 5^4$$

Five is *raised to the power four* as there are *four* fives multiplied together, and so on.

We could work out the value of these powers. Thus $5 \times 5 = 25$; hence $5^2 = 25$. $5 \times 5 \times 5 = 125$; hence $5^3 = 125$, and so on.

The power notation is convenient short-hand when strings of the same number are multiplied together. Be careful not to confuse $5 \times 2$ (which is 10) and $5^2$ (which is $5 \times 5 = 25$).

## COMBINING POWERS

Adding powers of a number is equivalent to multiplication. Consider $5^2 \times 5^3$.

$$
\begin{aligned}
5^2 \times 5^3 &= (5 \times 5) \times (5 \times 5 \times 5) \\
&= 5 \times 5 \times 5 \times 5 \times 5 \\
&= 5^5
\end{aligned}
$$

Thus $\qquad 5^2 \times 5^3 = 5^{2+3} = 5^5$

**Examples**
$$2^3 \times 2^4 = 2^{3+4} = 2^7$$
$$10^2 \times 10^3 \times 10^4 = 10^{2+3+4} = 10^9$$

Subtracting powers of a number is equivalent to division. Consider $5^3 \div 5^2$.

$$5^3 \div 5^2 = \frac{5 \times \cancel{5} \times \cancel{5}}{\cancel{5} \times \cancel{5}} = 5^1$$

Thus $\qquad 5^3 \div 5^2 = 5^{3-2} = 5^1$

**Examples**

$$2^5 \div 2^2 = 2^{5-2} = 2^3$$
$$10^4 \div 10^3 = 10^{4-3} = 10^1$$

Multiplying powers of a number is equivalent to raising it to one power and then immediately to another. Consider $(5^2)^4$.

$$(5^2)^4 = 5^2 \times 5^2 \times 5^2 \times 5^2$$
$$= 5 \times 5 \times 5 \times 5 \times 5 \times 5 \times 5 \times 5$$
$$= 5^8$$

Thus $\qquad (5^2)^4 = 5^{2 \times 4} = 5^8$

**Examples**

$$(3^3)^2 = 3^{3 \times 2} = 3^6$$
$$(10^3)^3 = 10^{3 \times 3} = 10^9$$

**EXERCISE 4a**

1. Write as powers
   (a) $2 \times 2 \times 2$
   (b) $3 \times 3 \times 3 \times 3$
   (c) $4 \times 4 \times 4$
   (d) $7 \times 7 \times 7 \times 7 \times 7 \times 7$
   (e) $9 \times 9 \times 9 \times 9 \times 9 \times 9 \times 9$.

2. Work out the values of
   (a) $2^4$  (b) $3^3$  (c) $7^2$  (d) $4^1$  (e) $3^4$
   (f) $4^3$  (g) $2^5$  (h) $6^3$  (i) $10^4$  (j) $10^6$.

3. Arrange these numbers into order, smallest first:
   (a) $32, 3^2, 2^3, 23, 3 \times 2$
   (b) $6^2, 26, 2^6, 2 \times 6, 62$
   (c) $4^3, 4 \times 3, 43, 3^4, 34$.

4. Simplify the following, giving your answers as powers:
   (a) $2^5 \times 2^3$  (b) $3^4 \times 3^2$  (c) $2^5 \div 2^3$  (d) $3^4 \div 3^2$
   (e) $(2^5)^3$  (f) $(3^4)^2$  (g) $(10^2)^3$  (h) $(10^3)^3$.

5. (a) Work out the values of
      (i) $2^2$  (ii) $2^4$  (iii) $2^6$  (iv) $2^8$.
   (b) Do the values of $2^4$ and $2^2$ multiplied together give $2^6$?
   (c) Use your answers to show that
      (i) $2^8 \div 2^6 = 2^2$  (ii) $(2^4)^2 = 2^8$.

6. Write as powers of 10
   (a) one hundred  (b) one thousand  (c) one million.

61

7. Deduce from your answers to Question 6 the power of 10 that represents
   (a) one hundred thousand
   (b) one hundred million
   (c) one American billion (one thousand million)
   (d) one English billion (one million million).

## ZERO AS A POWER

Consider $5^4 \div 5^4$. When any number is divided by itself the answer is 1. (For example $2 \div 2 = 1$; $11 \div 11 = 1$, etc.) Thus $5^4 \div 5^4 = 1$. However, if we apply the rules of powers, then

$$5^4 \div 5^4 = 5^{4-4} = 5^0$$

Hence $$5^0 = 1$$

We could have shown the same with *any* number, not just 5. *Any* number raised to the power zero is one. Thus, for example,

$$7^0 = 1$$

$$\left(\frac{1}{4}\right)^0 = 1$$

Only zero itself is an exception to this rule. $0^0$ cannot be evaluated.

## NEGATIVE POWERS

Consider $5^2 \div 5^6$.

$$5^2 \div 5^6 = 5^{2-6} = 5^{-4}$$

But $$5^2 \div 5^6 = \frac{5 \times 5}{5 \times 5 \times 5 \times 5 \times 5 \times 5}$$

$$= \frac{1}{5 \times 5 \times 5 \times 5}$$

$$= \frac{1}{5^4}$$

So $5^{-4}$ is the same as $\frac{1}{5^4}$.

In general, a negative power means the *reciprocal* of the number or 'one over the number'. Thus

$$4^{-2} = \frac{1}{4^2} = \frac{1}{16}$$

$$7^{-1} = \frac{1}{7}$$

$$10^{-3} = \frac{1}{10^3} = \frac{1}{1000}$$

## FRACTIONS AS POWERS

Consider $5^{\frac{1}{2}}$. If $5^{\frac{1}{2}}$ is squared, we get

$$(5^{\frac{1}{2}})^2 = 5^{\frac{1}{2} \times 2} = 5^1$$

$$(5^{\frac{1}{2}})^2 = 5.$$

It follows that $\qquad 5^{\frac{1}{2}} = \sqrt{5}$

i.e. the *square root* of 5.

Similarly, we could show that

$$2^{\frac{1}{3}} = \sqrt[3]{2} \qquad \text{i.e. the } \textit{cube root} \text{ of } \mathbf{3}$$

$$7^{\frac{1}{4}} = \sqrt[4]{7} \qquad \text{i.e. the } \textit{fourth root} \text{ of } 7$$

Now consider $5^{\frac{2}{3}}$.

$$5^{\frac{2}{3}} = (5^{\frac{1}{3}})^2 = (\sqrt[3]{5})^2$$

i.e. the square of the cube root of 5. Alternatively, if $5^{\frac{2}{3}}$ is cubed, we get

$$(5^{\frac{2}{3}})^3 = 5^{\frac{2}{3} \times 3} = 5^2$$

As $5^{\frac{2}{3}}$ cubed gives $5^2$, it follows that $5^{\frac{2}{3}} = \sqrt[3]{5^2}$, i.e. the cube root of 5 squared

$$5^{\frac{2}{3}} \underset{\text{cube root}}{\overset{\text{square}}{\diagdown}}$$

Similarly,

$$8^{\frac{2}{3}} = (8^{\frac{1}{3}})^2 = (\sqrt[3]{8})^2 = (2)^2 = 4$$

or $\qquad 8^{\frac{2}{3}} = (8^2)^{\frac{1}{3}} = \sqrt[3]{64} = 4$

**Examples** (*i*) $\quad 4^{\frac{1}{2}} = \sqrt{4} = 2$

(*ii*) $\quad 27^{\frac{1}{3}} = \sqrt[3]{27} = 3$

(iii) $27^{\frac{2}{3}} = (27^{\frac{1}{3}})^2 = (3)^2 = 9$

(iv) $4^{\frac{3}{2}} = (\sqrt{4})^3 = 2^3 = 8$

(v) $4^{-\frac{3}{2}} = (\sqrt{4})^{-3} = 2^{-3} = \dfrac{1}{8}$

(vi) $64^{-\frac{1}{3}} = \dfrac{1}{64^{\frac{1}{3}}} = \dfrac{1}{\sqrt[3]{64}} = \dfrac{1}{4}$

**EXERCISE 4b**  Find the values of

1. (a) $6^0$     (b) $3.4^0$     (c) $(\frac{1}{2})^0$     (d) $(8.35)^0$

2. (a) $2^{-1}$     (b) $3^{-2}$     (c) $10^{-2}$     (d) $10^{-4}$

3. (a) $3^{-1}$     (b) $4^{-2}$     (c) $2^0$     (d) $5^{-1}$

4. (a) $2^{-2}$     (b) $6^{-1}$     (c) $5^{-2}$     (d) $3^{-3}$

5. (a) $4^{-1}$     (b) $10^0$     (c) $7^{-2}$     (d) $2^{-3}$.

6. Work out the following, giving your answer both as a value and as a power of 2:

(a) $2^4 \div 2^3$     (b) $2^2 \times 2^{-1}$     (c) $2^2 \times 2^{-4}$     (d) $2^2 \div 2^{-1}$

(e) $2^{-2} \times 2^{-4}$     (f) $(2^{-2})^2$     (g) $2^{-2} \div 2^{-4}$     (h) $(2^{-2})^{\frac{1}{2}}$.

(i) $2^2 \times 2^{-2}$     (j) $2^1 \times 2^{-3}$     (k) $2^3 \div 2^5$     (l) $(2^2)^{-1}$.

7. Using your calculator, if you wish, write down the values of the following:

(a) $2^2, 3^2, 4^2, \ldots 12^2$       (b) $2^3, 3^3, 4^3, \ldots 10^3$

(c) $2^4, 3^4, 4^4, 5^4$.

Use your answers to Question 7 to find the values of the following. Do not use your calculator.

8. (a) $4^{\frac{1}{2}}$     (b) $81^{\frac{1}{2}}$     (c) $36^{\frac{1}{2}}$     (d) $9^{\frac{1}{2}}$

9. (a) $100^{\frac{1}{2}}$     (b) $4^{\frac{3}{2}}$     (c) $9^{\frac{3}{2}}$     (d) $25^{\frac{1}{2}}$

10. (a) $64^{\frac{1}{2}}$     (b) $144^{\frac{1}{2}}$     (c) $125^{\frac{1}{3}}$     (d) $64^{\frac{1}{3}}$

11. (a) $256^{\frac{1}{4}}$     (b) $49^{\frac{1}{2}}$     (c) $27^{\frac{1}{3}}$     (d) $125^{\frac{1}{3}}$

12. (a) $125^{\frac{2}{3}}$     (b) $100^{\frac{3}{2}}$     (c) $36^{\frac{3}{2}}$     (d) $8^{\frac{2}{3}}$

13. (a) $49^{-\frac{1}{2}}$     (b) $27^{-\frac{1}{3}}$     (c) $1000^{-\frac{1}{3}}$     (d) $100^{-\frac{3}{2}}$

14. (a) $216^{-\frac{1}{3}}$     (b) $343^{-\frac{1}{3}}$     (c) $256^{-\frac{1}{4}}$     (d) $625^{-\frac{1}{4}}$.

15. (a) $16^{\frac{1}{4}}$     (b) $16^{\frac{3}{4}}$     (c) $16^{-\frac{3}{4}}$     (d) $(16^{\frac{1}{4}})^5$

16. (a) $(-5)^0$     (b) $(-5)^1$     (c) $(-5)^2$     (d) $(-5)^3$.

17. (a) $(-8)^1$     (b) $(-8)^2$     (c) $(-8)^0$     (d) $(-8)^{\frac{1}{3}}$

18. (a) $8^{\frac{1}{3}}$     (b) $8^{-\frac{1}{3}}$     (c) $8^{\frac{2}{3}}$     (d) $8^{-\frac{2}{3}}$.

Find the value of $x$ in the following. Use your calculator if you think it will help:

19. (a) $121^x = 11$               (b) $64^x = 4$

    (c) $5^x = 1$                 (d) $9^x = \frac{1}{3}$.

20. (a) $2^x = 2$     (b) $125^x = \frac{1}{5}$     (c) $81^x = \frac{1}{3}$     (d) $(\frac{1}{2})^x = 2$.

21. $2^{-1} = \frac{1}{2}$. What is $(\frac{1}{2})^{-1}$?

If your calculator has a $\boxed{1/x}$ button, you can find $2^{-1}$ and $(\frac{1}{2})^{-1}$ using it. Explain.

What happens if you find $4^{-1}$ using the $\boxed{1/x}$ key, and then press the $\boxed{1/x}$ key a second time?

Try pushing the $\boxed{1/x}$ key several times with other numbers, besides 4. Can you explain what happens?

## STANDARD FORM

Any number, no matter how large or small, may be written in *standard form* or *scientific notation*; that is, as a number between 1 and 10 multipled by an appropriate power of 10. For example

$$253.7 = 2.537 \times 100 = 2.537 \times 10^2$$

Since the first part of standard form must be written as a value between 1 and 10, the decimal point in the original number (253.7) has to be moved two places to the left. This effectively divides the number by 100, so to compensate we multiply by 100 (written as $10^2$ in standard form).

**Examples**
$$1234.5 = 1.2345 \times 10^3$$
$$67890 = 6.7890 \times 10^4$$
$$96\,000\,000 = 9.6 \times 10^7$$

The decimal point in small numbers, such as $0.000543$, has to be moved to the right if the numbers are to be written as a value between 1 and 10. This multiplies the number so we compensate by using a *negative* power of 10 (so effectively dividing).

65

$$0.000543 = 5.43 \div 10000 = 5.43 \times 10^{-4}$$

$$0.068 = 6.8 \div 100 = 6.8 \times 10^{-2}$$

$$0.00789 = 7.89 \div 1000 = 7.89 \times 10^{-3}$$

## CALCULATORS AND STANDARD FORM

Calculators use standard form so that very large or very small numbers can be displayed in eight or ten digits.

For example, the number 123 456 789 000 could not be shown, in the ordinary way, on an eight or even a ten digit calculator display: the calculator automatically switches to standard form.

Try entering 12 345 678 × 10 000 into your calculator and see what happens. If yours is an eight digit calculator, you should find it displays only part of the number, perhaps:

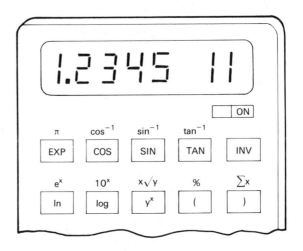

Fig. 4.1

Most eight digit calculators will *not* round the last digit correctly (did yours?). However, although the number is too long for the display, it is still stored inside the calculator. Now divide the number by 10 000 and you will recover the 'lost' figures. Try it and see.

If you have a ten digit calculator, experiment with an even bigger number, say 2 123 456 789 × 1000 and see what happens.

You can enter a number into a calculator using the EXP key

(EXP is short for exponential — another word for the power of a number).

66

For example 123 000 000 can be keyed into a calculator as follows:

| 1 | . | 2 | 3 | EXP | 8 |

(since $123\,000\,000 = 1.23 \times 10^8$ in standard form).

Similarly, $0.000\,000\,123$ can be keyed in as

| 1 | . | 2 | 3 | EXP | 7 | +/− |

(since $0.000\,000\,123 = 1.23 \times 10^{-7}$).

## POWERS AND ARITHMETIC IN STANDARD FORM

### Multiplication and Division

Numbers written in standard or scientific form include powers of ten as part of the number. These powers of 10 multiply and divide each other just like any other powers. For this reason it is best to separate the powers of 10 and deal with them on their own.

**Example** $(3.9 \times 10^2) \times (1.1 \times 10^4)$.

Rearranging the problem to bracket the powers of 10 together we have

$$(3.9 \times 1.1) \times (10^2 \times 10^4) = (3.9 \times 1.1) \times 10^{2+4}$$
$$= 4.29 \times 10^6$$

**Example** $(1.44 \times 10^{-3}) \div (7.2 \times 10^{-6}) = (1.44 \div 7.2) \times (10^{-3} \div 10^{-6})$
$$= 1.44 \div 7.2 \times 10^{-3 - (-6)}$$
$$= 0.2 \times 10^{-3+6}$$
$$= 0.2 \times 10^3$$

However, this number is not yet in standard form since 0.2 is not a number between 1 and 10. Using $0.2 = 2 \times 10^{-1}$ we continue

$$0.2 \times 10^3 = (2 \times 10^{-1}) \times 10^3 = 2 \times 10^{-1+3} = 2 \times 10^2$$

**Example** $\dfrac{(1.1 \times 10^{-3})^2}{6.05 \times 10^4} = \dfrac{(1.1)^2 \times (10^{-3})^2}{6.05 \times 10^4}$

$$= \dfrac{1.21}{6.05} \times \dfrac{10^{-6}}{10^4}$$

$$= 0.2 \times 10^{-6\,-4}$$
$$= (2 \times 10^{-1}) \times 10^{-10}$$
$$= 2 \times 10^{-11}$$

## Addition and Subtraction

Addition and subtraction of numbers written in standard form is more tricky. In fact the powers of 10 make the problem *more* difficult; it is best to convert the numbers into ordinary decimals and then add or subtract in the usual way.

**Examples** (*i*) $\qquad 1.1 \times 10^2 + 2.4 \times 10^3 = 110 + 2400 = 2510$
$$= 2.510 \times 10^3$$

(*ii*) $\qquad 9.1 \times 10^{-2} - 4.3 \times 10^{-3} = 0.091 - 0.0043 = 0.0867$
$$= 8.67 \times 10^{-2}$$

**EXERCISE 4c**   Write the following in standard form:

1. (a) 78.9          (b) 542.1          (c) 32 000
   (d) 32 000 000     (e) 110 000      (f) 931.62.

2. (a) 0.0134        (b) 0.000 51      (c) 0.01
   (d) 0.000 011      (e) 0.000 002    (f) 0.003 10.

3. (a) 3456            (b) 0.3456         (c) 0.000 345 6
   (d) 0.000 000 034 56        (e) 0.000 000 003 456.

4. (a) $52 \times 10^2$       (b) $0.5 \times 10^3$      (c) $278.1 \times 10^6$
   (d) $3054.7 \times 10^7$.    (e) $12.1 \times 10^4$    (f) $813.6 \times 10^2$.

5. (a) 325.4          (b) 0.007 23      (c) 0.21
   (d) 239 012        (e) 42.478       (f) 11.213.

6. (a) 32 000        (b) 17 000 000    (c) 532 000
   (d) 320.21        (e) 483.231      (f) 832 001 000.

With*out* a calculator work out the following, giving your answers in standard form:

7. $(2 \times 10^4) \times (3 \times 10^5)$         8. $(5 \times 10^{-7}) \div (4 \times 10^{-3})$

9. $(8.4 \times 10^3) \times (1.1 \times 10^{-2})$     10. $(3.3 \times 10^3) \div (1.1 \times 10^{-2})$

11. $(5 \times 10^{-7}) \times (4 \times 10^{-3})$       12. $(1.5 \times 10^5) \times (8 \times 10^{-2})$

13. $\dfrac{1.2 \times 10^5}{3 \times 10^2}$              14. $\dfrac{1.6 \times 10^4}{4 \times 10^2}$

15. $\dfrac{4.5 \times 10^5}{9 \times 10^1}$          16. $\dfrac{3.6 \times 10^7}{6 \times 10^4}$

17. $\dfrac{2.4 \times 10^3}{1.2 \times 10^{-2}}$          18. $\dfrac{4.2 \times 10^4}{2.1 \times 10^{-2}}$

19. $\dfrac{3.2 \times 10^5}{1.6 \times 10^{-1}}$          20. $\dfrac{4.4 \times 10^6}{1.1 \times 10^{-4}}$

21. $(2.3 \times 10^3) + (2.2 \times 10^2)$      22. $(2.3 \times 10^3) - (2.2 \times 10^2)$

23. $3.2 \times 10^4 + 5.4 \times 10^3$         24. $(3.91 \times 10^{-2}) - (2.5 \times 10^{-3})$

25. $5.11 \times 10^{-2} - 9.87 \times 10^{-4}$     26. $(4.2 \times 10^{-1}) - (3.2 \times 10^{-2})$.

27. With*out* using your calculator show that
$$\frac{1.2 \times 10^8 \times 3.6 \times 10^5}{4 \times 10^{-3} \times 1.8 \times 10^2}$$
is $6 \times 10^{13}$.

Now work out the question with your calculator, using the $\boxed{\text{EXP}}$ and the $\boxed{(}$ and $\boxed{)}$ keys.

Could you work out the answer on a calculator that has no memory or $\boxed{(}\,\boxed{)}$ keys, without writing anything down?

Use your calculator to work out these; take care to double check by estimating mentally the approximate answers.

28. $\dfrac{2 \times 10^3 \times 6 \times 10^2}{1.2 \times 4 \times 10^{12}}$      29. $\dfrac{4.2 \times 10^{-3} \times 8.1 \times 10^{11}}{1.8 \times 10^{12} \times 3.6 \times 10^{-13}}$

30. $\dfrac{2.73 \times 10^{-6} \times 3.63}{9.009 \times 10^{-3}}$      31. $\dfrac{3.6 \times 10^5 \times 1.2 \times 10^{12}}{6 \times 10^{-6} \times 1.44 \times 10^{-11}}$

32. $\dfrac{2.43 \times 10^{-8} \times 5.12 \times 10^{-9}}{8.1 \times 10^{10} \times 6 \times 10^{11}}$     33. $\dfrac{1.44 \times 10^3 \times 5.6 \times 10^{-7}}{5.4 \times 10^6 \times 3 \times 10^8}$.

34. The planet Pluto is 7 300 000 000 miles from the Sun. The star, Alpha Centauri, is 23 520 000 000 000 miles from the Sun. A light year is 5 880 000 000 000 miles.

(a) Write these astronomical distances in scientific notation.

(b) Estimate to 1 s.f. the number of light years between the Sun and Alpha Centauri.

(c) Estimate to 1 s.f. the number of miles in a light day.

35. The mass of an atom of hydrogen is approximately $1.66 \times 10^{-24}$ g, and that of an atom of oxygen is approximately $2.66 \times 10^{-23}$ g.

   (a) Find, giving the answer in standard form to three significant figures, the mass of a molecule of water, which consists of two atoms of hydrogen and one of oxygen.

   (b) The given masses are correct to three significant figures. Find the maximum possible error in your answer to (a), and show that this answer is not necessarily *correct* to three significant figures.

   For parts (c) and (d), use your answer to (a), approximating it to *two* significant figures.

   (c) Find, giving your answer in standard form, the approximate number of molecules in 1 g of water.

   (d) Find, to the nearest whole number, the percentage by mass of oxygen in water. (LU)

36. Investigate $(-1)^n$ for different values of $n$.

   What happens if $n$ is

   (a) an even number,

   (b) an odd number,

   (c) a negative number,

   (d) a fraction,

   (e) zero?

37. Can you find two numbers, $x$ and $y$ so that

$$x^y = y^x$$

   Are there other possibilities?

# 5 SETS

## SET NOTATION

Numbers or objects may be bracketed together to form a *set*. A set is usually denoted by a capital letter and its members are written inside curly brackets. For example, integers or whole numbers form a set, usually called $Z$, where

$$Z = \{\ldots, -3, -2, -1, 0, 1, 2, 3, \ldots\}$$

Or we might define a set, $F$, to be the factors of 6:

$$F = \{1, 2, 3, 6\}$$

The symbol $\in$ denotes that a number or object *belongs to* a set. A member of a set is often called an *element*, so $\in$ could also be translated as *'is an element of'*. $\notin$ means the opposite: *does not belong to*. Thus

$$4 \in Z \qquad \text{but} \qquad 4 \notin F$$

means that 4 belongs to the set of whole numbers, $Z$, but not to $F$, the set of factors of 6.

Some elements of a set may be grouped together to form a *subset*. For example, the set of natural numbers, $N = \{1, 2, 3, \ldots\}$ and is a subset of $Z$, the set of *all* whole numbers. We write

$$N \subset Z \qquad \text{or} \qquad Z \supset N$$

meaning that $N$ *is a subset of* $Z$ or $Z$ *contains the set* $N$. Similarly

$$F \subset Z \qquad \text{and} \qquad Z \supset F$$

The opposite, *'is not a subset of'*, is written $\not\subset$.

$n(A)$ means *the number of elements in set $A$*. Thus $n(F) = 4$ because set $F$ consists of 4 elements. $F$ is a *finite* set, i.e. it has a finite number of elements. $Z$ is an *infinite* set: the list of whole numbers runs on for ever.

The set containing no elements at all is called the *empty* or *null* set, denoted $\emptyset$ or $\{\ \}$. Thus $n(\emptyset) = 0$.

The set of all possible elements, usually defined at the beginning of each problem, is denoted by $\mathcal{E}$ or $\mathcal{U}$. Thus a question may begin $\mathcal{E} = \{x: 0 \leqslant x \leqslant 20\}$ meaning that the universal set is to be the set of all numbers, $x$, from 0 to 20. Numbers outside that range are not to be considered.

# VENN DIAGRAMS

The relationships between sets may be illustrated by *Venn diagrams*. Each set is shown within a rectangular universal set, overlapping or containing other sets as appropriate. For example, the set of natural numbers, $N$ is a subset of the set of all whole numbers, $Z$. This would be written as $N \subset Z$ in set language, and illustrated by the Venn diagram in Fig. 5.1.

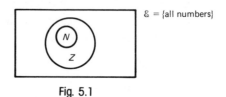

Fig. 5.1

When sets have some elements in common, they are shown to overlap each other on a Venn diagram (see Fig. 5.2). Elements in *both* sets form the *intersection* of $A$ and $B$, written in set language as $A \cap B$.

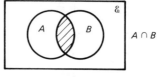

Fig. 5.2

Sets that have no elements in common appear on a Venn diagram as sets which do not overlap (Fig. 5.3).

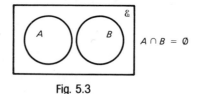

Fig. 5.3

*All* the elements of two sets belonging to one set or the other or to both sets make up the *union* of $A$ and $B$, written in set language as $A \cup B$ (see Fig. 5.4).

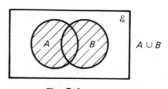

Fig. 5.4

Elements that lie outside a given set, $A$, form the *complement* of $A$, written $A'$ (Fig. 5.5).

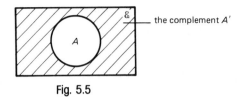

Fig. 5.5

**Example** Three sets, $A, B, C$, are defined as follows:

$$A = \{0, 1, 2, 3, 4\} \qquad B = \{1, 3\} \qquad C = \{2, 4, 6, 8\}$$

where $\& = \{0, 1, 2, 3, 4, 5, 6, 7, 8, 9\}$.

By looking closely at the elements in each set we can see that the two elements in $B$ (i.e. 1 and 3) occur in $A$ as well; thus $B$ is a subset of $A$. $C$ and $B$ have no elements in common. $A$ and $C$ both contain elements 2 and 4, and so intersect. A Venn diagram makes this information clearer (Fig. 5.6).

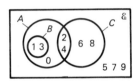

Fig. 5.6

Notice how easy it is to see from Fig. 5.6 that $B$ is a subset of $A$, and that $A$ (but not $B$) intersects with $C$. Moreover, by placing the elements of each set in their proper places on the diagram, it is possible to read off certain results:

$$A \cap C = \{2, 4\}$$
$$A \cup C = \{0, 1, 2, 3, 4, 6, 8\}$$
$$B \cap C = \emptyset \quad \text{(i.e. } B \text{ and } C \text{ have no elements in common)}$$
$$A \cap B' = \{0, 2, 4\}$$
$$n(A \cap B') = 3$$

**EXERCISE 5a**

1. Write in words the meaning of the following in set language:
   (a) $A \supset B$    (b) $2 \in C$    (c) $C \not\subset D$    (d) $n(C) = 10$.

2. Write in set language the following statements:
   (a) set $X$ contains set $Y$
   (b) the set $S$ is not empty
   (c) $\frac{1}{2}$ does not belong to set $Z$

73

(d) the number of elements in set $Z$ is 5

(e) set $A$ is not a subset of $B$

(f) use only numbers from 1 to 30

(g) set $C$ has three members.

3. If $Z = \{$whole numbers$\}$, $E = \{$even numbers$\}$, $O = \{$odd numbers$\}$, is it true that

(a) $E \neq Z$     (b) $E \subset Z$     (c) $n(E) = 20$   (d) $Z \supset O$?

4. $\& = \{$all towns and cities in the world$\}$, $C = \{$capital cities$\}$, $B = \{$British cities$\}$, $W = \{$Welsh cities$\}$. Is it true that

(a) $C \not\subset B$            (b) $W \in B$            (c) $W \subset B$

(d) London $\in B$      (e) Cheltenham $\subset C$

(f) Cardiff $\notin W$      (g) $n(W) < n(B)$?

5.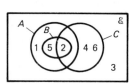

Fig. 5.7

If $\& = \{1, 2, 3, 4, 5, 6\}$, $A = \{1, 2, 5\}$, $B = \{2, 5\}$, $C = \{2, 4, 6\}$, as shown on the Venn diagram (Fig. 5.7), list the elements of

(a) $A \cap B$     (b) $B \cup C$     (c) $A'$     (d) $A \cap B'$.

Find

(e) $n(A \cap B)$         (f) $n(B \cup C)$         (g) $n(A')$

(h) $n(A \cap B')$.

6. If $E = \{$Bristol, Manchester, London, Liverpool, Edinburgh$\}$ and $C = \{$Paris, Bonn, Rome, London, Edinburgh$\}$, list the cities in the sets

(a) $E \cap C$     (b) $E \cup C$     (c) $C' \cap E$     (d) $C \cap E'$.

7. $T = \{$multiples of 3 up to 39$\}$ and $F = \{$multiples of 4 up to 40$\}$.

(a) List the elements of $T$

(b) List the elements of $F$.

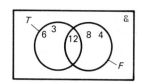

Fig. 5.8

Copy the Venn diagram from Fig. 5.8 and mark on it the members of $T$ and $F$. (The first few have been done for you.)

(c) Write down three multiples common to 3 and 4.

(d) What is the LCM of 3 and 4?

8.

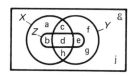

Fig. 5.9

$\& = \{a, b, c, d, e, f, g, h, j\}$. Sets $X$, $Y$ and $Z$ are as shown in Fig. 5.9. Which of the following are true?

(a) $Z \subset X \cap Y$     (b) $Z \supset X \cup Y$

(c) $Z \subset X \cup Y$     (d) $Z \cap X = \{b\}$

(e) $Z \cap X = \{b, d\}$    (f) $Z \cup (X \cap Y) = \{d, h\}$

(g) $Z' = \{a, c, f, g, h, j\}$   (h) $Z' \cap X = \{a, c, h\}$

(i) $Z' \cup Y' = \{a, c, j\}$    (j) $n(X \cap Y) = 1$.

9. $\& = \{$letters of the alphabet$\}$, $A = \{a, b, c, d, e\}$, $V = \{a, e, i, o, u\}$, $B = \{b, c\}$. Show the sets $A$, $V$ and $B$ on a Venn diagram. Is it true that

(a) $A \cap V = \{a, e\}$   (b) $A \cup V = A$   (c) $A \supset B$

(d) $A \subset B$      (e) $A \cap B \in A$   (f) $A \cup B = A$

(g) $B' \cap A = \{a, d, e\}$   (h) $y \in V' \cap A'$.   (i) $n(B) = 2$?

Describe in words the letters belonging to $V'$.

10.

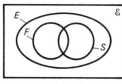

Fig. 5.10

$\& = \{1, 2, 3, \ldots, 11, 12\}$, $E = \{2, 4, 6, 8, 10, 12\}$, $F = \{4, 8, 12\}$, $S = \{6, 12\}$. Copy the Venn diagram in Fig. 5.10 and place the numbers 1 to 12 in appropriate regions. List the members of

(a) $E \cap F \cap S$    (b) $E \cap (F \cup S)'$   (c) $E' \cap F$.

The statement in set language $E' \cap F = \emptyset$ could be interpreted, in everyday language, to mean 'no odd number is a multiple of four'. State, in a similar fashion, the meaning of

(d) $E' \cap S = \emptyset$      (e) $E \cap S' \neq \emptyset$      (f) $F \subset E$.

11. $\& = \{$houses in my road$\}$, $T = \{$terraced houses$\}$, $S = \{$semi-detached houses$\}$.

(a) What in everyday language is meant by

(i) $n(T) = 20$                (ii) $n(S) = 30$

(iii) $n(\&) > 50$             (iv) $T \cup S \neq \&$?

(b) Describe a house belonging to $T' \cap S'$.

If $B = \{$bungalows$\}$ write down set language statements equivalent to

(c) None of the terraced houses in my road are bungalows.

(d) Some of the bungalows in my road are semi-detached.

12.

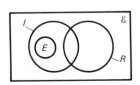

Fig. 5.11

The Venn diagram in Fig. 5.11 shows the relationship between the sets $I = \{$isosceles triangles$\}$, $E = \{$equilateral triangles$\}$, $R = \{$right-angled triangles$\}$. Is it true that

(a) all isosceles triangles are also equilateral triangles

(b) all equilateral triangles are also isosceles triangles

(c) isosceles triangles can never be right-angled triangles

(d) equilateral triangles can never be right-angled triangles?

13. $\& = \{$pupils who come to your school$\}$, $P = \{$pupils who bring a packed lunch$\}$, $L = \{$pupils who have a school lunch$\}$, $C = \{$pupils who come to school by car$\}$, $S = \{$pupils in the sixth form$\}$. Describe someone who is a member of

(a) $P \cap C$      (b) $C \cup S$      (c) $C' \cap L$      (d) $(S \cup L)'$.

Write a statement in set language to describe $x$ who brings a packed lunch and does not come to school by car.

## NUMBER PROBLEMS

Venn diagrams are useful in clarifying the numbers of elements in different sets.

**Example** In a class of 32, 8 do not study any languages; 20 study French and 10 study German. How many students are doing both French and German?

Since $8 + 20 + 10 = 38$, it follows that some pupils *must* be taking two languages, since there are only 32 people in the entire class.

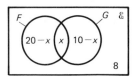

Fig. 5.12

Let there be $x$ pupils taking both French and German.

We could write this mathematically as $n(F \cap G) = x$.

The number just taking French is then $20 - x$.

Similarly, the number just taking German is $10 - x$.

The total number of pupils in the class is 32, hence

$$8 + (20 - x) + (10 - x) + x = 32$$

This gives a simplified equation

$$38 - x = 32$$

Hence

$$x = 6$$

**EXERCISE 5b**    1.

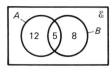

Fig. 5.13

The Venn diagram in Fig. 5.13 shows the *number* of elements in each region. Find

(a) $n(A \cap B)$    (b) $n(A)$    (c) $n(B)$    (d) $n(A \cup B)$.

If $n(\mathcal{E}) = 30$, find

(e) $n((A \cup B)')$    (f) $n(A')$.

**2.**

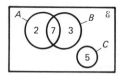

Fig. 5.14

The five statements below refer to the Venn diagram (Fig. 5.14). The figures in the diagram represent the number of elements in each subset. In each case, state whether the statement is true or false; if you think it is false, state the correct number of elements in the given set.

(a)  $n(A) = 2$          (b)  $n(A \cap B \cap C) = 0$

(c)  $n(A \cup B \cup C) = 17$     (d)  $n(A \cup B) = 5$

(e)  $n(B \cap C') = 3$.                              (JMB)

3.  At a computer users' club, 38 members were present for the meeting one evening. 5 of the members present were able to program in three computer languages: ALGOL, BASIC and COBOL. Including these 5, altogether 11 members knew ALGOL and BASIC, 12 knew COBOL and BASIC and 6 knew COBOL and ALGOL.

Some of this information is shown on the Venn diagram (Fig. 5.15).

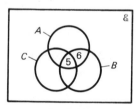

Fig. 5.15

Given that the sets $A$, $B$ and $C$ all contain 18 members, copy and complete the Venn diagram and so find the following:

(a)  the number of members knowing no COBOL, $n(C')$

(b)  the number who know ALGOL but not BASIC, $n(A \cap B')$

(c)  the number who know none of these three languages, $n(A' \cap B' \cap C')$.

4.  One Monday morning, 244 people were asked which of three competing Sunday newspapers, the *Observer*, the *Sunday Times* and the *Sunday Telegraph*, they had read the day before.

2 people had read all three
7 people had read both the *Sunday Times* and *Observer*
8 people had read both the *Observer* and *Sunday Telegraph*
13 people had read the *Sunday Times* and *Sunday Telegraph*
34 people had read only the *Observer*
48 people had read only the *Sunday Telegraph*
50 people had read only the *Sunday Times*.

Draw a Venn diagram to illustrate this information. How many people

(a) had not read any of these three newspapers?

(b) had only seen one of them?

(c) had not seen the *Sunday Times*?

5. Fifty pupils had a trip to the seaside. 24 pupils went bathing, 24 pupils went fishing and 24 did some shopping. A further more detailed check was also taken. 2 pupils had done all three things. 11 pupils had been shopping and bathing only. 6 pupils had been bathing and fishing only. 4 pupils had been shopping and fishing only.

Draw a Venn diagram showing intersecting sets

$B$ = {number of pupils who had been bathing}

$F$ = {number of pupils who had been fishing}

$S$ = {number of pupils who had been shopping}

Show the number of pupils in each region, and answer the following questions.

(a) How many pupils did not do any of these activities?

(b) How many only bathed?

(c) How many went fishing but did not go bathing?   (EAEB)

6.

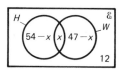

Fig. 5.16

There are 88 houses in my street. Each week 54 take *The Worplesdon Herald* magazine; 47 take *The Worplesdon World*. 12 houses do not take a weekly magazine at all. If $x$ houses take both, use the Venn diagram in Fig. 5.16 to form an equation in $x$. Find $x$.

7. Of the 88 families in my street, 52 have dogs. 28 families have no pet at all but there are 20 cats also living in the street. If $x$ families have both a cat and a dog, how many (in terms of $x$) have *just* a dog and no cat? Draw a Venn diagram to show the numbers of families without pets, those with just a dog, those with just a cat and those with both a dog and a cat. Form an equation in $x$ and solve it.

8. Of the 88 families living in my street, 15 have no children at all, 22 families have just boys; 21 families have just girls. How many families have both boys and girls?

9. In a class of 30, 24 students do woodwork, 16 do metalwork and 5 take no craft lessons at all. How many pupils do both woodwork and metalwork?

10. In a club of 25 cricketers 2 are wicket-keepers and never play as anything else. 15 are regarded as strong batsmen and 12 as strong bowlers. How many are regarded *both* as strong bowlers and strong batsmen?

11. In a language school of 40 all the pupils are doing French. 8 also study Spanish and 17 are learning German. If 18 do French and no other language, how many do all three?

12.

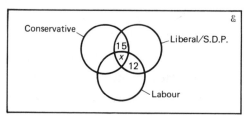

Fig. 5.17

In a sample of 100 voters, 15 said that, at some time in their lives, they had voted Conservative and Liberal/S.D.P. but never Labour. 12 said they had voted Labour and Liberal/S.D.P. but never Conservative. 2 people said they had voted on different occasions for Conservative and Labour, but never Liberal. 25 always voted Conservative and nothing else. 27 always voted Labour. 11 always voted Liberal/S.D.P.

Copy and complete the Venn diagram in Fig. 5.17 and find out how many voters in this sample have voted for all three parties at one time or another.

# 6 BASIC ALGEBRA

In algebra, letters are used to represent numbers. There are several reasons why this may be convenient. For example, in Chapter 4 we proved that $5^0 = 1$ (see page 62). We could prove in exactly the same way that $2^0 = 1$ or $4^0 = 1$ or even $(3.456)^0 = 1$, for the result applies to *all* numbers. The result was written at length: *any number raised to the power zero is one.* However, the result could have been written in a shorter form using algebra. For, on the understanding that $x$ represents any number, $x^0 = 1$ means the same thing.

Often, quite complicated ideas can be expressed quickly and easily with algebra. For example, *any number greater than one has a square-root greater than one but less than the number itself* could be written: $1 < \sqrt{x} < x$.

Another reason for replacing a number with a letter is that, often, we do not yet know the value of that number.

**Example** A friend thinks of a number, doubles it and adds three. He tells me the answer is nine. What number did he first think of?

Let the number be represented by the letter $x$:

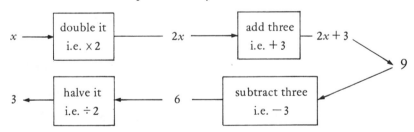

Hence $x = 3$, meaning the number my friend first thought of is three. (See Chapter 7 for a full treatment of the use of algebra in solving problems.)

## SUBSTITUTING INTO FORMULAE

Perhaps the most common use of algebra is to express mathematical relationships as formulae. For example, it is usual to give the area of a circle as $\pi r^2$ rather than as '*pi times the square of the radius*'.

Working out a quantity from the values of the various letters in the formula is easy: just replace each letter by the number given for it.

**Example** If $T = a + 3b$, find $T$ when $a = 5$ and $b = 6$.

Replacing the letters $a$ and $b$ by their value, we get
$$T = 5 + (3 \times 6)$$
$$= 5 + \quad 18$$
$$= 23$$

**Example** If $P = (3x + 2y)^2$, find $P$ when $x = 3$ and $y = 1.5$
$$P = (3 \times 3 + 2 \times 1.5)^2$$
$$= (\quad 9 \quad + \quad 3 \quad )^2$$
$$= 12^2$$
$$= 144$$

**EXERCISE 6a**    Work out the following formula from the values given. [Take $\pi$ as $\frac{22}{7}$.]

1. $P = 2a + 2b$      Find $P$ when $a = 6$, $b = 4$

2. $F = ma$      Find $F$ when $m = 60$ and $a = -\frac{3}{4}$

3. $E = mgx$      Find $E$ when $m = 0.4$, $g = 10$ and $x = 3.2$

4. $A = \frac{1}{2}bc$      Find $A$ when $b = 7$, $c = 5$

5. $p = 1 - q$      Find $p$ when $q = \frac{3}{16}$

6. $v = u + at$      Find $v$ when $u = 5$, $a = -2$ and $t = 2$

7. $y = mx + c$      Find $y$ when $m = -2$, $x = 3$, $c = 5$

8. $E = \frac{1}{2}mv^2$      Find $E$ when $m = 2.4$, $v = 2.1$

9. $r = \sqrt{x^2 + y^2}$      Find $r$ when $x = 5$ and $y = 12$

10. $A = \left(\dfrac{a + b}{2}\right)d$      Find $A$ when $a = 5$, $b = 12$ and $d = 2\frac{1}{2}$

11. $A = \pi r^2$      Find $A$ when (a) $r = 14$ (b) $r = 1.4$

12. $V = \frac{4}{3}\pi r^3$      Find $V$ when (a) $r = 3$ (b) $r = 0.3$

13. $s = ut + \frac{1}{2}at^2$      Find $s$ when $u = 6$, $a = 5$ and $t = 3$

14. $v^2 = u^2 + 2as$      Find $v$ when $u = 5$, $a = 6$ and $s = 2$

15. $T = 2\pi\sqrt{\dfrac{L}{g}}$      Find $T$ when $g = 10$ and $L = 4.9$

82

**16.** $S = 2\pi(r + h)$      Find $S$ when $r = 0.45$ and $h = 0.25$

**17.** $P = \dfrac{mv^2}{r}$      Find $P$ when $m = 3$, $r = 8$ and $v = 0.4$

**18.** $S = \dfrac{a(1 - r^n)}{1 - r}$      Find $S$ when $a = 3$, $r = \frac{1}{3}$ and $n = 4$

**19.** $s = \sqrt{np(1 - p)}$      Find $s$ when $n = 12$, $p = \frac{1}{4}$

**20.** $\dfrac{1}{f} = \dfrac{1}{u} + \dfrac{1}{v}$      Find $f$ when $u = 6$ and $v = 8$.

## SIMPLIFYING ALGEBRAIC EXPRESSIONS

Sometimes a formula is written in a correct, but clumsy, form. With a little extra work it might be written in a simpler, more elegant way. For example, the perimeter, $P$, of a square with sides of length $x$ could be given as the formula $P = x + x + x + x$. Such a formula is accurate but is not well written; it can be simplified to the neater and shorter form $P = 4x$.

**Examples** ($i$)    $8x^2 \times 2x$

     $= (8 \times 2) \times (x^2 \times x)$

     $= 16x^3$      Simple numbers should be multiplied or divided out; letters should be written to the lowest possible power.

   ($ii$)    $\dfrac{10x^3}{5x}$

     $= \dfrac{\overset{2}{\cancel{10}}\overset{x^2}{\cancel{x^3}}}{\underset{}{\cancel{5}}\cancel{x}}$      Cancel 5 with 10 and $x$ into $x^3$.

     $= 2x^2$

As different letters represent different numbers, it is *not* possible to combine them in a single term.

**Examples** ($i$)    $3x - 2y$      This cannot be simplified any further.

   ($ii$)    $8x^2 \times 2y$

     $= (8 \times 2) \times (x^2 \times y)$    Here we can simplify $8 \times 2$, but the $x^2$ and $y$ stay as they are.

     $= 16x^2y$

(iii) $\dfrac{p^2q^2 \times pq}{p^2q}$

Here the letters $p$ and $q$ appear several times and the expression can be made shorter by cancelling out $p^2$ and $q$.

$= \dfrac{\cancel{p^2}q^2 \times p\cancel{q}}{\cancel{p^2}\cancel{q}}$

$= q^2p$

Do not try to add or subtract different powers of one letter; and do not try to cancel down just one side of an addition or subtraction sign.

**Examples** (i)  $x^2 + x$

This cannot be simplified further. Although $x^2$ and $x$ are related, they represent different numbers.

(ii)  $\dfrac{a+b}{b}$

Trying to cancel out just one side of an addition (or subtraction) sign to give $\dfrac{a+\cancel{b}}{\cancel{b}}$ is a common error. In fact, in this case, no simplification is possible: $b$ is not a common factor of both the top and bottom.

**EXERCISE 6b**  Simplify as far as possible; if no simplification is possible then explain why.

1.  $3 \times a$

2.  $5 \times b \; + \; 2 \times b$

3.  $a + a + a + a + a$

4.  $a \times a \times a \times a$

5.  $6a + 3b + 2a + b$

6.  $3x^2 + 2x^2 + x^2$

7.  $2mn + mn - mn$

8.  $m + m + p - m - p + 2p + m$

9.  $ab + a + ab + b + ab$

10.  $3x + 3y + 2x + 4y$

11.  $3x^3 + 2x^2x - 3y$

12.  $6 + 3xy - 4xy + x$

13.  $3p^2 \times 4pq$

14.  $6d^2e \times 5df$

15.  $5pq^2 \times 6p^2q$

16.  $3m^2n \times 3m$

17.  $\dfrac{12mn}{4}$

18.  $\dfrac{25rst}{5r}$

19.  $\dfrac{21j^2s^3f^2}{7js^2f}$

20.  $\dfrac{jk}{7jk}$

21.  $\dfrac{6m^2n^2}{mn}$

22.  $\dfrac{a^2bc^3}{abc}$

84

23. $\dfrac{p+q}{p}$

24. $\dfrac{j+2k}{2}$

25. $\dfrac{x^2+y}{xy}$

26. $\dfrac{m^2+n^2}{mn}$

27. $\dfrac{3a^2+4b^2}{3ab}$

28. $\dfrac{2r^3+3st}{3st}$

29. $\dfrac{10a+5b}{5}$

30. $\dfrac{12p+4q}{4}$

31. $\dfrac{6ab+3ab^2}{3a}$

32. $\dfrac{25x^2y-10x^3}{5x}$

## BRACKETS

Algebra is a very precise code, demanding careful attention to detail. Small differences in the way a formula is written can completely alter its meaning. In particular, brackets are important because they change the order in which calculations are done: brackets are *always worked out first*.

**Example** $3x + 2$.

means take the number $x$, multiply it by 3 and then add 2 to the result, but

$3(x + 2)$

means take the number $x$, add 2 first and *then* multiply by 3. In this case the 2 is also multiplied by 3.

$$3(x + 2) = 3x + 6$$

To illustrate the difference, let $x = 4$:

$$3x + 2 = 3 \times 4 + 2 = 12 + 2 = 14$$

but $$3(x + 2) = 3 \times (4 + 2) = 3 \times 6 = 18.$$

## EXPANDING BRACKETS

Sometimes it is useful to rewrite a formula removing the brackets. The brackets are said to have been *expanded* into a string of algebraic terms.

**Examples** (*i*)
$$2 + 3(x + 4) = 2 + 3 \times x + 3 \times 4$$
$$= 2 + 3x + 12$$
$$= 3x + 14$$

Notice that *both* the $x$ and the 4 that were originally inside the the brackets are multiplied by 3.

If a negative number precedes the bracket, the sign of *both* terms inside the bracket will change.

(*ii*)
$$5 - (x + 2) = 5 - x - 2$$
$$= 3 - x$$

The sign of the 2 changes as well as the sign of the $x$.

(*iii*)
$$6 - (x - 4) = 6 - x + 4$$
$$= 10 - x$$

as $-(-4)$ is equivalent to $+4$.

Brackets may also be multiplied by brackets.

**Examples** (*i*)  $(x + 3)(x + 2)$

$= x(x + 2) + 3(x + 2)$     Each term in the first bracket must

$= x^2 + 2x + 3x + 6$     multiply each term in the second bracket. The remaining brackets are then multi-

$= x^2 + 5x + 6$     plied out. Finally, $2x + 3x$ can be simplified to $5x$.

Again, be careful with negative signs:

(*ii*)  $(x - 4)(2x - 3)$

$= x(2x - 3) - 4(2x - 3)$     The first bracket must multiply each term in the second bracket, but this time one of the terms is negative (i.e. $-4$).

$= 2x^2 - 3x - 8x + 12$     The multiplication is completed, remembering that $-4 \times (-3) = 12$.

$= 2x^2 - 11x + 12$     Finally, the string is simplified as far as possible.

Brackets may also be raised to a power. Thus $(m - 2n)^2$ means $(m - 2n)(m - 2n)$. It is best to write out the multiplication in full, and then complete it stage by stage:

86

**Example**

$$(m - 2n)^2 = (m - 2n)(m - 2n)$$
$$= m(m - 2n) - 2n(m - 2n)$$
$$= m^2 - 2mn - 2mn + 4n^2$$
$$= m^2 - 4mn + 4n^2$$

Notice that this is *not* the same as $(m)^2 - (2n)^2$.

**EXERCISE 6c**  Expand the following brackets, simplifying your results as far as possible.

1. $5 + 2(x + 3)$

2. $2x + x(3 + x)$

3. $5ab + a(b + 3)$

4. $4xy + 3(x + y)$

5. $2pq + p(q + q^2)$

6. $3(a + b) + a(1 + b)$

7. $5(c - d) + 3(c - d)$

8. $3mn + 2n(m - n)$

9. $7(p - 2q) + q(p - 2)$

10. $5(r - s) + 2(s - 1) + 3(1 - r)$

11. $6 - (3x + y)$

12. $2 - (u + v)$

13. $9 - (w + x)$

14. $8 - (y + z)$

15. $11 - 3(a - b)$

16. $3 - 2(m - n)$

17. $13 - 5(c - d)$

18. $1 - 4(p - q)$

19. $(u + 6)(2 + u)$

20. $(v + 5)(v - 3)$

21. $(n + p)(p + 2)$

22. $(2n + m)(m + 2n)$

23. $(c + 5d)(5c + 3d)$

24. $(4e + 3f)(3e + 4f)$

25. $(j + k)(j - k)$

26. $(m + n)(m - 3n)$

27. $(p - 3q)(p - 2q)$

28. $(q - r)(2q - r)$

29. $(2x - 3y)(2x - 4y)$

30. $(5u - 3v)(3u - 7v)$

31. $(a + b)^2$

32. $(a + 2b)^2$

33. $(a - b)^2$

34. $(3e - f)^2$

35. $(2e + 3f)^2$

36. $(5g - 2f)^2$

37. $a + 3(5 + a + b)$

38. $(a + 3)(5 + a + b)$

39. $(c + d)(3 + c - d)$

40. $(e + f)(2 - e - f)$

41. $c + d(3 + c - d)$

42. $e + f(2 - e - f)$

# ALGEBRAIC FRACTIONS

Algebraic fractions obey the same rules of cancelling down, adding and subtracting, multiplying and dividing as ordinary fractions.

**Example** $\dfrac{x}{2} + \dfrac{x}{3}$.

The lowest common denominator is $2 \times 3 = 6$ (as 2 and 3 have no factors in common). Over this denominator:

$$\frac{x}{2} \quad \text{has equivalent} \quad \frac{x \times 3}{2 \times 3} = \frac{3x}{6}$$

and

$$\frac{x}{3} \quad \text{has equivalent} \quad \frac{x \times 2}{3 \times 2} = \frac{2x}{6}$$

Thus

$$\frac{x}{2} + \frac{x}{3} = \frac{3x}{6} + \frac{2x}{6} = \frac{5x}{6}$$

**Example** $\dfrac{2}{a} + \dfrac{3}{b}$.

This time the denominators are algebraic. As $a$ and $b$ represent different numbers with no factors in common, the lowest common denominator is $a \times b = ab$. Over this denominator:

$$\frac{2}{a} \quad \text{has equivalent} \quad \frac{2 \times b}{a \times b} = \frac{2b}{ab}$$

and

$$\frac{3}{b} \quad \text{has equivalent} \quad \frac{3 \times a}{b \times a} = \frac{3a}{ab}$$

So

$$\frac{2}{a} + \frac{3}{b} = \frac{2b}{ab} + \frac{3a}{ab} = \frac{2b + 3a}{ab}$$

**Example** $\dfrac{4x - 3}{2} + \dfrac{1}{3}$.

If the top (or bottom) of the algebraic fraction is in two parts, like $4x - 3$, it is very easy to separate them incorrectly. It is a good idea to put brackets around the parts as a *first step*. Thus $4x - 3$ becomes $(4x - 3)$.

In this example, the lowest common denominator is 6, so we write:

$$\frac{4x-3}{2} = \frac{(4x-3)}{2} = \frac{(4x-3)\times 3}{2\times 3} = \frac{12x-9}{6}$$

So

$$\frac{4x-3}{2} + \frac{1}{3} = \frac{12x-9}{6} + \frac{2}{6} = \frac{12x-7}{6}$$

**Example** $\dfrac{3a^2b^2}{c} \div \dfrac{6b^2c}{d}$.

$$\frac{3a^2b^2}{c} \div \frac{6b^2c}{d} = \frac{3a^2b^2}{c} \times \frac{d}{6b^2c}$$

Cancelling down by 3 and by $b^2$ we get

$$\frac{\cancel{3}a^2\cancel{b^2}}{c} \times \frac{d}{\cancel{6}\cancel{b^2}c} = \frac{a^2d}{2c^2}$$

**EXERCISE 6d**   Work out the following, expressing your answers as single fractions in their lowest terms.

1. $\dfrac{a}{3} + \dfrac{a}{5}$

2. $\dfrac{2b}{3} + \dfrac{b}{6}$

3. $\dfrac{c}{3} + \dfrac{2d}{7}$

4. $\dfrac{3e^2}{4} - \dfrac{f}{2}$

5. $\dfrac{g}{4} + \dfrac{g^2}{3}$

6. $\dfrac{g}{4} - \dfrac{g^2}{3}$

7. $\dfrac{y}{6} + \dfrac{2y}{3}$

8. $\dfrac{2x-1}{3} - \dfrac{x}{2}$

9. $\dfrac{3x+2}{2} + \dfrac{x}{3}$

10. $\dfrac{5j+2}{3} - \dfrac{j}{2}$

11. $\dfrac{2k-2}{3} + \dfrac{3k}{4}$

12. $\dfrac{7k-1}{2} - \dfrac{k}{3}$

13. $\dfrac{m+1}{2} + \dfrac{m+2}{3}$

14. $\dfrac{n+1}{4} + \dfrac{n+2}{3}$

15. $\dfrac{3p-2}{4} - \dfrac{p+3}{2}$

16. $\dfrac{q-r}{2} + \dfrac{q+r}{3}$

17. $\dfrac{s-t}{4} - \dfrac{t+u}{5}$

18. $\dfrac{1}{j} + \dfrac{1}{k}$

19. $\dfrac{2}{l} - \dfrac{3}{m}$

20. $\dfrac{4n}{p} + \dfrac{5p}{q}$

21. $\dfrac{6q}{r} - \dfrac{2}{3q}$

22. $\dfrac{5q}{r} - \dfrac{2rs}{q}$

23. $\dfrac{8q}{r} + \dfrac{3r}{q}$

24. $\dfrac{11s}{3t} - \dfrac{3s}{4t}$

25. $\dfrac{t}{2u} - \dfrac{3t}{4u}$

26. $\dfrac{2w}{3v} - \dfrac{w}{2v}$

27. $\dfrac{3x}{5y} - \dfrac{x}{2y}$

28. $\dfrac{11s}{3t} \times \dfrac{ut}{3s}$

29. $\dfrac{p}{2q} \times \dfrac{q}{r}$

30. $\dfrac{s^2}{2t} \times \dfrac{t}{s}$

31. $\dfrac{1}{uv} \div \dfrac{2}{v}$

32. $\dfrac{3}{xy} \div \dfrac{5}{y}$

33. $\dfrac{8}{ab} \div \dfrac{4a}{b}$

34. $\dfrac{2u}{3vw} \div \dfrac{v}{6w}$

35. $\dfrac{6m^2p}{q} \div \dfrac{1}{2pq}$

36. $\dfrac{4}{5d^2e} \div \dfrac{4}{3de}$

37. $\dfrac{a^3b^2}{c} \div \dfrac{c^2bd}{a^2}$

38. $\dfrac{a^3}{12bc} \div \dfrac{3}{4bc}$

39. $\dfrac{x}{y^2z} \div \dfrac{x^2}{yz}$

40. $fg^2 \times \dfrac{f}{g}$

41. $pq^2 \times \dfrac{p}{q}$

42. $m^2n^2 \div \dfrac{m}{n}$

## ALGEBRAIC POWERS

The rules for combining powers apply to algebraic values in exactly the same way as they apply to ordinary numbers. Thus $y \times y \times y$ would be shortened to $y^3$; $y^4$ would mean $y \times y \times y \times y$, etc.

**Examples** (i) $\quad y^2 \times y^3 = y^{2+3} = y^5$

(ii) $\quad y^5 \div y^7 = y^{5-7} = y^{-2}$, i.e. $\dfrac{1}{y^2}$

(iii) $\quad (y^2)^3 = y^{2 \times 3} = y^6$

(iv) $\quad y^{\frac{1}{2}} = \sqrt[2]{y}$ and $y^{\frac{3}{4}} = (\sqrt[4]{y})^3$ or $\sqrt[4]{y^3}$

(v) $\quad y^0 = 1$.

In algebraic problems involving more than one letter, be careful not to muddle up powers of *different* letters. Thus $x^2y^3$ cannot be simplified, though $y^2y^3$ would be written as $y^5$.

**Examples** (vi) $\quad p^3q^2 \times pq = p^{3+1} \times q^{2+1} = p^4q^3$

(vii) $\quad p^3q \div pq^2 = p^{3-1} \times q^{1-2} = p^2q^{-1}$

(viii) $\quad \sqrt{p^4q^6} = \sqrt{p^4} \times \sqrt{q^6} = p^2q^3$.

**EXERCISE 6e**  Simplify the following as far as possible:

1. (a) $p \times p \times p \times p \times p$        (b) $p^3 \times p^2 \times p$

    (c) $(p^3)^2$                         (d) $(p^3)^{-2}$

2. (a) $\dfrac{1}{q \times q \times q \times q}$  (b) $\dfrac{1}{q} \times \dfrac{1}{q} \times \dfrac{1}{q}$

   (c) $(q^{-2})^{-1}$  (d) $q^0$

3. (a) $x^2y \times x^3$  (b) $(x^2y)^2$

   (c) $x^2y \times x^{-1}y$  (d) $x^2y \times x^{-2}y^{-2}$

4. (a) $yz^3 \div z^2$  (b) $y^3z \div y^4$

   (c) $y^3z^{-1} \div x$  (d) $y^3z^{-1} \div y^{-1}z^{-1}$

5. (a) $\sqrt{a} \times \sqrt{a}$  (b) $\sqrt{a} \times a^0$

   (c) $\sqrt{a^2b^2}$  (d) $(a^{\frac{1}{4}})^{-1}$

6. (a) $(a \times a^3)^2$  (b) $(a^3 \times \sqrt{a})^2$

   (c) $(a^{-\frac{1}{3}} \times a^4)^{-1}$  (d) $(\sqrt{a} \times a^2)^{\frac{1}{2}}$

7. (a) $x^0y^2 \times x^0y^0$  (b) $p^3q^2 \times pq^2r$

   (c) $\dfrac{m^2}{n} \times m^2n^2$  (d) $(mn^2)^2$

8. (a) $p^{-2} \times \dfrac{1}{p^2}$  (b) $(y^{-2})^{-3}$

   (c) $q^{-2} \div q^2$  (d) $x^{-\frac{1}{2}} \div x^{\frac{1}{2}}$

9. (a) $a^{-\frac{3}{4}} \times a^{-\frac{1}{4}}$  (b) $\sqrt{(pq^{2r})}$

   (c) $\sqrt[3]{p^{-3}q^6}$  (d) $\dfrac{tu^{-\frac{1}{2}}}{t^{\frac{1}{2}}u^{-\frac{1}{2}}}$

10. (a) $\dfrac{a^3b^2}{c} \times \dfrac{c^2}{a^2b}$  (b) $\dfrac{x^7y^3}{z^2} \times \dfrac{x^2z}{y^7}$

11. (a) $2p^0q^2r \div p^{-1}qr^2$  (b) $\dfrac{3m^2n^2}{p^2} \div pm^2n^2$

## FACTORISING

Just as it is sometimes helpful to rewrite a formula so that the brackets are eliminated, so on other occasions it might be easier to deal with a long string of algebraic terms if they are grouped into brackets. This process, the reverse of expanding brackets, is called *factorising*.

## Factorising by Grouping Terms

**Examples** (*i*)    $3xy + 2x$

$$= x(3y + 2)$$

The two terms have $x$ in common.

Thus $x$ can be written outside a bracket such that it multiplies the terms inside the bracket to give $3xy + 2x$.

(*ii*)   $4y^2z + yz$

$$= yz(4y + 1)$$

Similarly, the two terms in this example contain the factors $yz$ which can be written outside a bracket as shown.

(*iii*) $ac - ad + bc - bd$

There is nothing common to *all four* terms in this case. So we look for *pairs* with common factors. Here

$$ac - ad = a(c - d)$$

$$= a(c - d) + b(c - d)$$    and

$$bc - bd = b(c - d)$$

$$= (c - d)(a + b)$$

$(c - d)$ is now a common factor that can be written outside a *second* bracket.

(*iv*) $pr - 2qr + 2qs - ps$

Again, there is nothing common to all four terms so we take pairs with common factors as in Example (*iii*).

$$= r(p - 2q) + s(2q - p)$$
$$= r(p - 2q) - s(p - 2q)$$

This time, however, we cannot continue as simply for $(p - 2q) \neq (2q - p)$. We must adjust the signs, as shown, using $(2q - p) = -(p - 2q)$

$$= (p - 2q)(r - s)$$

Now we can proceed as before.

**EXERCISE 6f**    Factorise the following:

1. $6 + 2m$

2. $3 + 12e$

3. $15 + 36p$

4. $5f - 15fg$

5. $16q - 8qr$

6. $7x - 21x^2$

7. $5q - q^2$

8. $11x - 121xy$

9. $21m^2n + 28mn$

10. $lm^2n - lmn$

11. $y^2z + yz^2$

12. $2a^2b + 6a^2$

13. $6mq - 3mr^2$

14. $nm + n + 2m + 2$

15. $pq + p + 2q + 2$

16. $15 + 3l + 5k + kl$

17. $4j + 8 - ij - 2i$

18. $6 + 2d - cd - 3c$

92

19. $fh + fi + gh + gi$

20. $ac + ad + bc + bd$

21. $tv + 2tw + uv + 2uw$

22. $2eg + eh + 2fg + fh$

23. $ru + rt - su - st$

24. $2jl - jm + 2kl - km$

25. $2wx - 3yx + 2wz - 3yz$

26. $3nq - pr + 3nr - pq$

27. $2a^3y - 2a^3z - by + bz$

28. $s^2u + tu - s^2v - vt$

29. $9pm^2 - 6pn - 6qm^2 + 4qn$

30. $2w^2y + 2yx - w^2z - zx$

31. $6tv + 6uw + 4uv + 9tw$

32. $8ac + 2ad + 12bc + 3bd$

33. $6x^2z - 6xy - 4yz + 9x^3$

34. $10e^2 - 5eh + 12fe - 6fh$

35. $6jm - 3jn - 10m + 5n$

36. $6uw + 3vx - 2ux - 9vw$

37. $ab + bc + bd$

38. $3e + ef^2 + eg$

39. $2q + qm + qn^2$

40. $3a^2 + 6a^2b + 3a^2c^2$

## Factorising Quadratic Expressions

A *quadratic* expression is a string of three algebraic terms of the form $ax^2 + bx + c$. For example, $x^2 + 5x + 6$ is a quadratic expression. This may be factorised by rewriting $5x$ as $3x + 2x$, and grouping terms:

$$x^2 + 5x + 6 = x^2 + 3x + 2x + 6$$
$$= x(x + 3) + 2(x + 3)$$
$$= (x + 3)(x + 2)$$

Notice that 3 and 2 not only add up to 5 (so $5x = 3x + 2x$) but also multiply to give 6. Other quadratics can be factorised if the number at the end has a pair of factors which add up to the number of $x$s.

**Example** $x^2 - 6x + 8$.

We need to find a factor pair of $+8$ whose sum is $-6$. The possibilities are

| | *possible factor pairs* | *sum* | |
|---|---|---|---|
| | $+1, +8$ | $+9$ | ✗ |
| $+8$ | $-1, -8$ | $-9$ | ✗ |
| | $+4, +2$ | $+6$ | ✗ |
| | $-4, -2$ | $-6$ | ✓ |

Thus we can rewrite the quadratic:

$$x^2 - 6x + 8 = x^2 - 2x - 4x + 8$$
$$= x(x-2) - 4(x-2)$$
$$= (x-2)(x-4)$$

Quadratics such as $2x^2 + 5x - 3$ which begin with more than one $x^2$ are factorised in much the same way, although there is an extra step: the first number must be multiplied with the last, and factor pairs of *that product* considered as before.

**Example** $2x^2 + 5x - 3$

$2 \times (-3) = -6$

Find the factor pair of $2 \times (-3) = -6$ which has a sum of $+5$.

|  | *possible factor pairs* | *sum* |  |
|---|---|---|---|
|  | $+1, -6$ | $-5$ | ✗ |
| $-6$ | $-1, +6$ | $+5$ | ✓ |
|  | $+2, -3$ | $-1$ | ✗ |
|  | $-2, +3$ | $+1$ | ✗ |

Thus
$$2x^2 + 5x - 3 = 2x^2 - x + 6x - 3$$
$$= x(2x-1) + 3(2x-1)$$
$$= (2x-1)(x+3)$$

If the $x^2$ term in the quadratic is negative, then the procedure is no different, although care must be taken with signs. Remember that $-x^2$ means $-1x^2$ and be sure to rearrange the terms into the usual order if necessary.

**Example** $2x - x^2 + 3$.

Rearranging the order and remembering that $-x^2 = -1x^2$:

$$-x^2 + 2x + 3$$

$-1 \times (+3) = -3$

So we must find a factor pair of $-3$ that has a sum of $+2$, i.e. $+3$ and $-1$.

94

$$-x^2 + 2x + 3 = -x^2 + 3x - x + 3$$
$$= x(-x + 3) + 1(-x + 3)$$
$$= (-x + 3)(x + 1)$$

The term $(-x + 3)$ is correct, but clumsy; it is better to change the order putting the positive term first, i.e. $(3 - x)$. So

$$2x - x^2 + 3 = (3 - x)(x + 1)$$

Some quadratics, for example $6x^2 - 31xy + 5y^2$ contain *two* variables (in this case, $x$ and $y$). The procedure for factorising these is virtually identical.

**Example** $6x^2 - 31xy + 5y^2$

$6 \times (+5) = +30$

Find the factor pair of $6 \times (+5) = +30$ which has a sum of $-31$: clearly $-30$ and $-1$ will work. Thus

$$6x^2 - 31xy + 5y^2 = 6x^2 - xy - 30xy + 5y^2$$
$$= x(6x - y) - 5y(6x - y)$$
$$= (6x - y)(x - 5y)$$

Two important quadratic factorisations that should be remembered are:

(*i*)  $x^2 + 2xy + y^2 = (x + y)^2$
(*ii*)  $x^2 - 2xy + y^2 = (x - y)^2$.

**EXERCISE 6g**  Factorise these quadratics:

1. $x^2 + 6x + 8$        2. $x^2 + 10x + 16$

3. $x^2 + 12x + 27$      4. $x^2 + 8x + 15$

5. $x^2 + 7x + 10$       6. $x^2 + 3x - 18$

7. $x^2 + 3x - 10$       8. $x^2 - 11x + 28$

9. $x^2 + 4x + 3$        10. $x^2 - 6x + 5$

11. $24 + 11x + x^2$      12. $20 + 9x + x^2$

13. $y^2 + 19y + 34$      14. $y^2 + 18y + 65$

15. $z^2 - 7z - 44$       16. $x^2 + x - 30$

17. $n^2 + 5n - 36$       18. $p^2 - 5pq - 66q^2$

19. $x^2 - 11xy + 18y^2$

20. $x^2y^2 - 11xy + 24$

21. $2x^2 + 7x + 6$

22. $6x^2 + 13x + 5$

23. $2x^2 + 15x + 7$

24. $3x^2 + 7x + 2$

25. $2x^2 + 11x + 15$

26. $3x^2 + 22x - 16$

27. $4x^2 + 19x - 5$

28. $5x^2 - 21x + 4$

29. $7x^2 - 9x + 2$

30. $12v^2 - 145v + 12$

31. $6c^2 + 13c + 6$

32. $21r^2 - 32r - 5$

33. $10t^2 - 9t - 7$

34. $3l^2 - 8l + 4$

35. $10p^2 - 29p - 21$

36. $4s^2 + 35s + 24$

37. $2f^2 - 21f + 54$

38. $3m^2 + 13m - 10$

39. $8e^2 + 43e - 30$

40. $6d^2 + d - 22$

41. $-6x^2 - x + 1$

42. $-6x^2 - 5x + 6$

43. $2 + x - 10x^2$

44. $5 - 17x - 12x^2$

45. $1 + x - 2x^2$

46. $6 + x - 2x^2$

47. $12 + 5x - 3x^2$

48. $7 + 34x - 5x^2$

49. $33x - 4x^2 - 8$

50. $35x - 6 - 11x^2$

51. $13x - 3x^2 - 14$

52. $17x - 4x^2 - 13$

53. $46g - 7g^2 + 21$

54. $15 - 2x^2 - 7x$

55. $37k + 55 + 6k^2$

56. $15 - 4l^2 - 17l$

57. $4 - 36m^2 + 7m$

58. $m^2 - 24n^2 + 10mn$

59. $p^2 - 24q^2 - 5pq$

60. $12p^2 - 49q^2 - 28pq$.

## Difference of Two Squares

Consider $(a - b)(a + b)$.

$$\begin{aligned}
(a - b)(a + b) &= (a - b)a + (a - b)b \\
&= a^2 - ba + ab - b^2 \\
&= a^2 - b^2
\end{aligned}$$

Thus it follows that

$$a^2 - b^2 = (a - b)(a + b)$$

where $a$ and $b$ are *any* numbers.

**Examples** ($i$) $\quad 25 - x^2 = 5^2 - x^2$

$$= (5 - x)(5 + x)$$

($ii$) $\quad 4a^2 - b^2 = (2a)^2 - b^2$

$$= (2a - b)(2a + b)$$

($iii$) $\quad 3p^2 - 12q^2 = 3(p^2 - 4q^2)$

$$= 3(p^2 - (2q)^2)$$

$$= 3(p - 2q)(p + 2q)$$

($iv$) $\quad 6.3^2 - 3.7^2 = (6.3 - 3.7)(6.3 + 3.7)$

$$= 2.6 \times 10$$

$$= 26$$

($v$) $\quad 97^2 - 9 = 97^2 - 3^2$

$$= (97 + 3)(97 - 3)$$

$$= 9400$$

**EXERCISE 6h**  Using the difference of two squares rule, factorise the following:

1. $3^2 - y^2$

2. $p^2 - q^2$

3. $r^2 - s^2$

4. $p^2 - (3q)^2$

5. $(mn)^2 - p^2$

6. $u^2 v^2 - 3^2$

7. $25 - y^2$

8. $121 - w^2$

9. $81 - r^2$

10. $144 - 25x^2$

11. $81s^2 - t^2$

12. $36y^2 - x^2$

13. $9t^2 - 4u^2$

14. $121f^2 - 49j^2$

15. $64s^2 - 49t^2$

16. $18r^2 - 2s^2$

17. $8d^2 - 2e^2$

18. $20a^2 - 80b^2$

19. $12d^2 - 48e^2$

20. $50c^2 - 98$

21. $200 - 32z^2$.

$8(5 - 2z)(5 + 2z)$

*Without* using long multiplication, work out

22. $97^2 - 3^2$

23. $81^2 - 19^2$

24. $123^2 - 23^2$

25. $300^2 - 290^2$

26. $51.6^2 - 48.4^2$

27. $0.009^2 - 0.001^2$

28. $1257^2 - 743^2$

29. $998^2 - 4$

30. $1009^2 - 81$.

## MISCELLANEOUS EXERCISE 6

1. Copy Fig. 6.1.

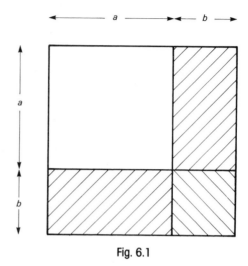

Fig. 6.1

Use it to prove diagramatically that $(a + b)^2 = a^2 + 2ab + b^2$.

Can you devise a similar illustration to show that

$$(a - b)^2 = a^2 - 2ab + b^2?$$

2. We know that $x + (y + z) = (x + y) + z$, i.e. it does not matter how we pair off a succession of additions. Does the same rule work for other operations? For example, does

$$x - (y - z) = (x - y) - z$$
$$x \times (y \times z) = (x \times y) \times z$$
$$x \div (y \div z) = (x \div y) \div z$$

Investigate by substituting in numbers of your own choosing.

3. We know that $x \times (y + z) = (x \times y) + (x \times z)$.

However, does the relationship still work if we swap the $\times$ and $+$ signs? That is, does

$$x + (y \times z) = (x + y) \times (x + z)?$$

Substitute numbers of your own choosing to show that, in general, this relationship does *not* hold.

Can you find three numbers, $x$, $y$ and $z$, which are exceptions (that is, they *do* work)?

Investigate for other operations. For example, does

$$x \times (y \div z) = (x \times y) \div (x \times z)$$

work for all numbers? If not, are there exceptions which *do* work?

4. Given that $x + y = 5$ and that $x \times y = 3$, work out the value of

   (a) $(x + y)^2$        (b) $\dfrac{1}{x} + \dfrac{1}{y}$.

5. Write down the first eight lines of Pascal's triangle.

   Now copy and continue the following

   $(a + b)^0 = 1$

   $(a + b)^1 = a + b$

   $(a + b)^2 = a^2 + 2ab + b^2$

   $(a + b)^3 = (a + b)(a^2 + 2ab + b^2)$

   $\qquad\quad\; = a^3 + 3a^2b + 3ab^2 + b^3$

   $(a + b)^4 = \ldots$

   $(a + b)^5 = \ldots$

   Can you see the relationship between Pascal's triangle and the expansion of $(a + b)^n$?

   Predict the result of $(a + b)^6$ and $(a + b)^7$ before you work them out.

6. Use the difference of squares rule to work out
   (a) $8^2 - 7^2$     (b) $23^2 - 22^2$     (c) $78^2 - 77^2$.
   Prove algebraically that $(n + 1)^2 - n^2 = (n + 1) + n$ for any number, $n$.

7. Look at this pattern:

   $$5^2 - 0^2 = 25$$
   $$6^2 - 1^2 = 35$$
   $$7^2 - 2^2 = 45$$
   $$8^2 - 3^2 = 55$$

   Investigate and generalise.

   Can you find any similar patterns?

8. (a) $(n-1)$, $n$ and $(n+1)$ are three consecutive numbers (like 2, 3, 4). Explain why a set of any three consecutive numbers must contain at least one even number and a multiple of 3.

(b) Using your calculator if necessary find
(i) $2^3 - 2$     (ii) $3^3 - 3$     (iii) $4^3 - 4$
(iv) $10^3 - 10$     (v) $13^3 - 13$.

Can you see a pattern?

(c) By first factorising by $n$ and then using the difference of two squares rule prove that the value of $n^3 - n$ must always be a multiple of 6 for any whole number, $n$.

(d) Investigate factors of $n^4 - n$, $n^5 - n$, $n^6 - n$ ... and so on.

9. If $x$ and $y$ are two positive numbers, such that $0 < x < 1$ and $0 < y < 1$, is it always true that

$$(x + y) - (x \times y) < 1?$$

Investigate.

# 7 ALGEBRAIC EQUATIONS AND PROBLEM SOLVING

## LINEAR EQUATIONS

The two sides of an equation are in a state of balance. For example

$$2 + 3 = 4 + 1$$

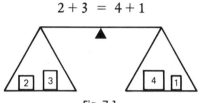

Fig. 7.1

(see Fig. 7.1). Balance is preserved *only* if both sides are treated in *exactly* the same way. Thus, we may

(*i*)  Add the same amount to both sides (Fig. 7.2(a)):

$$2 + 3 + 1 = 4 + 1 + 1$$

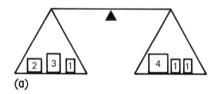

(a)

(*ii*) Subtract the same amount from both sides (Fig. 7.2(b)):

$$2 + 3 + 1 = 4 + 1 + 1$$
$$-2 \qquad\quad -2$$

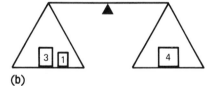

(b)

giving

$$3 + 1 = 4$$

(*iii*) Multiply the *whole* of both sides by the same amount (Fig. 7.2(c)):

$$2 \times (3 + 1) = 2 \times 4$$

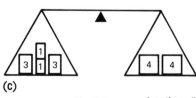

(c)

giving

Fig. 7.2  (continued)

$$(2 \times 3) + (2 \times 1) = 2 \times 4$$

or

$$6 + 2 = \overset{.}{8}$$

(*iv*) Divide the *whole* of both sides by the same amount (Fig. 7.2(d)):

$$\frac{6}{2} + \frac{2}{2} = \frac{8}{2}$$

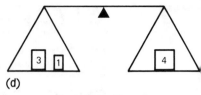

(d)

Fig. 7.2 (continued)

giving $3 + 1 = 4$

We may also square (or square root) the *whole* of both sides. Thus, for example

$$3 + 1 = 4$$
$$\Rightarrow \quad (3 + 1)^2 = 4^2$$

Do *not* square individual items, however, for then each term is multiplied by something *different*; balance is lost (Fig. 7.3) and the resulting equation is *false*.

$$3^2 + 1^2 = 9 + 1 = 10$$

but $\quad 4^2 = 16$

So $\quad 3^2 + 1^2 \neq 4^2$

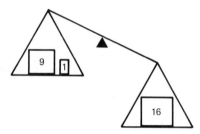

Fig. 7.3

**Example** Solve $6x + 7 = 5 - 2x$.

Add $2x$ to both sides:

$$6x + 7 + 2x = 5 - 2x + 2x$$
$$8x + 7 = 5$$

Subtract 7 from both sides:

$$8x + 7 - 7 = 5 - 7$$
$$8x = -2$$

Finally, divide both sides by 8:

$$\frac{8x}{8} = \frac{-2}{8}$$

giving $\qquad x = -\frac{1}{4}$

*Check* $\qquad 6 \times (-\frac{1}{4}) + 7 = 5\frac{1}{2}$

$\qquad 5 - 2 \times (-\frac{1}{4}) = 5\frac{1}{2}$ ✓

**Example** Solve $2(3x-2) = 20-3(x+2)$.

The brackets make the problem more complicated so multiply them out as the first step, taking care with the negative signs:

$$6x-4 = 20-(3x+6)$$
$$6x-4 = 20-3x-6$$
$$6x-4 = 14-3x$$

Add $3x$ to both sides:

$$6x-4+3x = 14-3x+3x$$

Simplify and add 4 to both sides:

$$9x-4+4 = 14+4$$
$$9x = 18$$

Finally, divide both sides by 9:

$$\frac{9x}{9} = \frac{18}{9}$$
$$x = 2$$

*Check*
$$2(3 \times 2 - 2) = 8$$
$$20 - 3(2 + 2) = 8 \checkmark$$

**Example** Solve $\dfrac{x-2}{3} - \dfrac{x+1}{6} = \dfrac{x-1}{10}$.

In this case, it is the algebraic fractions that make the equation difficult to solve. Remember that the algebraic parts $x-2, x+1$ and $x-1$ must be treated as single terms, so as a first step, write three brackets as follows:

$$\frac{(x-2)}{3} - \frac{(x+1)}{6} = \frac{(x-1)}{10}$$

Now the lowest common multiple of the denominators 3, 6 and 10 is 30. So as the next step, multiply the whole of both sides by 30 (written as a fraction $\frac{30}{1}$)

$$\frac{30}{1} \times \frac{(x-2)}{3} - \frac{30}{1} \times \frac{(x+1)}{6} = \frac{30}{1} \times \frac{(x-1)}{10}$$

Cancel down: $\qquad 10(x-2)-5(x+1) = 3(x-1)$

Multiply out: $\qquad 10x-20-5x-5 = 3x-3$

Simplify: $\qquad\qquad\qquad\quad 5x-25 = 3x-3$

103

Subtract $3x$ and add 25 to both sides:

$$2x = 22$$

$$x = 11$$

*Check*

$$\frac{11-2}{3} - \frac{11+1}{6} = 1$$

$$\frac{11-1}{10} = 1 \checkmark$$

**EXERCISE 7a**  Find $x$ from the following equations. Show each step in your reasoning, and check your answers in the original equation.

1. $3x + 7 = 19$   4

2. $5x - 2 = 13$

3. $2x - 1 = 1$   3

4. $5 + 7x = 19$

5. $11 + 3x = 6x + 2$   1

6. $8 + 5x = 3 + 4x$

7. $3x - 2 = x - 1$   2

8. $11x - 6 = 3x + 10$

9. $5 - 7x = -9$

10. $8 - 3x = -1$

11. $1 - 3x = 6x + 2$

12. $2 - 5x = 7x - 6$

13. $3(x - 2) = 12$

14. $2(x + 1) - 1 = 17$

15. $5(2x - 4) = 4$

16. $4(2 - x) = 3(x - 9)$

17. $8 - (x + 3) = 4$

18. $5 + (2x + 1) = 0$

19. $3 - 2(x + 1) = 8$

20. $14 - 3(2x + 3) = 2$

21. $12 - \frac{2}{3}(2x + 1) = 6$

22. $11 - \frac{1}{4}(5x + 2) = 8$

23. $9 - \frac{1}{2}(x + 3) = 3$

24. $3 - \frac{1}{5}(x + 3) = 1$

25. $15 - 3(2x - 1) = 9$

26. $1 - 5(2x - 3) = 6$

27. $5 + 3(x - 1) = 2(x + 3)$

28. $6 + 4(x - 1) = 12x + 2$

29. $11 - 7(x - 1) = 3(x + 1) - 9$

30. $17 - 3(x - 1) = 24 + x$

31. $12 - 2(2x - 1) = \frac{1}{2}(x + 1)$

32. $11(x + 2) + 3(x + 1) = 17(2x - 1) + 2$

33. $x^2 - 8 = 1$

34. $3x^2 - 5 = 7$

35. $x^3 + 3 = 11$

36. $2x^3 - 7 = 9$

37. $18 - x^2 = 9$

38. $20 - 3x^2 = 8$

39. $\dfrac{12}{x} = 4$

40. $\dfrac{17}{x} = 34$

41. $\sqrt{x} + 6 = 10$

42. $17 - \sqrt{x} = 7 + \sqrt{x}$

43. $\dfrac{x+2}{3} = 4$

44. $\dfrac{x-3}{5} = 1$

45. $\dfrac{3x+5}{8} = x$

46. $\dfrac{2x-16}{3} = 2x$

47. $\dfrac{2x+6}{5} = 3x-4$

48. $\dfrac{5x-7}{2} = 4$

49. $\dfrac{7x-1}{2} = 13-x$

50. $\dfrac{2x-5}{3} = 25-x$

51. $\dfrac{x-2}{3} = \dfrac{x+4}{5}$

52. $\dfrac{3x-5}{6} = \dfrac{9-x}{9}$

53. $\dfrac{x+1}{6} = \dfrac{1-x}{4}$

54. $\dfrac{x-2}{7} = 2 + \dfrac{3-x}{14}$

55. $\dfrac{x-1}{2} + \dfrac{x+1}{3} = \dfrac{2x+5}{6}$

56. $\dfrac{2x-4}{2} + \dfrac{x+1}{10} = \dfrac{2x+1}{5}$

57. $\dfrac{2x+1}{2} - \dfrac{x+2}{4} = \dfrac{x+10}{8}$

58. $\dfrac{2x-1}{3} - \dfrac{2x+1}{4} = \dfrac{x-4}{12}$

59. $\dfrac{3x-1}{2} - \dfrac{x-1}{6} = \dfrac{x+8}{3}$

60. $\dfrac{x+1}{3} - \dfrac{x-1}{9} = \dfrac{x+8}{18}$

## REARRANGING FORMULAE

Formulae may be rearranged in precisely the same way as simple equations – that is, each side must be added to, subtracted from, multiplied or divided *exactly* as the other.

**Example** Rearrange the formula $y = mx + c$ to express $x$ in terms of $y$, $m$ and $c$.

$$y = mx + c$$

Subtract $c$ from both sides:

$$y - c = mx$$

Divide each side by $m$:

$$\frac{y-c}{m} = \frac{mx}{m}$$

Hence

$$\frac{y-c}{m} = x$$

105

**Example**  Rearrange the formula $q = \sqrt{\dfrac{2r}{p}}$ to make $p$ the subject.

Square both sides:

$$q^2 = \left(\sqrt{\frac{2r}{p}}\right)^2$$

giving

$$q^2 = \frac{2r}{p}$$

Multiply both sides by $p$:

$$p \times q^2 = p \times \frac{2r}{p}$$

$$pq^2 = 2r$$

Divide both sides by $q^2$:

$$\frac{pq^2}{q^2} = \frac{2r}{q^2}$$

Hence

$$p = \frac{2r}{q^2}$$

**EXERCISE 7b**  Rearrange the formulae below to make the given letter the subject. Show each step in your reasoning.

1.  $P = 4a;\quad a$

2.  $V = ir;\quad$ (a) $i$ (b) $r$

3.  $F = ma;\quad m$

4.  $A = 2\pi r;\quad \pi$

5.  $E = mgx;\quad x$

6.  $I = \dfrac{Prt}{100};\quad r$

7.  $A = \frac{1}{2}ab;\quad b$

8.  $V = \frac{1}{3}abx;\quad x$

9.  $p = 1 - q;\quad q$

10.  $t = \dfrac{o}{a};\quad$ (a) $o$ (b) $a$

11.  $v = u + at;\quad$ (a) $u$ (b) $a$

12.  $v^2 = u^2 + 2as;\quad$ (a) $a$ (b) $u$

13.  $S = 2\pi(r + x);\quad x$

14.  $E = \frac{1}{2}mv^2;\quad$ (a) $v^2$ (b) $v$

15.  $A = \pi r^2;\quad r$

16.  $y = mx + c;\quad$ (a) $c$ (b) $x$

17.  $V = \frac{4}{3}\pi r^3;\quad r$

18.  $r = \sqrt{x^2 + y^2};\quad$ (a) $y^2$ (b) $y$

19.  $P = \dfrac{mv^2}{r};\quad$ (a) $r$ (b) $v$

20.  $s = ut + \frac{1}{2}at^2;\quad$ (a) $u$ (b) $a$

21. $A = \left(\dfrac{a+b}{2}\right)x;$        (a) $x$      (b) $a$

22. $s = \sqrt{np(1-p)};$    $n$

23. $T = 2\pi\sqrt{\dfrac{l}{g}};$       (a) $l$      (b) $g$

24. $\dfrac{1}{f} = \dfrac{1}{u} + \dfrac{1}{v};$       (a) $\dfrac{1}{u}$      (b) $u$

## PROBLEMS LEADING TO SIMPLE EQUATIONS AND FORMULAE

**Example** The perimeter of a rectangle is 36 cm. If it is twice as long as it is wide, what is its area?

As we do not yet know the lengths of the rectangle's sides we must use letters. Let the width be $w$. Then the length must be twice this, i.e. $2w$.

Fig. 7.4

The perimeter is

$$2w + w + 2w + w = 6w$$

But we are told that the perimeter is 36 cm. So now we can make the simple equation:

$$6w = 36$$

giving $w = 6$ cm.

Thus the rectangle is 6 cm wide, and, therefore, 12 cm long.

$$\text{area} = \text{length} \times \text{breadth} = 12\,\text{cm} \times 6\,\text{cm} = 72\,\text{cm}^2$$

**Example** This year, a man is four times the age of his son. In five years' time he will be three times as old as his son. How old is the man now?

Let the son's current age be $x$ years. His father is four times as old or $4x$ years. In five years time, *both* father and son will be five years older. So the son's future age is $x + 5$ years and the father's is $4x + 5$ years. But in five years, the father is three times his son's age. That is

$$4x + 5 = 3(x + 5)$$

107

Expanding the bracket, we get the equation

$$4x + 5 = 3x + 15$$

Subtracting $3x$ and 5 from both sides gives

$$4x + 5 - 3x - 5 = 3x + 15 - 3x - 5$$

$$x = 10$$

Thus the son is currently 10 years old and his father is therefore 40. (And in five years, the son will be 15 and his father 45 — three times as old.)

**EXERCISE 7c**

1. (a) I ask a friend to think of a number, double it and add four. He tells me his answer is 18. Show that this can be written algebraically as $2x + 4 = 18$. What number did my friend think of?

   (b) Another friend, playing the same game, tells me his answer is 66. What number did he first think of?

2. My friend now asks me to think of a number, add 5 to it, double the result and then take away 7. If my answer is 13, what number did I first think of?

3. I think of another number, treble it, subtract 14, multiply by 10 and divide by two. If my answer is $-100$, what (negative) number did I think of?

4. Three consecutive numbers (i.e. like $3, 4, 5$) are $n$, $n + 1$ and $n + 2$. If the sum of the three numbers is 42, form an equation and find the three numbers.

5. Three consecutive *even* numbers are $n$, $n + 2$ and $n + 4$. What is the fourth? If the sum of the first and the fourth of these numbers is 26, what are the four numbers?

6. The perimeter of a rectangle is 28 cm. If the length is 10 cm more than the width, find the sides of the rectangle.

7. The perimeter of a rectangle is 64 cm. If the length of the rectangle is three times the width, find the area of the rectangle.

8. The perimeter of an isosceles triangle is 35 cm. If the two sloping sides are both twice the length of the base, find the length of the base.

9. Find, in terms of $l$, the perimeter of the shape in Fig. 7.5. If the perimeter is 60 cm, find the area.

Fig. 7.5

10. The height of a triangle is half the length of its base, $b$ cm. If the area of the triangle is 9 cm², find $b$.

11. A young girl is one-third of her mother's age. In ten years time, she will be one-half her mother's age; how old will the girl be then?

12. The elder of two brothers is exactly twice the age of the other. Three years ago, the elder brother was three times the other's age. How old are the boys now?

13. At the greengrocer's, carrots cost $q$ pence per kilogram, potatoes cost $q + 5$ pence per kilogram and Brussels sprouts cost $2q + 3$ pence per kilogram. If I buy 2 kg of carrots, 5 kg of potatoes and 1 kg of sprouts, find, in terms of $q$, how much I have spent.

    The bill comes to £1.54. What is the cost of the sprouts?

14. At the newsagent I buy a copy of *The Worplesdon Times* for $t$ pence, a chocolate bar for $t - 5$ pence and two magazines for $2t + 3$ pence each. If the bill comes to £1.27, what is the cost of my newspaper?

15. Three consecutive numbers (like 1, 2, 3) are $n$, $n + 1$ and $n + 2$. The total of the three numbers is 18. Find $n$.

16. Three consecutive odd numbers (like 3, 5, 7) are $2n + 1$, $2n + 3$ and $2n + 5$. Find the three numbers given that their total is 51.

17. The tanks at a filling station currently hold $x$ litres of petrol. A petrol tanker arrives containing three times this much. When 75 000 litres have been transferred from the tanker to the filling station's tanks, they each then contain exactly the same amount. Find $x$.

18. Clive buys a home computer for £$x$. At the same time he buys a disk-drive for £$x$/5 and a colour monitor for £$x$/2. If he spends a total of £680, find the cost of the computer.

19. At the local supermarket, frozen chicken costs $x$ pence per pound and fresh chicken costs half as much again.

    If the difference in price is 48 pence per pound, find the cost of a fresh chicken weighing 3 pounds.

20. A bus company charges a minimum fare of 20 pence for a journey of up to one fare stage, and then an extra $q$ pence for each fare stage reached (so that a journey passing one fare stage costs $20 + q$ pence).

(a) Find, in terms of $q$, the cost of a journey that passes
    (i) 2    (ii) 5    (iii) $x$ $(x > 2)$ fare stages.

(b) If the journey passing 5 fare stages costs me 75 pence, find the value of $q$.

(c) If the journey passing $x$ fare stages costs me 97 pence, find $x$.

21. The same bus company proposes to revise the fares by raising the minimum fare to 25 pence and charging $3r$ pence for the first fare stage, $2r$ pence for the second and then $r$ pence for each subsequent fare stage.

(a) Find, in terms of $r$, the cost of a journey that passes
    (i) 2    (ii) 5    (iii) $x$ $(x > 2)$ fare stages.

(b) If the journey passing 5 fare stages costs me 89 pence, find the value of $r$.

(c) If the journey passing $x$ fare stages costs me 73 pence, find $x$.

## SIMULTANEOUS EQUATIONS

It is only possible to solve equations for *two* unknown values if there are *two* equations to work on simultaneously.

**Example** Find $x$ and $y$ if

$$2x + y = 8 \qquad [1]$$

and

$$3x - y = 7 \qquad [2]$$

If we add together the left-hand sides of the two equations, then the result must equal the two right-hand sides added together. Moreover, if we add the two left-hand sides, then $+y$ and $-y$ will cancel, leaving an equation that contains only $x$.

$$2x + y = 8$$
$$3x - y = 7$$

Adding gives

$$5x = 15$$

Hence

$$x = \frac{15}{5} = 3$$

Now, if $x = 3$, we can say that, from Equation [1]

$$(2 \times 3) + y = 8$$

or $\qquad\qquad 6 + y = 8$

Therefore $\qquad\qquad y = 2$

Thus the solution to Equations [1] and [2] is $x = 3$, $y = 2$.

*Check* $\qquad\qquad 2 \times 3 + 2 = 8$

$\qquad\qquad 3 \times 3 - 2 = 7$ ✓

Sometimes it is necessary to multiply one or both equations so that the number of *y*s in each equation is the same. Also, if the signs of the *y*s in both equations are the same, then the equations must be *subtracted* (not added).

**Example** Find $x$ and $y$ if

$$3x - 2y = 1 \qquad\qquad [1]$$
$$x - 5y = 9 \qquad\qquad [2]$$

First, we must multiply Equation [1] by 5 and Equation [2] by 2 so that both equations then contain $10y$.

Multiplying Equation [1] by 5 gives

$$15x - 10y = 5$$

Multiplying Equation [2] by 2 gives

$$2x - 10y = 18$$

*Subtracting* Equation [2] from Equation [1] leaves

$$13x = -13$$

Hence $\qquad\qquad x = -1$

Putting $x = -1$ in Equation [1] gives

$$(3 \times -1) - 2y = 1$$
$$-3 - 2y = 1$$

Adding 3 to both sides:

$$-2y = 4$$

Dividing by $-2$: $\qquad\qquad y = \dfrac{4}{-2} = -2$

Thus the solution to Equations [1] and [2] is $x = -1$, $y = -2$.

*Check* $\qquad\qquad 3 \times (-1) - 2 \times (-2) = 1$

$\qquad\qquad (-1) - 5 \times (-2) = 9$ ✓

**EXERCISE 7d**   Solve the following pairs of simultaneous equations; in each case check your answers with the original equations.

1. $x + y = 5$
   $x - y = 3$

2. $2x + y = 12$
   $4x - y = 6$

3. $2x + 3y = 17$
   $4x - 3y = 7$

4. $5x + y = 10$
   $3x - y = 2$

5. $2a + b = 12$
   $a + b = 7$

6. $3p - q = 8$
   $3p - 2q = 7$

7. $2y + z = 7$
   $y + z = 5$

8. $p - 7q = 5$
   $p - 5q = 9$

9. $y + x = 8$
   $x - y = 2$

10. $3m - n = 11$
    $3m - 2n = 13$

11. $p + 2q = 7$
    $3p - 4q = 21$

12. $c + d = 4$
    $3d - c = 16$

13. $5x + 2y = 19$
    $7x - y = 19$

14. $x + 4y = 3$
    $2x - 8y = -2$

15. $3x + y = 7$
    $y + x = 5$

16. $2y + 7z = -13$
    $4y + 5z = -8$

17. $4g - 5h = 3$
    $6g - 7h = 4$

18. $12f - 6e = -2$
    $7e - 3f = 6$

19. $3m - 5n = -2.5$
    $9m + 8n = -5.2$

20. $4p - 2q = -7$
    $3p - q = 5$

21. $4a - 3b = 6$
    $2a + 6b = 13$

22. $x + 2y = 6$
    $3x + y = 6$

23. $m + n = 6$
    $3m - 2n = 8$

24. $x + y = 6$
    $2x - 3y = 6$

## PROBLEMS LEADING TO SIMULTANEOUS EQUATIONS

**Example**   The two points $(3, 11)$ and $(2, 8)$ lie on the line $y = mx + c$. Find $m$ and $c$.

As the point $(3, 11)$ lies on the line, so the equation of the line $y = mx + c$ must work for $y = 11$ and $x = 3$, i.e. $11 = 3m + c$. Similarly, since the point $(2, 8)$ lies on the line, $y = 8$ and $x = 2$

must also satisfy the equation $y = mx + c$, hence $8 = 2m + c$. Now we have two equations that can be solved simultaneously:

$$11 = 3m + c \qquad [1]$$

$$8 = 2m + c \qquad [2]$$

Subtracting Equation [2] from Equation [1] gives

$$3 = m$$

Substituting back into the first equation gives

$$11 = 3 \times 3 + c$$

Hence $\qquad\qquad c = 2$

**Example** A taxi company charges a minimum fare of $m$ pence for any journey up to 1 mile and then $q$ pence per mile after that. If a journey of 2 miles costs £1.10 and a journey of 8 miles costs £2.90, what is the minimum charge and the cost per mile outside the 1 mile limit?

A journey of 2 miles costs $m + q$ pence and a journey of 8 miles costs $m + 7q$ pence. We are told that the 2 mile journey costs £1.10 (110 pence) and that the 8 mile journey costs £2.90 (or 290 pence). Thus

$$m + q = 110 \qquad [1]$$

and $\qquad\qquad m + 7q = 290 \qquad [2]$

Subtracting Equation [1] from Equation [2]:

$$6q = 180$$

$$q = 30 \text{ pence}$$

Substituting the value of $q$ back into Equation [1]:

$$m + 30 = 110$$

$$m = 80 \text{ pence}$$

Thus the taxi firm's minimum charge is 80p and the cost per mile after the first mile is 30p.

*Check*  Journey of 2 miles costs $80p + 30p = $ £1.10

Journey of 8 miles costs $80p + 7 \times 30p = $ £2.90. ✓

**EXERCISE 7e**

1. Two numbers, $x$ and $y$, have a sum of 15 and a difference of 3. Find $x$ and $y$.

2. Find two numbers which have a difference of 12 and a sum of 24.

113

3. Two apples and a banana cost 36p. Just one apple and a banana cost 26p. What is the cost of an apple? What is the cost of a banana?

4. Five tins of peas and three tins of beans cost £1.53; one tin of peas and two tins of beans cost 60 pence. Find the cost per tin of peas and beans.

5. Two adults' tickets and one child's ticket to the theatre cost £7.50. Two children's and one adult's tickets cost £6.00. Find the cost of the tickets.

6. I buy 30 stamps at the post office. Some are second-class (costing 13p each) and the rest are first-class (costing 18p each). If the total cost is £4.40, how many first-class stamps did I buy?

7. I have in my pocket a total of 82p in loose change, made up of $x$ 5p pieces and $y$ 2p pieces. If the numbers were the other way round — that is, if I had $x$ 2p pieces and $y$ 5p pieces — I would have only 58p. Write down two equations in $x$ and $y$ and solve them simultaneously.

8. I pay a bill for £520 with $x$ £10 notes and $y$ £5 notes. If I use 72 notes altogether, find $x$ and $y$.

9. At the garage the other day I bought 25 litres of petrol and one litre of oil for £11.20; today I have just bought a further 20 litres of petrol and 5 litres of oil for £11.90. What is the price of a litre of petrol?

10. A man normally works at £$x$ per hour for a 35 hour week. He is paid £$y$ per hour of overtime. One week he works 38 hours and receives £120; the next week he works 41 hours and receives £135. What are his normal and overtime rates of pay?

11. A bus company charges a basic fare of $m$ pence, and $q$ pence for each fare stage passed. One journey takes me past three fare stages and costs 40p; another journey, passing five fare stages, costs 56p. What is the minimum fare? How much would a journey passing eight fare stages cost?

12. (a) A line has the equation $y = mx + c$. If the points $x = 2$, $y = 13$ and $x = 3$, $y = 18$ lie on this line, find $m$ and $c$.
    (b) Another line, also of the form $y = nx + d$, goes through the points $(2, 1)$ and $(5, 7)$. Find $n$ and $d$.
    (c) A line passes through the points $(1, 5)$ and $(3, 17)$. Find the equation of this line.

13. The value, $T$, of a term in a series is given by the formula $T = a + (n-1)d$ where $a$ and $d$ are constants. When $n = 2$, $T = 9$ and when $n = 4$, $T = 17$. Find $a$ and $d$.

14. The velocity of a particle is given by the formula $v = u + at$. When $t = 3$, $v = 17$ and when $t = 5$, $v = 25$. Find $a$ and $u$.

15. The distance, $s$, travelled by a particle is given by the formula $s = ut + \frac{1}{2}at^2$. If $s = 2$ when $t = 1$ and $s = 0$ when $t = 3$ find $a$ and $u$.

16. Given that $v^2 = u^2 + 2as$, that $v = 4$ when $s = 3$ and that $v = 5$ when $s = 10.5$ use simultaneous equations to find

    (a) $a$          (b) $u^2$          (c) $u$.

# QUADRATIC EQUATIONS

## Quadratics that Factorise

The solution of quadratic equations that factorise depends upon a peculiar property of zero, namely that if the product of two numbers is zero then one of the numbers must be zero.

**Example** $x^2 + 4x = 0$.

Factorising: $x(x + 4) = 0$.

So *either* $\qquad\qquad\qquad x = 0$

*or* $\qquad\qquad (x + 4) = 0$     i.e. $x = -4$

Thus there are two possible answers: $x = 0$ or $x = -4$.

*Check* $\quad 0^2 + 4 \times 0 = 0$   and   $(-4)^2 + 4 \times (-4) = 0$ ✓

**Example** $x^2 + 5x + 6 = 0$.

Since the left-hand side of the equation is a quadratic expression that factorises to $(x + 3)(x + 2)$ (see page 93), we may say

$$x^2 + 5x + 6 = 0$$

$$(x + 3)(x + 2) = 0$$

But if these two expressions, $(x + 3)$ on the one hand and $(x + 2)$ on the other, multiply to give zero, then one of them *must* be zero.

115

So *either* $(x + 3) = 0$   giving   $x = -3$

*or* $(x + 2) = 0$   giving   $x = -2$.

The equation has *two* possible solutions: $x = -3$ or $-2$.

*Check* $(-3)^2 + 5 \times (-3) + 6 = 0$   and
$(-2)^2 + 5 \times (-2) + 6 = 0$   ✓

**Example** $6x^2 - 11x + 8 = 3$.

Subtracting 3 from both sides:

$$6x^2 - 11x + 8 - 3 = 3 - 3$$

Hence $\qquad 6x^2 - 11x + 5 = 0$

Factorising: $\qquad (6x - 5)(x - 1) = 0$

So either $\quad 6x - 5 = 0 \Rightarrow 6x = 5 \Rightarrow x = \frac{5}{6}$

or $\qquad x - 1 = 0 \Rightarrow x = 1$

The solutions are $x = \frac{5}{6}$ or $x = 1$.

Sometimes, considerable rearranging is necessary.

*Check* $6 \times (\frac{5}{6})^2 - 11 \times (\frac{5}{6}) + 8 = 3$   and
$6 \times (1)^2 - 11 \times (1) + 8 = 3$   ✓

**Example** Solve the equation $x = \dfrac{7}{6 + x}$.

Multiplying both sides by $(6 + x)$:

$$x(6 + x) = 7$$

Multiplying the bracket out and subtracting 7 from both sides:

$$6x + x^2 - 7 = 0$$

Rearranging into the usual order:

$$x^2 + 6x - 7 = 0$$

Hence $\qquad\qquad x^2 - x + 7x - 7 = 0$

$$x(x - 1) + 7(x - 1) = 0$$

$$(x - 1)(x + 7) = 0$$

So either $x = 1$ or $x = -7$.

*Check* $\qquad \dfrac{7}{6 + (1)} = 1$ and $\dfrac{7}{6 + (-7)} = -7$   ✓

116

**EXERCISE 7f**   *Throughout this exercise check your answers in the original equations.*

Write down the solutions to the following:

1. $(x-2)(x-3) = 0$

2. $(x+4)(x-3) = 0$

3. $(p+3)(p+2) = 0$

4. $x(x-2) = 0$

5. $xy = 0$

6. $x(x-1)(x-2) = 0$. (*Note*: there are *three* possible answers.)

Solve these equations by factorising:

7. $x^2 + 3x = 0$

8. $x^2 - 2x = 0$

9. $z^2 - 4z = 0$

10. $5z - z^2 = 0$

11. $p^3 - p^2 = 0$

12. $2x^2 - x = 0$

13. $r^2 - 5r = 0$

14. $s^2 - 3s = 0$

15. $r^5 + 3r^4 = 0$

16. $r^3 + r^2 = 0$.

Solve the following quadratic equations by factorising them first:

17. $x^2 + 6x + 8 = 0$

18. $a^2 + 6a - 16 = 0$

19. $b^2 - 2b - 15 = 0$

20. $x^2 - 7x + 10 = 0$

21. $2x^2 + 5x - 3 = 0$

22. $4c^2 - 12c + 5 = 0$

23. $11c^2 + 8c - 3 = 0$

24. $12x^2 + 13x + 3 = 0$

25. $5x^2 - 3x - 2 = 0$

26. $5d^2 + 2d - 7 = 0$

27. $12x^2 - 23x - 2 = 0$

28. $4q^2 + 19q + 12 = 0$.

Rearrange these equations to give zero on the right-hand side and solve them by factorising:

29. $x^2 + 6x = 27$

30. $x^2 + x = 2$

31. $6x^2 + x = 2$

32. $3x^2 + 14x = 5$

33. $a^2 - 11a + 30 = 2$

34. $2x^2 + 13x - 2 = -20$

35. $6x^2 + 9x - 5 = 1$

36. $17x = 10x^2 + 3$

37. $15 - x^2 = 23x + 3x^2 + 30$

38. $2x^2 + 5x + 3 = 12x$

39. $21b^2 + 2b = 24b + 8$

40. $6x^2 - 5 = 13x$

41. $20w^2 = 28 - 19w$

42. $x^2 - 6x = 3x + 2x - 24$

43. $y(2y + 7) = -6$

44. $q(5q + 14) = 3$

117

45. $x - 1 = \dfrac{2}{x}$

46. $x + 4 = \dfrac{5}{x}$

47. $x - 3 = \dfrac{10}{x}$

48. $x + 1 = \dfrac{2}{x}$

49. $a = \dfrac{2}{(a+1)}$

50. $x = \dfrac{3}{(x-2)}$

51. $b = \dfrac{6}{b-5}$

52. $y = \dfrac{1}{2y-1}$

53. $c = \dfrac{15}{7+2c}$

54. $z = \dfrac{4}{15z+4}.$

## Quadratics that do not Factorise

If the quadratic will not factorise, then there is a formula to use.

If $$ax^2 + bx + c = 0$$

then $$x = \frac{-b \pm \sqrt{b^2 - 4ac}}{2a}$$

**Example**  Solve $7x^2 + 4x - 1 = 0$.

Comparing this equation with $ax + bx + c$

$$a\,x^2 \quad +b\,x \quad +c$$
$$7\,x^2 \quad +4\,x \quad -1$$

we see that we should put $a = 7$, $b = 4$ and $c = -1$ into the above formula:

$$x = \frac{-4 \pm \sqrt{4^2 - (4 \times 7 \times -1)}}{2 \times 7}$$

$$= \frac{-4 \pm \sqrt{16 - (-28)}}{14}$$

So either $$x = \frac{-4 + \sqrt{44}}{14} = 0.188 \quad (3 \text{ d.p.})$$

or $$x = \frac{-4 - \sqrt{44}}{14} = -0.760 \quad (3 \text{ d.p.})$$

**Example** $4z^2 - 2 = 3z + 11$.

First, we must ensure that the right-hand side is zero and that the terms are in order ($z^2$ first, then $z$ and then the number).

Subtracting $3z + 11$ from both sides and arranging into order gives:

$$4z^2 - 3z - 13 = 0$$

$$\boxed{4}\,z^2 \quad \boxed{-3}\,z \quad \boxed{-13} = 0$$
$$\boxed{a}\,z^2 \quad \boxed{+b}\,z \quad \boxed{+c} = 0$$

Comparing with

$$az^2 + bz + c$$

we see that $a = +4$, $b = -3$ and $c = -13$. Substituting these values into the formula gives

$$z = \frac{-(-3) \pm \sqrt{(-3)^2 - (4 \times 4 \times -13)}}{2 \times 4}$$

Now, $-(-3) = +3$ and $(-3)^2 = +9$, so

$$z = \frac{+3 \pm \sqrt{+9 + 208}}{8}$$

$$= \frac{+3 \pm \sqrt{217}}{8} = \frac{+3 \pm 14.731}{8}$$

Hence

$$z = \frac{+3 + 14.731}{8} = 2.22 \quad \text{(2 d.p.)}$$

or

$$z = \frac{+3 - 14.731}{8} = -1.47 \quad \text{(2 d.p.)}$$

It is worth remembering that the square root of a negative number does not exist, so $b^2 - 4ac$ *must always* be a positive quantity. If you make it negative, do not ignore the minus sign: go back and check your arithmetic. Remember, too, that *any* number squared is positive, so $b^2$ is *always* positive, even if $b$ itself is negative (as in this example).

**EXERCISE 7g**  Use the formula $x = \dfrac{-b \pm \sqrt{b^2 - 4ac}}{2a}$ to solve the following quadratic equations, giving your answers to 2 d.p. where appropriate:

1. $x^2 + 3x + 2 = 0$          2. $2x^2 + 5x + 2 = 0$

3. $3x^2 + 7x + 2 = 0$          4. $2x^2 + 2x - 3 = 0$

119

5. $x^2 + x - 5 = 0$

6. $x^2 - 8x + 5 = 0$

7. $x^2 - 6x + 3 = 0$

8. $x^2 - 4x - 4 = 0$

9. $x^2 - 3x - 2 = 0$

10. $3x^2 - 2x - 7 = 0$

11. $-2y^2 - 5y + 2 = 0$

12. $-y^2 - 2y + 5 = 0$

13. $-z^2 - 3z + 6 = 0$

14. $p - p^2 + 3 = 0$.

Rearrange these equations to make the right-hand side zero and then solve by formula:

15. $a^2 + a - 2 = 1$

16. $2a - a^2 = -2$

17. $m^2 - 2m = 3 - 4m$

18. $3z^2 - 2z = z^2 + 1$

19. $2b^2 + 3 = 2 - 5b$

20. $3a^2 - 12a = -3 - 19a$

21. $3y(y + 1) = 1$

22. $2x^2 + 10x = x - 3$

23. $4 - y = \dfrac{2}{y}$

24. $y = \dfrac{2}{(2y + 1)}$

25. $x - 2 = \dfrac{2}{x}$

26. $z = \dfrac{3}{3 + z}$

27. $2x = \dfrac{1}{5x - 1}$

28. $3x = \dfrac{4}{3x + 2}$.

## PROBLEMS LEADING TO QUADRATIC EQUATIONS

**Example** Two consecutive *even* numbers have a product of 168. What are they?

Let the first number be $x$. Then the next (i.e. consecutive) even number is $x + 2$. The product of these two numbers is $x \times (x + 2)$ and is to be 168, i.e.

$$x(x + 2) = 168$$

or $$x^2 + 2x - 168 = 0$$

Factorising in the usual way:

$$(x + 14)(x - 12) = 0$$

giving

$$x = -14 \quad \text{so that the second number is } -12$$

or $$x = +12 \quad \text{so that the second number is } +14.$$

**Example** A rectangular, open-topped water tank is to be made out of $14\,\text{m}^2$ of sheet metal so that it is $4\,\text{m}$ long and has a square cross-section, as shown in Fig. 7.6(a). If the tank is $x$ metres high and $x$ metres wide, find $x$ and the volume of the tank.

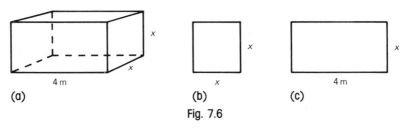

(a)    (b)    (c)

**Fig. 7.6**

The area of each of the two square ends is $x \times x = x^2$ (Fig. 7.6(b)). So the area of the two of them is $2x^2$. The area of the rectangle bottom and of each of the two rectangular sides is $4 \times x = 4x$ (Fig. 7.6(c)). So the area of these three sides together is $12x$. Thus the area of all five sides of the tank is $2x^2 + 12x$ square metres.

But the area of the sides must equal the area of sheet metal required to build the tank, i.e. $14\,\text{m}^2$. Thus

$$2x^2 + 12x = 14$$
$$2x^2 + 12x - 14 = 0$$

Dividing both sides by 2:

$$x^2 + 6x - 7 = 0$$

and factorising in the usual way:

$$(x + 7)(x - 1) = 0$$

giving $\qquad x = -7 \quad \text{or} \quad +1$

But $x$ represents the side length of a water tank which cannot be a negative quantity, so the answer $x = -7$ cannot be allowed. Therefore $x$ must be $1\,\text{m}$. The volume of the tank is

$$4\,\text{m} \times 1\,\text{m} \times 1\,\text{m} = 4\,\text{m}^3$$

Generally, there are *two* answers to a quadratic equation. However, it often happens that one answer makes no practical sense so (as in the example above) has to be disallowed, leaving only *one* possible solution.

**EXERCISE 7h** *In most of these questions there are two answers; if one answer is not allowable, say why.*

1. I think of a number, square it and add the original number to the result. The total is 42. What two numbers could I have thought of?

121

2. A friend thinks of a number, squares it, doubles the result and then adds the original number to make a total of 36. What could the original number have been? He then tells me that his original number was *not* a whole number. What is his number?

3. A girl thinks of a number, squares it and then adds three times the original number to give a total of 40. What could her number have been? What must it be if she says she chose a a positive number?

4. If the area of the rectangle shown in Fig. 7.7 is $54\,\text{cm}^2$, find $x$.

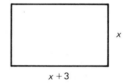

Fig. 7.7

5.

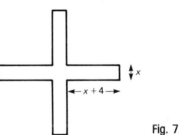

Fig. 7.8

If the area of the cross shape shown in Fig. 7.8 is $93\,\text{cm}^2$, find $x$.

6. A rectangular garden is laid out with lawns and paths as shown in Fig. 7.9. If the paths are both $x$ metres wide, and the garden is 20 m by 15 m, show that the area of the lawn is given by $(20-x)(15-x)\,\text{m}^2$. If, in fact, the area of the lawn is $234\,\text{m}^2$, find $x$.

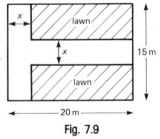

Fig. 7.9

7. The living room in my house is 3 ft longer than its width. If the area of the room is 304 square feet, work out its length and width.

8. The width of the main bedroom in my house is 5 ft less than its length. The area of the room is 204 square feet. Find its length and width.

122

9. A block of wood is 10 cm high, $5x$ cm long and $2x + 3$ wide. Given that its volume is 1000 cm³, find $x$.

10. A rectangular tank is 2 m high and $1\frac{1}{2}$ m longer than it is wide. If the volume of the tank is 9 m³, find the length and breadth.

11. A small closed tank has a square cross-section of side length $x$ cm and is 30 cm high (Fig. 7.10). If the surface area of the tank (including the top) is 3200 cm², find $x$.

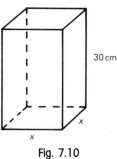

30 cm

Fig. 7.10

12. A rectangular carpet fits in the centre of a room leaving a border $x$ ft wide all the way round, as shown.

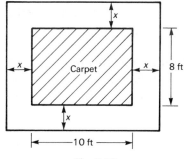

Fig. 7.11

Given that the carpet measures 10 ft by 8 ft and that the area of the room is 168 square feet, form an equation in $x$ and so find the measurements of the room.

13. A rectangular lawn is laid in the centre of a garden with a 1 m wide footpath on all four sides. Given that the lawn is twice as long as it is wide and that the area of the garden (i.e. lawn and path together) is 144 m² find the length and breadth of the lawn.

14. Two consecutive whole numbers are $n$ and $n + 1$. Write down an algebraic expression for the sum of their squares. Find the value of $n$ given that this sum of squares is

(a) 421            (b) 221.

15. It can be shown that a figure with $n$ sides has $\frac{1}{2}n(n-3)$ diagonals.

   (a) Use the formula to show that a six-sided figure (a hexagon) has 9 diagonals. Draw such a six-sided figure and all 9 diagonals.

   (b) How many sides has a figure with   (i) 54   (ii) 77 diagonals?

16. The sum of the first $n$ whole numbers, i.e. $1 + 2 + 3 + \ldots + n$, is given by the formula $\frac{1}{2}n(n+1)$. Use this formula to

   (a) show that $1 + 2 + 3 + 4 + \ldots + 12 = 78$

   (b) find $n$ if $1 + 2 + 3 + 4 + \ldots + n = 120$.

17. A marble is rolled along the ground. It travels for just over 5 seconds before coming to a complete halt. During that time the distance travelled by the marble is given by the formula

   $$\text{distance from starting point} = 4.2t - 0.4t^2 \text{ metres}$$

   where $t$ is the number of seconds for which it has been travelling $(t \leqslant 5)$.

   (a) How far has it travelled after 3 seconds?

   (b) How long does it take for the marble to travel 10.8 metres?

18. Pythagoras' theorem says that the square of the longest side (the hypotenuse) of a right-angled triangle is equal to the sum of the squares of the other two sides (see Fig. 7.12).

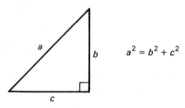

Fig. 7.12

   (a) Fig. 7.13 shows a right-angled triangle in which the shortest side is of length $x$ cm, the hypotenuse is $x + 8$ and the third side is $x + 7$. Use Pythagoras' theorem to find $x$.

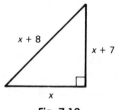

Fig. 7.13

(b) In another right-angled triangle the second side is 3 cm longer than the shortest side and the hypotenuse is 6 cm longer than the shortest side. Find the lengths of the three sides.

(c) In a third right-angled triangle, the shortest side is 9 cm shorter than the hypotenuse, and the second side is 8 cm shorter than the hypotenuse. Find the lengths of the three sides.

## MISCELLANEOUS EXERCISE 7

1. (a) Use the formula $T = a + (n-1)d$ to find
   (i) $T$ when $a = 2$, $d = 3$ and $n = 5$;
   (ii) $n$ when $a = 3$, $d = 4$ and $T = 31$.

   (b) Use the equation $T - mg = mf$ to find
   (i) the value of $T$ when $m = 10$, $g = 32$ and $f = 15$;
   (ii) the value of $f$ when $m = 4$, $g = 32$ and $T = 140$.
   (SUJB)

2. (a) Simplify

   (i) $(3p - 5q)(2p + 3q)$  (ii) $\dfrac{a-3}{2} - \dfrac{a-4}{3}$.

   (b) Factorise
   (i) $15ab^2 - 5a^2b + 25ab$  (ii) $4x - 4y - xy + y^2$
   (iii) $3ab^2 - 6a^2b$  (iv) $x^2 - 6x + 5$.
   (SUJB)

3. Solve the following pairs of simultaneous equations:
   (a) $4x + y = 9$     (b) $3x - 4y = -6$  (c) $5x + 7y = -1$
   $\quad 7x - y = 2$      $\quad 5x + 2y = 16$      $\quad 4x + 3y = 7$.

4. Factorise
   (a) $6xy + 2x$       (b) $3x^2 + 2x^3y$       (c) $12x^2y^2 + 4xy$
   (d) $mn + 2m^2 + 2pm + pn$     (e) $2rt - st - 2rv^2 + sv^2$
   (f) $x^2 + 5x - 14$          (g) $2x^2 + x - 21$.

5. Solve the following quadratic equations (to 3 s.f., if necessary):
   (a) $x^2 + 9x + 20 = 0$       (b) $x^2 - x = 6$
   (c) $3x^2 = x + 2$            (d) $3x^2 - x - 5 = 0$
   (e) $2x^2 + 3x - 11 = 0$      (f) $x^2 - 3x - 1 = 2$.

6. Every rectangle in the sequence shown below has all its vertices (corners) at dots on the grid. The table gives the area, $A$, of each rectangle and the number of dots, $p$, on its perimeter.

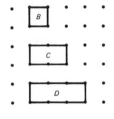

| Shape | Area $A$ | Number of dots on perimeter $p$ |
|---|---|---|
| B | 1 | 4 |
| C | 2 | 6 |
| D | 3 | 8 |
| E | | |

Fig. 7.14

(a) Draw the next rectangle in the sequence and copy and complete the table.

(b) Write down a formula expressing $p$ in terms of $A$. Hence, using your formula, find
  (i) the number of dots on the perimeter of a rectangle which has an area of 13 square units,
  (ii) the area of a rectangle with 40 dots on its perimeter.

(c) For more complicated shapes, the area $A$ is found using the formula

$$A = \tfrac{1}{2}p + d - 1$$

where  $p$ = the number of dots on the perimeter

and  $d$ = the number of dots *inside* the shape.

  (i) Use the formula to find $A$ if $p = 15$ and $d = 6$.
  (ii) For the shape shown in Fig. 7.15 write down the values of $p$ and $d$, and using the above formula, find the value of $A$.

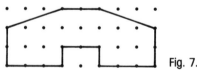

Fig. 7.15

  (iii) For a different shape, $A = 12$ and $p = 12$. Calculate the value of $d$.
  (iv) Another shape has an area of 15 square units and there are 8 dots inside the shape. Find the number of dots on its perimeter.
  (v) Re-arrange the formula $A = \tfrac{1}{2}p + d - 1$ to express $p$ in terms of $A$ and $d$. (SEREB)

126

7. Consider the formula $L = \dfrac{(X+3)(1-2X)}{X}$.

    (a) What is the value of $L$ when $X = 2$?

    (b) What values of $X$ will make $L = 0$?

    (c) If the formula is written in the form $L = \dfrac{aX^2 + bX + C}{X}$

       what is the value of $b$?　　　　　　　　　　(SUJB)

8. Give the solution sets of the following:

    (a) $(x-4)^2 = x^2 - 8x + 16$　　　(b) $(x-4)^2 = x^2$

    (c) $(x-4)^2 = -8x$　　　　　　　(d) $(x-4)^2 = 16$

    Explain why the equation $(x-4)^2 = -x^3$ cannot have a positive root. Given that this equation has a root which is a negative integer, find this root.　　　　　　　(LU)

9. It is given that $x = 1 - 2p$ and $y = 2 + 3p$.

    (a) Calculate the value of

       (i) $x$ when $p = -3$,　(ii) $p$ when $y = 3$.

    (b) Find a formula for $p$ in terms of $x$.

    (c) Given that $xy = -\frac{1}{2}$, show that $12p^2 + 2p - 5 = 0$.

    (d) Solve the equation $12p^2 + 2p - 5 = 0$, giving each answer correct to two decimal places.　　　　　(AEB '82)

10. It is stated that you can find the temperature by counting the chirps of the snowy tree cricket: the relation is given as

$$T = 40 + \frac{N}{4}$$

where $T$ is the temperature in degrees Fahrenheit and $N$ is the number of chirps per minute.

    (a) State the temperature if the chirping rate is 60 per minute.

    (b) What chirping rate would you expect if $T = 65$?

    (c) At what temperature will the cricket cease to chirp?

    (d) The relation between $T$, temperature in degrees Fahrenheit, and $C$, temperature in degrees Centigrade, is

$$T = 32 + \tfrac{9}{5}C$$

    Find a formula for $C$ in terms of $N$, giving your answer as simply as you can.　　　　　　　　　(O & C)

11. I buy $n$ boxes of sweets, each of which contains $x$ sweets. The sweets are divided equally between $y$ children.

    (a) How many sweets in total did I buy?

    (b) How many sweets did each child receive?

12. In a shop, apples cost 8 pence each, oranges cost $x$ pence each and baskets cost 12 pence each.

    (a) Find

        (i)   the cost of 7 apples in a basket,

        (ii)  the cost, in terms of $y$, of $y$ apples in a basket,

        (iii) the cost, in terms of $x$, of 6 oranges in a basket,

        (iv) the cost, in terms of $a$, $b$ and $x$, of $a$ apples and $b$ oranges in a basket.

    (b) Express in terms of $y$, the number of apples that can be bought in a basket for $y$ pence.     (WJEC)

13. A man buys $x$ boxes of tea at a cost of £$z$ for each box. He takes all of this tea and divides it into $n$ packets each of mass $y$ grams.

    (a) What is the mass of tea in each of the original boxes in grams.

    (b) How much has the tea in each packet cost him?     (Ox)

14. A mother and her grown-up daughter both work. Together they bring home a total of £189 per week.

    (a) Suppose the daughter earns £$x$ per week, write down, in terms of $x$ an algebraic expression for the amount the mother earns.

    (b) The mother's income is twice the daughter's. Use this fact to write down, again in terms of $x$, a second expression for the amount the mother earns.

    (c) Write down an equation and solve it to find the value of $x$.

    (d) How much does the mother earn?

15. If I buy $x$ kg of oranges at 60p/kg and $y$ kg of lemons at 75 p/kg, my bill would be £1.95. In fact, I buy $y$ kg of oranges and $x$ kg of lemons so my bill comes to £2.10. Form two equations, each in terms of $x$ and $y$, and solve them to find $x$ and $y$.

16. Two workmen compare their weekly wages. Their rates of pay are £$b$ per hour for the basic wage and £$c$ per hour for overtime.

One man works a basic week of 35 hours and 10 hours overtime and receives £122.50. The other man works a basic week of 40 hours and 5 hours overtime and receives £117.50.

Write down two equations, each in terms of $b$ and $c$, and solve them simultaneously to find the two rates of pay.     (SUJB)

17. A rectangular piece of paper ABCD is $(x-3)$ cm by $x$ cm. A corner piece, BEF, 4 cm by 9 cm, is removed, as shown in Fig. 7.16.

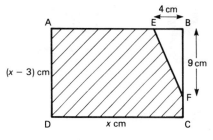

Fig. 7.16

(a) What, in terms of $x$, was the area of the original rectangular piece of paper?

(b) What is the area of the triangular piece removed?

(c) Show that the area of the remaining paper, AEFCD, (shown shaded in Fig. 7.16) is $x^2 - 3x - 18$.

(d) If, in fact, the area of the shaded part is 190 cm², find the length and breadth of the original paper.

18. In the rectangle $ABCD$ (Fig. 7.17), $AB = x$ cm and $BC = 1$ cm. The line $LM$ is drawn so that $ALMD$ is a square.

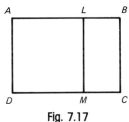

Fig. 7.17

Write down, in terms of $x$,

(a) the length $LB$,

(b) the ratios $\dfrac{AB}{BC}$ and $\dfrac{BC}{LB}$.

(c) If $\dfrac{AB}{BC} = \dfrac{BC}{LB}$, obtain a quadratic equation in $x$. Hence find $x$ correct to two decimal places. (LU)

19. It is said of the roots of the equation

$$x^2 - nx + 1 = 0$$

(a) that they add up to number $n$,

(b) that the second root is the reciprocal of the first.

Investigate.

129

# 8 FUNCTIONS AND MAPPINGS

## FUNCTIONS

The relationship between the members of one set, called the *domain*, and those of another, called the *co-domain* or the *range*, can be shown on an *arrow diagram*. The relationship need not be mathematical. For example, the arrow diagram in Fig. 8.1 illustrates the relationship 'keeps'.

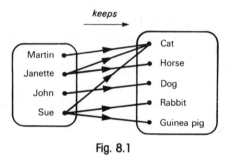

Fig. 8.1

Thus Martin keeps a cat, Janette keeps a cat and a horse, John keeps a dog and Sue keeps a cat, a guinea pig and a rabbit.

Mathematical relationships can be illustrated this way, too. For example Fig. 8.2 shows members of the set {0, 1, 2} linked with their *images* in the set {0, 1, 2, 3, 4, 5} after squaring.

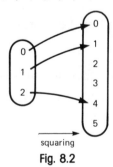

squaring

Fig. 8.2

The arrow diagram illustrates the *mapping* $x \rightarrow x^2$. Other algebraic processes or *functions* can be defined as mappings. For example,

$$f: x \rightarrow 2x + 3$$

$$f: x \rightarrow y, \quad y = 2x + 3$$

both describe the operation (*the function f*) such that a number, $x$, is doubled and then 3 added.

A third way of writing this is

$$f(x) = 2x + 3$$

This notation is particularly useful, for we can go on to write

$$f(1) = 2 \times 1 + 3 = 5$$
$$f(2) = 2 \times 2 + 3 = 7$$
$$f(3) = 2 \times 3 + 3 = 9$$

and so on.

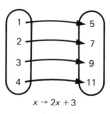

$$x \rightarrow 2x + 3$$

Fig. 8.3

Manipulating functions is exactly like rearranging equations.

**Example**  $f(x) = 3 + x$  and  $g(x) = 5 - x$.  Find $x$ if

(a) $f(x) = 6$   (b) $f(x) = g(x)$.

(a) $f(x) = 6$ implies $3 + x = 6$. Subtracting 3 from both sides gives $x = 3$.

(b) $f(x) = g(x)$ implies

$$3 + x = 5 - x$$

Rearranging:      $x + x = 5 - 3$

$$2x = 2$$

$$x = 1$$

1. Find the images of the following, using the mapping $x \rightarrow 2x$:

  (a) 1     (b) 3     (c) 4     (d) $\frac{1}{3}$     (e) 0
  (f) $-5$     (g) $-\frac{1}{4}$.

2. Find the images of the following under the mapping
   $x \rightarrow 4x + 3$:

  (a) 0     (b) 4     (c) $-2$     (d) $\frac{1}{2}$     (e) $-\frac{1}{2}$
  (f) $\frac{3}{4}$     (g) $-\frac{3}{4}$.

3. Copy and complete the following arrow graphs:

(a)

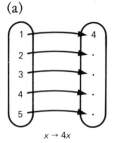

$x \to 4x$

(b)

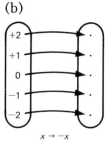

$x \to -x$

(c)

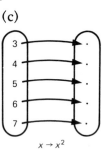

$x \to x^2$

(d)

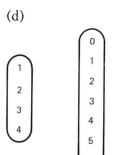

$x \to 2x - 2$

(e)

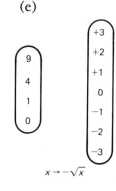

$x \to -\sqrt{x}$

(f)

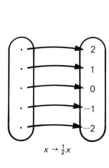

$x \to \frac{1}{2}x$

4. Draw arrow graphs to show the image of each member of the given domain under the given function.

  (a) $f\colon x \to 3x + 1$        $\{-2, -1, 0, +1, +2\}$

  (b) $g\colon x \to y,\ y = 1 - \frac{1}{2}x$    $\{-4, -2, 0, +2, +4\}$

  (c) $h(x) = 3x + 2$        $\{-2, -1, 0, +1, +2\}$

  (d) $j(x) = 10 - \sqrt{x}$       $\{0, 1, 4, 9, 16\}$.

5. If the function $g$ is defined by $g\colon x \to y,\ y = \dfrac{1}{x}$, what are the images of

  (a) 2      (b) 3      (c) 1      (d) $-2$      (e) $-1$

  (f) $\frac{1}{2}$      (g) $\frac{1}{3}$      (h) $\frac{1}{4}$      (i) $-\frac{1}{2}$      (j) $-\frac{1}{3}$?

6. Given that $f(x) = 5x$ find

  (a) $f(0)$    (b) $f(1)$    (c) $f(5)$    (d) $f(-1)$    (e) $f(-3)$.

7. Given that $f(x) = 2x - 1$ find

  (a) $f(1)$    (b) $f(2)$    (c) $f(3)$    (d) $f(-1)$    (e) $f(-2)$.

8. Given that $f(x) = x^3$ find

  (a) $f(0)$    (b) $f(1)$    (c) $f(2)$    (d) $f(-1)$    (e) $f(-2)$.

9. The function $f$ is defined by $f(x) = 2x^2 + 4$. Find
   (a) $f(1)$   (b) $f(2)$   (c) $f(-1)$   (d) $f(-2)$   (e) $f(-3)$
   (f) $f(0)$   (g) $f(\frac{1}{2})$   (h) $f(\frac{1}{4})$   (i) $f(-\frac{1}{2})$   (j) $f(-\frac{1}{4})$.

10. If $f: x \to 3x - 1$, solve the following equations:
    (a) $f(x) = 5$     (b) $f(x) = 14$     (c) $f(x) = -4$
    (d) $f(x) = 0$     (e) $f(x) = \frac{1}{2}$     (f) $f(x) = \frac{1}{8}$.

11. If $f(x) = 2x + 3$ solve the following equations
    (a) $f(x) = 3$     (b) $f(x) = 9$     (c) $f(x) = 27$
    (d) $f(x) = -5$     (e) $f(x) = 0$     (f) $f(x) = 4$.

12. If $f: x \to \frac{1}{2}x$ and $g: x \to 2x + 3$, solve the following:
    (a) $f(x) = 0$     (b) $g(x) = 0$     (c) $f(x) = -2$
    (d) $g(x) = -2$     (e) $f(x) = g(2)$     (f) $f(x) = g(5)$
    (g) $f(2) = g(x)$     (h) $f(5) = g(x)$     (i) $f(-1) = g(x)$.

13. Solve the following equations, given that $f: x \to x - 1$ and $g: x \to 2x + 2$:
    (a) $f(x) = 3$     (b) $g(x) = 3$     (c) $f(x) = -1$
    (d) $g(x) = -1$     (e) $f(x) = g(1)$     (f) $f(x) = g(0)$
    (g) $g(x) = f(-1)$     (h) $g(x) = f(-2)$     (i) $g(x) = f(x)$.

14. If $f: x \to 5 - 2x$ and $g: x \to 3x$, solve the following equations:
    (a) $f(x) = g(0)$     (b) $g(x) = f(0)$     (c) $f(-1) = g(x)$
    (d) $f(x) = g(-1)$     (e) $f(x) = g(\frac{1}{2})$     (f) $f(x) = g(x)$.

15. If $f(x) = x^2$ and $g(x) = (x + 1)^2$, solve the equations
    (a) $f(x) = g(x)$     (b) $f(x) = g(3)$     (c) $g(x) = f(3)$.

16. If $f(x) = (x - 1)^2$ and $g(x) = (2x - 1)^2$, find the solution set to the equations
    (a) $f(x) = 9$     (b) $g(x) = x$     (c) $f(x) = g(x)$.

# COMPOUND FUNCTIONS

If *two* functions act together, they are said to form a *compound* or *composite* function.

**Example** Two functions are defined as follows:

$$f: x \to 2x$$

$$g: x \to x - 2$$

Find the image of 3 when (a) $f$ acts first, followed by $g$, (b) $g$ acts first, followed by $f$.

(a) The image of 3 under the function $f$ is

$$f(3) = 2 \times 3 = 6$$

Now the image of 6 under $g$ is

$$g(6) = 6-2 = 4$$

In summary

$$
\begin{array}{ccc}
f & & g \\
3 \quad\longrightarrow\quad 6 & & \longrightarrow\quad 4
\end{array}
$$

Notice that we could write this process as $g[f(3)]$ or $gf(3)$. Thus $gf$ represents the function $f$ *followed by* $g$. (This is often a source of great confusion, so take careful note. You may find it helpful to draw square brackets of your own whenever you are asked to evaluate a compound function, i.e. $gf(x)$ becomes $g[f(x)]$.

(b) If $g$ acts first upon 3, then

$$g(3) = 3-2 = 1$$

Then, in turn $\qquad f(1) = 2 \times 1 = 2$

In summary

$$
\begin{array}{ccc}
g & & f \\
3 \quad\longrightarrow\quad 1 & & \longrightarrow\quad 2
\end{array}
$$

Clearly, the order in which the functions operate is crucial. This time we have found the composite function $f[g(3)]$ or $fg(3)$, where $fg$ represents the function $g$ *followed by* $f$.

Algebraically, the effect of the compound function $gf$ acting on $x$ is

$$gf(x) = g[f(x)] = g[2x] = 2x-2$$

and the effect of $fg$ is

$$fg(x) = f[g(x)] = f[x-2] = 2(x-2) = 2x-4$$

**Example** If $f(x) = x^2$ and $g(x) = x-2$, find the following:

(a) $gf(3) = g[f(3)] = g(9) = 9-2 = 7$

(b) $fg(3) = f[g(3)] = f(1) = 1^2 = 1$

(c) $gf(x) = g[f(x)] = g(x^2) = x^2-2$

(d) $fg(x) = f[g(x)] = f(x-2) = (x-2)^2$.

1. If $f(x) = 5x$ and $g(x) = 2x + 1$, find
   (a) $f(1)$     (b) $g(1)$     (c) $f(2)$     (d) $g(2)$
   (e) $g[f(1)]$   (f) $f[g(1)]$   (g) $g[f(2)]$   (h) $f[g(2)]$.

2. If $f(x) = \dfrac{1}{x}$ and $g(x) = x^2$, find
   (a) $f(2)$     (b) $g(2)$     (c) $f(3)$     (d) $g(3)$
   (e) $f[g(2)]$   (f) $f[g(3)]$   (g) $g[f(2)]$   (h) $g[f(3)]$.

3. Two functions are defined as $f: x \to 3x$ and $g: x \to x - 1$.
   Find
   (a) $f(3)$     (b) $g(3)$     (c) $f(2)$     (d) $g(9)$
   (e) $g[f(3)]$   (f) $f[g(3)]$   (g) $g[f(0)]$   (h) $f[g(0)]$.
   Show that the composite function $gf(x) = 3x - 1$.
   Find a similar algebraic expression for the composite function $fg(x)$.

4. Two functions are defined as follows: $h: x \to 4x$ and $j: x \to x + 2$. Find
   (a) $h(1)$     (b) $j(1)$     (c) $hj(1)$     (d) $jh(1)$.
   Show that the composite function $hj(x) = 4x + 8$, and find $jh(x)$.

5. Three functions are $f: x \to 2x$,     $g: x \to -x$ and $h: x \to x + 4$. Find
   (a) $fg(1)$     (b) $gf(1)$     (c) $fh(1)$     (d) $hf(1)$
   (e) $gh(1)$     (f) $hg(1)$.
   Show that $fg(x) = gf(x) = -2x$.

6. Four functions are $f: x \to x^2$,     $g: x \to x - 2$,
   $h: x \to \sqrt{x}$, and $j: x \to x + 2$. Find
   (a) $fg(2)$     (b) $gf(2)$     (c) $ff(2)$     (d) $fh(4)$
   (e) $gg(4)$     (f) $fg(x)$     (g) $ff(x)$     (h) $fh(x)$.

7. If $f: x \to 2x + 1$ and $g: x \to \frac{1}{2}(x - 1)$, find
   (a) $fg(2)$     (b) $gf(4)$     (c) $fg(3)$     (d) $gf(7)$.
   Show that $fg: x \to x$.     Find $gf(x)$.

8. If $f: x \to x^2$, $g: x \to x - 3$ and $h: x \to \frac{1}{2}x$, find algebraic expressions for

(a) $fg$      (b) $gf$      (c) $fh$      (d) $hf$

(e) $gh$      (f) $hg$.

9. Two functions are defined by $f: x \to x^3$ and $g: x \to x^4$. Find algebraic definitions for the composite functions

(a) $fg$      (b) $gf$.

Hence show that $fg(x) = gf(x)$.

10. If $f: x \to 4x$ and $g: x \to 5x$, show that $fg(x) = gf(x)$.


## INVERSE FUNCTIONS

Suppose a function $f$ maps $x$ on to a value $y$. Then the *inverse function*, $f^{-1}$, will reverse the process, that is, map the value $y$ back on to $x$.

By definition, the composite function $f^{-1}f$ maps $x$ back on to itself, so $f^{-1}f$ is an *identity function*, $f^{-1}f: x \to x$.

Finding the inverse of a function depends upon tracing it back step by step.


**Example** Find the inverse of $f: x \to 2x + 3$.

The upper flow diagram shows each stage of the function $f$. First, multiply by 2 to get $2x$, then add three. Working the process in reverse, that is starting from the right-hand side and working leftwards doing the exact opposite at each stage, we first subtract 3 and then halve the result. Hence

$$f^{-1}: x \to \tfrac{1}{2}(x - 3)$$

*Check*      $f(4) = 2 \times 4 + 3 = 11$

$f^{-1}(11) = \tfrac{1}{2}(11 - 3)$

$= 4$    ✓

136

**Example** Find the inverse of $g: x \rightarrow \dfrac{2x-3}{5}$.

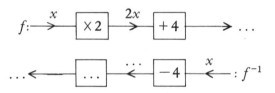

$$g: \quad \xrightarrow{x} \boxed{\times 2} \xrightarrow{2x} \boxed{-3} \xrightarrow{2x-3} \boxed{\div 5} \xrightarrow{\quad} \dfrac{2x-3}{5}$$

$$\dfrac{5x+3}{2} \xleftarrow{\quad} \boxed{\div 2} \xleftarrow{5x+3} \boxed{+3} \xleftarrow{5x} \boxed{\times 5} \xleftarrow{x} : g^{-1}$$

Thus $g^{-1}: x \rightarrow \dfrac{5x+3}{2}$.

*Check* $g(4) = \dfrac{2 \times 4 - 3}{5} = \dfrac{8-3}{5} = \dfrac{5}{5} = 1$

$g^{-1}(1) = \dfrac{5 \times 1 + 3}{2} = \dfrac{8}{2} = 4$ ✓

**EXERCISE 8c**

1. Complete the following flow diagram to find the inverse of the function, $f: x \rightarrow 2x + 4$

$$f: \xrightarrow{x} \boxed{\times 2} \xrightarrow{2x} \boxed{+4} \xrightarrow{\quad} \ldots$$

$$\ldots \xleftarrow{\quad} \boxed{\ldots} \xleftarrow{\ldots} \boxed{-4} \xleftarrow{x} : f^{-1}$$

2. The flow charts illustrate the functions $f: x \rightarrow \dfrac{x}{3} - 1$ and

$g: x \rightarrow \dfrac{3x+2}{4}$. Trace them back to find $f^{-1}$ and $g^{-1}$.

(a) $\quad f: \xrightarrow{x} \boxed{\div 3} \xrightarrow{x/3} \boxed{-1} \xrightarrow{\quad} \dfrac{x}{3} - 1$

(b) $\quad g: \xrightarrow{x} \boxed{\times 3} \xrightarrow{3x} \boxed{+2} \xrightarrow{3x+2} \boxed{\div 4} \xrightarrow{\quad} \dfrac{3x+2}{4}$

Find the inverses of the following functions defining them in the style $f: x \rightarrow 2x$. In each case, find (a) $f(4)$ and (b) $f^{-1}[f(4)]$.

3. $f: x \rightarrow 2x$　　　　　　　4. $f: x \rightarrow 4x$

5. $f: x \rightarrow 5x + 6$　　　　　6. $f: x \rightarrow 3x + 5$

7. $f: x \rightarrow 6x - 2$　　　　　8. $f: x \rightarrow \frac{1}{2}x + 1$

9. $f: x \to \frac{1}{4}x - 2$

10. $f: x \to \frac{x+2}{3}$

11. $f: x \to \frac{x-5}{2}$

12. $f: x \to \frac{x-4}{8}$

13. $f: x \to \frac{1}{x}$

14. $f: x \to \frac{4}{x}$

15. $f: x \to -x$

16. $f: x \to x^2 - 1$

17. $f: x \to 2x^2 + 1$

18. $f: x \to 3x^2 + 2$

19. $f: x \to (x-1)^2$

20. $f: x \to \sqrt{2x+1}$.

21. If $g: x \to 3x + 1$, find
    (a) $g^{-1}$      (b) $g(2)$      (c) $g^{-1}(7)$.

22. If $p: x \to 5 - 2x$, find
    (a) $p^{-1}$      (b) $p(-1)$      (c) $p^{-1}(7)$.

23. If $j: x \to (1 - \frac{1}{3}x)$, find
    (a) $j^{-1}$      (b) $j(6)$      (c) $j^{-1}(-1)$.

24. If $s: x \to \frac{1}{2}(1 - x)$, find
    (a) $s^{-1}$      (b) $s^{-1}(\frac{1}{4})$      (c) $s(\frac{1}{2})$.

25. If $f: x \to \frac{1}{4}(1 - \frac{1}{2}x)$, find
    (a) $f^{-1}$      (b) $f^{-1}(\frac{-1}{8})$      (c) $f(3)$.

## MISCELLANEOUS EXERCISE 8

1. The diagram (Fig. 8.4) shows that three subjects, History, Geography and Religious Education, are taught by five teachers A, B, C, D and E.

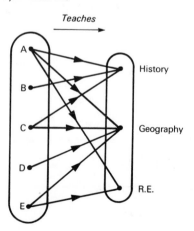

Fig. 8.4

From the diagram, write down which of the teachers

(a) teach History,

(b) teach Religious Education,

(c) teach all three subjects,

(d) teach one subject only,

(e) do not teach Geography.                                    (EMREB)

2. The arrow diagram in Fig. 8.5 illustrates the relationship 'is a prime factor of' but it is incomplete.

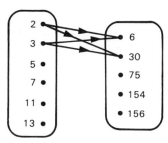

Fig. 8.5

Copy and complete it.

3. If $x \in \{\text{positive odd numbers}\}$, describe the image set of $x$ under the following functions:

(a) $f: x \rightarrow -x$      (b) $g: x \rightarrow 2x$      (c) $h: x \rightarrow x + 1$.

4. If $x \in \{\text{negative integers}\}$, describe the image set of $x$ under the following functions:

(a) $f: x \rightarrow -x$      (b) $g: x \rightarrow x^2$      (c) $h: x \rightarrow \dfrac{x}{x-1}$.

5. $f(x) = 2x; \ g(x) = x + 2; \ h(x) = x^2$.

Find the solution sets to the following equations:

(a) $f(x) = \frac{1}{2}$      (b) $g(x) = -\frac{1}{2}$      (c) $f(x) = x$

(d) $g(x) = x$      (e) $f(x) = g(x)$      (f) $h(x) = x$

(g) $h(x) = f(x)$      (h) $h(x) = g(x)$.

6. Functions $f$ and $g$ are defined for all values of $x$ by

$$f: x \rightarrow (x-2)^2$$
$$g: x \rightarrow 5(x-2)$$

(a) Find the values of $x$ for which $f(x) = \frac{1}{9}$.

(b) Factorise $(x-2)^2 - 5(x-2)$. Hence, or otherwise, find the values of $x$ for which $f(x) = g(x)$.

(c) Solve the equation $f(x) = 2x$, giving your answers correct to 2 decimal places.      (AEB '82)

7. $f: x \rightarrow 2x + 1$. Given that two simple functions, $h$ and $g$, are equivalent to $f$, i.e. $f(x) = hg(x)$, suggest definitions of $h$ and $g$.

8. Two functions are defined by
$$f: x \rightarrow 4 - x^2 \qquad \text{and} \qquad g: x \rightarrow (4 - x)^2.$$
   (a) Find $f(2)$ and $g(2)$ and hence show that $f(x) \neq g(x)$.
   (b) If $h$ and $i$ are two (simple) functions such that $f(x) = hi(x)$, which is first to act on $x$, $h$ or $i$?
   (c) Define the functions $h$ and $i$ algebraically.
   (d) Suggest a composite function, in terms of $h$ and $i$, equivalent to $g$.

9. (a) If $f: x \rightarrow 2x - 1$ show that $f^{-1}: x \rightarrow \frac{1}{2}(x + 1)$.
   (b) Find, expressed in a similar fashion, $g^{-1}$ if $g: x \rightarrow 3x$.
   (c) Find the composite functions
   (i) $f^{-1}g^{-1}$    (ii) $gf$    (iii) $(gf)^{-1}$.
   What can you say about $f^{-1}g^{-1}$ and $(gf)^{-1}$?

10. $f(x)$ denotes the remainder when an integer $x$ is divided by 10. Given that $x > 10$, find a possible value of $x$ in each of the following cases.
    (a) $f(x) = 4$      (b) $2f(x) = f(x)$      (c) $f(x^2) > 2 + f(x)$.
    (C)

11. A function $S$ is defined on two-digit numbers as the sum of the digits of the number. For example $S(26) = 2 + 6 = 8$; $S(97) = 9 + 7 = 16$. Find
    (a) $S(22)$      (b) $S(45)$      (c) $S(56)$.
    Given that $x < 20$, find possible values of $x$ in the following cases:
    (d) $S(x) = 3$      (e) $S(x) = 4x$      (f) $S(x) = \frac{1}{2}x$.

12. The function f is defined as follows for any positive integer $n$:
$$\text{if } n \text{ is even, } f(n) = \tfrac{1}{2}n$$
$$\text{if } n \text{ is odd, } f(n) = n + 1$$
    (a) Write down the values of f(9), ff(9) and fff(9).
    (b) Find the value of $n$ for which $f(n) = 7$, and two values of $n$ for which $f(n) = 8$.
    (c) Name the set of values of $n$ for which $f^{-1}(n)$ has two values, and the set for which it has only one value.

(d) Explain why, for any value of $n$ except 1 or 2, $\mathrm{ff}(n) < n$.

(e) A computer is programed so that when any positive integer $n$ is set into it, it finds and prints $\mathrm{f}(n)$, then sets $\mathrm{f}(n)$ into itself, finds and prints $\mathrm{ff}(n)$, then sets $\mathrm{ff}(n)$ into itself, and so on indefinitely. Show that if $n = 9$ the computer will eventually print 2, and describe what happens after that.                                      (LU)

13. A function is defined on *two* numbers, $x$ and $y$, such that

$$f(x, y) = x + y - xy$$

(a) Show that $\mathrm{f}(5, 2) = -3$.

(b) Find $\mathrm{f}(4, 3)$.

(c) Show that $\mathrm{f}(x, 0) = x$.

(d) Find possible values of $x$ if $\mathrm{f}(x, y) = 5$. Are there any other possibilities?

(e) If $\mathrm{f}(x, y) = 0$, find $y$ in terms of $x$.

(f) When is $\mathrm{f}(x, y) > 0$? Investigate.

# 9 STRAIGHT LINE GRAPHS

## PLOTTING A LINE

**Example** Draw the graph of $y = 3x + 4$ (for $0 \leqslant x \leqslant 4$).

Points on a graph have *coordinates* $(x, y)$. A series of points such that in each case the $y$-coordinates are related to the corresponding $x$-coordinates according to some function (such as $y = 3x + 4$) are said to trace out a path or *locus*.

We begin by choosing a series of convenient values of $x$ (say, 0, 1, 2, 3 and 4) and then, for each one, finding the corresponding $y$-coordinate using the relationship $y = 3x + 4$:

| $x$ | 0 | 1 | 2 | 3 | 4 |
|---|---|---|---|---|---|
| $y = 3x + 4$ | 4 | 7 | 10 | 13 | 16 |

Figure 9.1 shows the points $(0, 4)$, $(1, 7)$, $(2, 10)$, $(3, 13)$ and $(4, 16)$. The points have been plotted carefully and joined up. Clearly they lie on a straight line.

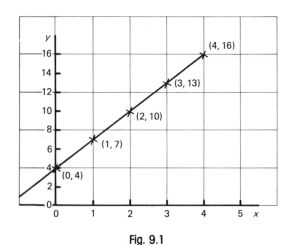

**Fig. 9.1**

Every point on the line has coordinates that satisfy the relationship $y = 3x + 4$. For example, $(1\frac{1}{2}, 8\frac{1}{2})$ lies on the line and $8\frac{1}{2} = (3 \times 1\frac{1}{2}) + 4$.

We can use the graph to read off values of $x$ and $y$ that are associated with each other. For example, if $x = 2\frac{1}{2}$, we can see from the graph (Fig. 9.2) that $y = 11\frac{1}{2}$; equally if $y = 14$, we can see that $x = 3\frac{1}{3}$.

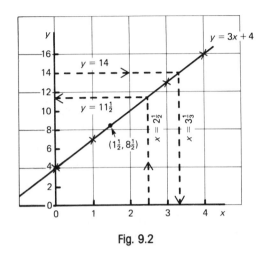

**Fig. 9.2**

In general, any equation of the sort

$$y = mx + c$$

(or any equation that can be rearranged into this form) can be represented on a graph by a straight line. Moreover, a line is fully defined by *two points*; so we need only find *two* pairs of co-ordinates to draw the graph of a line. It is simplest to find the $y$ value associated with $x = 0$ and the $x$ value associated with $y = 0$. It is sensible to find a third point as a check, but it is a waste of time and effort to find more than three points.

## SOLVING SIMULTANEOUS EQUATIONS GRAPHICALLY

**Example** Solve the equations

$$2x + y = 8$$

$$3x - y = 7$$

Note that both these equations can be rearranged into the form $y = mx + c$, so they both represent straight lines.

143

Now let us first find three points on the line $2x + y = 8$:

$2x + y = 8$

| x | y |
|---|---|
| 0 | 8 |
| 4 | 0 |
| 1 | 6 |

Similarly, find three points on the second line $3x - y = 7$:

$3x - y = 7$

| x | y |
|---|---|
| 0 | -7 |
| $\frac{7}{3}$ | 0 |
| 1 | -4 |

Now plot the two lines (as in Figure 9.3). The lines meet at the point $(3, 2)$. Thus $x = 3$ and $y = 2$ will fit both equations and is the solution to the simultaneous equations given.

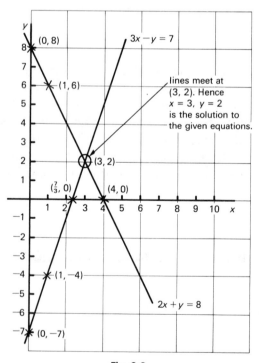

Fig. 9.3

*Check*

$$2x(3) + 2 = 8$$
$$3x(3) - 2 = 7 \checkmark$$

1. Plot the points $(0, 1), (1, 3), (2, 5), (3, 7)$. Join up the points. What do you notice? Is the point $(-1, -1)$ on your line? Is the point $(1\frac{1}{2}, 3)$ on your line?

2. Plot the following points on the same graph as you used in Question 1: $(1, 3), (0, 4), (5, -1), (-1, 5), (4, 4), (2, 2)$. Join them up to form a straight line. Which point does *not* lie on the line?

3. Complete the following table:

| $x$ | 0 | 1 | 2 | 3 | 4 | 5 | 6 | 7 | 8 |
|---|---|---|---|---|---|---|---|---|---|
| $y = 2x + 1$ | 1 | 3 | 5 | ... | ... | ... | ... | ... | ... |

Plot the points $(0, 1), (1, 3), (2, 5), (3, \ldots)$, etc. on a graph and show that they lie on a straight line. Do you need to find so many points to plot the graph? How many do you need?

4. Complete the following tables and plot the lines on *one* graph:

(a) $y = 5 - x$

| $x$ | $y$ |
|---|---|
| 0 | 5 |
|  | 0 |
| 1 |  |

(b) $y = x + 3$

| $x$ | $y$ |
|---|---|
| 0 |  |
|  | 0 |
| 1 |  |

(c) $y = x - 1$

| $x$ | $y$ |
|---|---|
|  |  |
|  |  |
| 2 |  |

What can you say about lines (a) and (b)? Where do they intersect?

What can you say about lines (b) and (c)? Where do they intersect?

5. Complete the following tables and plot the lines on one graph

(a) $y = x + 3$

| $x$ | $y$ |
|---|---|
| 0 |  |
|  | 0 |
| 3 |  |

(b) $y = 2x + 3$

| $x$ | $y$ |
|---|---|
| 0 |  |
|  | 0 |
| 3 |  |

(c) $y = 3x + 3$

| $x$ | $y$ |
|---|---|
| 0 |  |
|  | 0 |
| 3 |  |

What do you notice about the lines? How do you think this is related to the equations of the lines?

145

6. Complete the following tables and plot the lines of one graph

   (a) $y = x$  (b) $y = x + 4$  (c) $y = x - 4$

| $x$ | $y$ |
|-----|-----|
| 0   |     |
| 1   |     |
| 5   |     |

| $x$ | $y$ |
|-----|-----|
| 0   |     |
|     | 0   |
| 5   |     |

| $x$ | $y$ |
|-----|-----|
| 0   |     |
|     | 0   |
| 5   |     |

What do you notice this time? How do you think this is related to the equations of the lines?

7. Which of the following equations would be represented by straight line graphs?

   (a) $y = 3x + 8$  (b) $y = 4x - 5$  (c) $y = 2x$
   (d) $y = 5 - 2x$  (e) $y = x^3$  (f) $y = x^2 + 2x + 1$
   (g) $5x + 4y = 6$  (h) $y = 4$.

8. Complete the following tables and plot the lines on one graph:

   (a) $y = 7 - 2x$  (b) $y = 2x - 1$

| $x$ | $y$ |
|-----|-----|
| 0   |     |
|     | 0   |
| 1   |     |

| $x$ | $y$ |
|-----|-----|
| 0   |     |
|     | 0   |
| 1   |     |

What is their point of intersection? How is this related to the pair of simultaneous equations

$$y = 7 - 2x$$
$$y = 2x - 1$$

9. Use a graphical method to solve the following simultaneous equations. Check your answers in the original equations.

   (a) $x + y = 5$  (b) $2x + y = 12$  (c) $2x + 3y = 17$
   $\quad\;\; x - y = 3$  $\quad\;\; 4x - y = 6$  $\quad\;\; 4x - 3y = 7$

   (d) $5x + y = 10$  (e) $3x + y = 7$  (f) $5x + 2y = 19$
   $\quad\;\; 3x - y = 2$  $\quad\;\; y + x = 5$  $\quad\;\; 7x - y = 19$

10. The table below shows the number of American dollars equivalent to given amounts of British money.

| £ | 10 | 20 | 30 | 40 | 50 |
|---|----|----|----|----|----|
| $ | 14 | 28 | 42 | 56 | 70 |

Plot this information on a graph. (Plot £$x$ on the horizontal axis and $$y$ on the vertical axis. Your graph should be a straight line.)

Use your graph to find

(a) how many dollars are equivalent to (i) £15 (ii) £38.

(b) how many pounds are equivalent to (i) $14 (ii) $38.

11. The following table shows the length of a spring when it has been stretched by a load of $x$ kilograms.

| Load $x$ kg | 2 | 4 | 6 | 8 |
|-------------|---|---|---|---|
| Length $y$ cm | 6 | 7 | 8 | 9 |

Plot a graph showing the load carried by the spring and its stretched length. (Again, your graph should be a straight line.)

Use your graph to find

(a) the length of the spring when carrying loads of
   (i) 3 kg  (ii) 6.5 kg.

(b) the load on the spring when it has stretched to a length of 7.5 cm.

What is the 'natural length' of the spring? (i.e. its length when no load is attached).

# GRADIENTS AND INTERCEPTS

The *gradient* of a line measures its *slope*, i.e. how steep it is. The gradient can be found from two points known to lie on the line using the ratio

$$\text{gradient} = \frac{\text{distance up}}{\text{distance along}} \quad \text{or} \quad \frac{\text{change in } y \text{ value}}{\text{change in } x \text{ value}}$$

In the equation of a straight line, $y = mx + c$, the gradient is given by $m$.

The *intercept* of a line determines where the line cuts the $y$-axis. In the equation $y = mx + c$, the intercept is given by $c$.

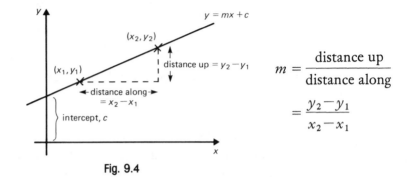

**Fig. 9.4**

Note that

(*i*) lines of the same gradient but different intercepts are parallel (Fig. 9.5(a)).

(*ii*) lines of the same intercept meet on the $y$-axis (Fig. 9.5(b)).

(*iii*) downward sloping lines have a negative gradient (Fig. 9.5(c)).

(*iv*) horizontal lines have zero gradient (Fig. 9.5(d)).

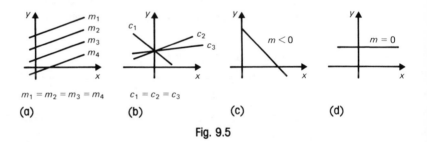

**Fig. 9.5**

**Example** What is the gradient of the line $2y + 3x - 7 = 0$?

Since we have the equation of the line in full, it should be possible to 'read off' the gradient by rearranging the equation into conventional $y = mx + c$ format:

Add 7 and subtract $3x$ from both sides:

$$2y = -3x + 7$$

Divide both sides by 2:

$$y = \frac{-3}{2}x + \frac{7}{2}$$

Hence the gradient is $\dfrac{-3}{2}$.

**Example** From the graph in Fig. 9.6, find the gradient of the line and where it cuts the $y$-axis. Hence write down the equation of the line.

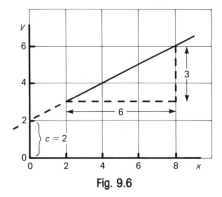

Fig. 9.6

The line passes through the points $(2, 3)$ and $(8, 6)$. The 'distance up' between these points is $6 - 3 = 3$, and the 'distance along' is $8 - 2 = 6$. Hence the gradient

$$m = \frac{\text{distance up}}{\text{distance along}} = \frac{3}{6} = \frac{1}{2}$$

By extending the line back to the $y$-axis, we can see that the intercept $c = 2$.

As $m = \frac{1}{2}$ and $c = 2$, the equation of the line is $y = \frac{1}{2}x + 2$.

**Example** Find the equation of the line passing through the points $(-1, 4)$ and $(5, 1)$.

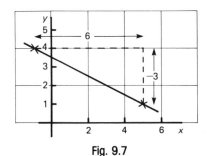

Fig. 9.7

From the graph in Fig. 9.7, it is obvious that this is a downward sloping line, with a *negative* gradient. The point $(-1, 4)$ lies above the point $(5, 1)$. But the gradient formula still applies, for the 'distance up' proves to be a negative quantity:

$$m = \frac{\text{distance up}}{\text{distance along}} = \frac{1 - 4}{5 - (-1)} = \frac{-3}{+6} = -\frac{1}{2}$$

149

Given this value for $m$, the equation of the line must be $y = -\frac{1}{2}x + c$. As the point $(5, 1)$ lies on the line, $x = 5$ and $y = 1$ will solve the equation:

$$1 = -\frac{1}{2} \times 5 + c$$
$$c = 3\frac{1}{2}$$

As $m = -\frac{1}{2}$ and $c = 3\frac{1}{2}$, the equation of the line is $y = -\frac{1}{2}x + 3\frac{1}{2}$.

**EXERCISE 9b**

1. What are (i) the gradients and (ii) the intercepts of the following lines:
   (a) $y = 4x + 3$      (b) $y = -x + 2$      (c) $y = 5 - 4x$
   (d) $y = 4 + 5x$      (e) $y - x = 3$      (f) $3y = 4 - 2x$.

2. Rearrange the equation $4y + 5x - 3 = 0$ into the usual $y = mx + c$ format. What is the gradient of this line? What is its intercept?

3. Rearrange the equation $6y - 2x + 5 = 0$ into the usual $y = mx + c$ format. What is the gradient of this line? What is its intercept?

4. Find (i) the gradients and (ii) the intercepts of the following lines:
   (a) $2y + 7x = 5$      (b) $9y + 3x - 5 = 0$
   (c) $5x + 9y = 8$      (d) $3x - 2y + 6 = 4$
   (e) $x - y = 0$      (f) $2y + 3 + 4x = 8$.

5. Three of the following lines are parallel to each other. Which?
   (a) $2y = 3x - 4$      (b) $3y = 2x - 4$      (c) $4y = 6x + 1$
   (d) $3y + 2x = 6$      (e) $2 + y = 4 + 1\frac{1}{2}x$
   (f) $y + x = 0$.

6. Which of the following statements are true?
   (a) $y = 3x - 1$ and $y = 2x - 1$ are parallel.
   (b) $y = 5x + 6$ and $5y = x + 6$ have the same intercept.
   (c) $y = 5x + 6$ and $5y = x + 6$ are parallel.
   (d) The gradient of $5y = x + 6$ is $\frac{1}{5}$.
   (e) $2y + 3x = 4$ and $2y - x = 4$ meet on the $x$-axis.
   (f) $2y + 3x = 4$ and $2y - x = 4$ meet on the $y$-axis.
   (g) $y = 4$ is a horizontal line.
   (h) $y = 4x$ goes through the point $(4, 1)$.
   (i) $x = 4$ is a vertical line.
   (j) The slope of $4x = 3y$ is $\frac{3}{4}$.

7. Find the equations of the following lines:

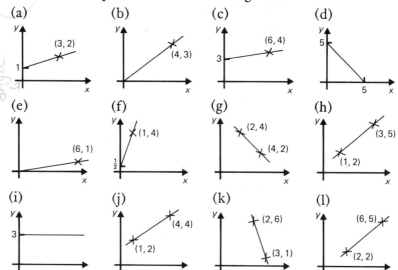

8. Find the gradients of the lines that pass through the points:
    (a) $(1,1)$ and $(4,4)$  (b) $(3,4)$ and $(5,6)$
    (c) $(3,9)$ and $(9,3)$  (d) $(0,0)$ and $(5,3)$
    (e) $(-1,3)$ and $(3,-1)$  (f) $(-2,-3)$ and $(2,3)$
    (g) $(2,3)$ and $(5,3)$  (h) $(3,0)$ and $(0,3)$.

9. Find the equations of the lines that pass through the points:
    (a) $(0,1)$ and $(5,6)$  (b) $(0,7)$ and $(6,4)$
    (c) $(2,7)$ and $(7,2)$  (d) $(4,1)$ and $(1,4)$
    (e) $(0,0)$ and $(3,2)$  (f) $(0,7)$ and $(5,7)$
    (g) $(-1,3)$ and $(-3,8)$  (h) $(3,-1)$ and $(4,1)$.

10. Match these six equations with the graphs shown in Fig. 9.8.
    (i) $y = 3x + 1$  (ii) $y = x - 2$  (iii) $y = 7 - x$
    (iv) $y = 6$  (v) $y = x^2 - 1$  (vi) $y = 20x$.

(a)  (b)  (c)

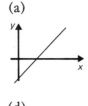  

(d)  (e)  (f)

Fig. 9.8

151

11. A line of gradient $+2$ and another of gradient $-2$ meet at the point P(3, 6), as shown in Fig. 9.9. Find the area of the triangle OPQ.

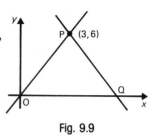

Fig. 9.9

## MISCELLANEOUS EXERCISE 9

1. Figure 9.10 shows three lines. The equations of these lines are
   (a) $y = 2$  (b) $y = 2x - 2$  (c) $y = 10 - x$.

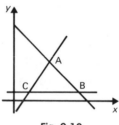

Fig. 9.10

Copy the diagram and indicate to which line each equation applies.

Find the coordinates of the points A, B and C and find the area of triangle ABC.

2. Write down the gradients of lines (a) to (h) in Fig. 9.11.

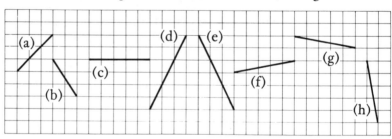

Fig. 9.11

3. The lines $y = 2x$ and $y = 5 - \frac{1}{2}x$ meet at right angles at a point P. Find the coordinates of P. If Q is the point (4, 8), show that Q lies on the line $y = 2x$. Draw an $8 \times 8$ grid; plot the points P and Q and the given two lines on your graph. Find the coordinates of two points R and S such that PQRS is a square. Find the equations of the lines QR and RS.

4. The lines $AB$ and $DE$ intersect at $F$ (Fig. 9.12). The equation of $AB$ is $4y - 3x = 12$ and the equation of $DE$ is $2y + 3x = 24$.

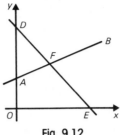

Fig. 9.12

(a) Write down the coordinates of the points $A$ and $D$ which lie on the $y$-axis and hence the length of $AD$.

(b) By drawing graphs of the two lines $AB$ and $DE$, or otherwise, find the coordinates of the point $F$.

(c) Calculate the areas of the triangle $ADF$ and the quadrilateral $OAFE$, given that $E$ is on the $x$-axis.     (WJEC)

5. The diagram (Fig. 9.13) shows the two lines

$$3x + 4y = 12,$$
$$2x - y = 2.$$

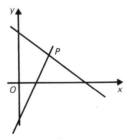

Fig. 9.13

*Sketch* a copy of this diagram and mark clearly which equation belongs to which line.

Calculate the coordinates of $P$, the point of intersection of the two lines.

Shade on your diagram the region defined by

$\{(x, y): y > 0\} \cap \{(x, y): 3x + 4y < 12\} \cap \{(x, y): 2x - y > 2\}.$
    (LU)

6. Find, graphically or otherwise, the solution set of the simultaneous equations

$$2x - y + 1 = 0$$
$$x - 4y + 18 = 0$$     (SUJB)

153

7. Draw a grid with axes marked from $-3$ to $+8$. Plot the points A$(-2,-1)$, B$(3,4)$ and C$(7,6)$. Draw the line AB and find its mathematical equation. Draw the line BC and find its equation. Find the coordinates of the point D so that ABCD is a parallelogram. *Write down* the gradients of the lines AD and DC.

8. The conversion of degrees Centigrade to degrees Fahrenheit can be shown as a line graph.

   Plot the three points given in the table below on a graph (put $°F$ on the vertical axis).

   | °C | 0 | 10 | 20 |
   |----|---|----|----|
   | °F | 32 | 50 | 68 |

   Join up the points to make a straight line. From your graph, estimate the Centigrade equivalents to

   (a) 40 °F　　　(b) 60 °F　　　(c) 75 °F.

   Estimate the Fahrenheit equivalents to

   (d) 15 °C　　　(e) 32 °C　　　(f) $-5$ °C.

   What is the gradient of the straight line? Where does it cut the vertical axis? Suggest an equation relating $y$ °F to the equivalent $x$ °C.

9. A salesman is paid a fixed salary of £2500 per annum together with a commission of 15% on his sales. Copy and complete the following table:

   | Sales | £1000 | £2000 | £6000 |
   |-------|-------|-------|-------|
   | Commission | £150 | | |
   | Salary | £2500 | | |
   | Total income | £2650 | | |

   Use the completed table to draw a graph of 'Sales' against 'Total income'.

   Use the graph to answer the following questions.

   (a) What is the salesman's total income when his sales are £2400?

   (b) What is the least amount of sales needed to produce a total income of not less than £3000?

   (c) In one year he is given a bonus of £750 and his total income is then £4000. What were his sales in that year?

   (ALSEB)

10. In an experiment, the results of measuring $x$ and $y$ are as follows:

| $x$ | 1 | 2 | 3 | 4 | 5 |
|-----|---|---|----|----|----|
| $y$ | 5 | 7 | 10 | 11 | 13 |

Plot these points on a graph and show that all but one of them lie on a straight line. Measure the gradient and intercept of the line and suggest an equation relating $x$ and $y$.

11. In an experiment to measure the current flowing in a piece of wire as voltage is varied, the following results were obtained:

| Voltage ($V$ volts) | 40 | 80 | 120 | 160 | 200 | 240 |
|---------------------|-----|------|------|------|------|------|
| Current ($I$ amps) | 7.1 | 14.0 | 21.3 | 29.0 | 35.3 | 42.4 |

Plot these points on a graph. (Put voltage on the horizontal axis.)

The points do not lie exactly on a straight line because of experimental error. However, the relationship is known to be a linear one. Draw in 'by eye' the line you think best fits the data (usually called the *line of best fit*).

Measure the gradient and intercept of your line and suggest an equation relating $V$ and $I$.

12. In another experiment the velocity of a projectile was measured over 12 seconds of motion. The following results were obtained:

| Time ($t$ seconds) | 2 | 4 | 6 | 8 | 10 | 12 |
|--------------------|------|------|------|-----|-----|-----|
| Velocity ($v$ m/s) | 24.8 | 20.1 | 15.0 | 9.9 | 5.0 | 0.0 |

Again, the points do not lie exactly on a straight line because of experimental error. None the less, it is known that the relationship is a linear one. Draw in the line of best fit 'by eye'.

Measure the gradient and intercept of your line and suggest an equation relating $t$ and $v$.

# 10 INEQUALITIES

The statement 'nine is greater than seven' is written mathematically as $9 > 7$. Similarly, 'seven is less than nine' is written as $7 < 9$. Statements such as these are known as *inequations* or *inequalities*.

They may be combined with an 'equals' sign; thus $\geqslant$ means 'greater than or equal to' and $\leqslant$ means 'less than or equal to'.

## INEQUALITIES ON THE NUMBER LINE

Simple inequalities (and sets defined in terms of inequalities) can be shown on a number line. Figure 10.1 illustrates the range $5 \leqslant x < 9$. Notice that 5 itself *is* included in the range; this is indicated by the solid circle (●). However, 9 is *not* included and its exclusion is indicated by the open circle (o).

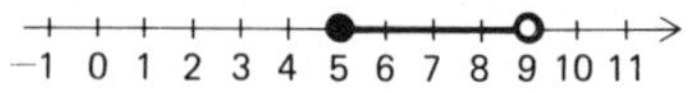

Fig. 10.1

**Example** If $A = \{-2 \leqslant x \leqslant 4\}$ and $B = \{1 < x < 8\}$, illustrate on the number line the set $A \cap B$.

As a member of $B$, $x$ must be greater than 1: as a member of $A$, $x$ must be less than or equal to 4. Thus, if $x \in A \cap B$ then $1 < x \leqslant 4$. Figure 10.2 illustrates $A \cap B$ on the number line.

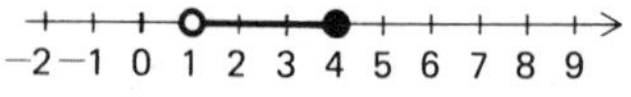

Fig. 10.2

## SIMPLIFYING INEQUALITIES

Inequalities behave in a similar fashion to equations. For example, we may add or subtract convenient numbers from both sides. Thus, to solve $x - 3 \geqslant 7$ we should proceed as follows

$$x - 3 \geqslant 7$$
$$x - 3 + 3 \geqslant 7 + 3$$
$$x \geqslant 10$$

However, it is only possible to multiply or divide *by positive numbers*. If we multiply both sides of the inequality $9 > 7$ by $+10$, we get $90 > 70$, which is true. But if we multiplied both sides by $-10$, the result '$-90 > -70$' is *false*. The effect of multiplying (or dividing) by a negative number is to reverse the inequality, for $-90 < -70$.

**Example** $-6x < -12$.

Divide both sides by $-6$ and *reverse the inequality*:

$$x > 2$$

On some occasions it is simpler to solve an inequality by trial and error.

**Example** $x \in \{1, 2, 3, 4, 5, 6, 7, 8\}$ and $f(x) = x^2 - 10x + 25$. Find the solution set to $f(x) > 4$.

Putting $x = 1$ gives

$$f(1) = (1)^2 - 10(1) + 25 = 1 - 10 + 25 = 16$$

i.e. $f(1) > 4$, so $x = 1$ is a solution. Similarly, we can show that $f(2) = 9$, so $x = 2$ is also a solution. However, putting $x = 3$ gives

$$f(3) = (3)^2 - 10(3) + 25 = 4$$

i.e. $f(3)$ is *not* greater than 4, and $x = 3$ is *not* a solution.

We can show in the same way that $x = 4, 5, 6$ and 7 gives values that are not greater than 4. However, $x = 8$ gives

$$f(8) = (8)^2 - 10(8) + 25 = 9$$

Thus the completed solution set is $x \in \{1, 2, 8\}$.

**EXERCISE 10a**

1. Use $>, <, \geqslant$ and $\leqslant$ signs to define the ranges indicated:

(a) ![number line 0 1 2 3 4 5 6]
(b) ![number line -3 -2 -1 0 1 2 3]
(c) ![number line -3 -2 -1 0 1 2 3]

(d) ![number line -2 -1 0 1 2 3]
(e) ![number line 101 102 103 104 105]

2. Illustrate the following ranges on a number line:

(a) $-3 \leqslant x \leqslant 2$     (b) $4 < x < 6$     (c) $3 < x \leqslant 5$

(d) $x > 4$     (e) $x \leqslant 2$     (f) $-3 \leqslant x \leqslant 0$.

3. If $A = \{-3 \leqslant x \leqslant 2\}$ and $B = \{0 \leqslant x < 4\}$. Illustrate sets $A$ and $B$ on a number line. Use your diagram to illustrate the following subsets:

   (a) $A \cap B$     (b) $A \cup B$     (c) $A'$     (d) $A' \cap B$.

4. The number lines shown in Fig. 10.3 illustrate the sets $A$ and $B$. Write down the ranges of the following subsets:

   (a) $A \cap B$     (b) $A \cup B$

   and illustrate them on a number line.

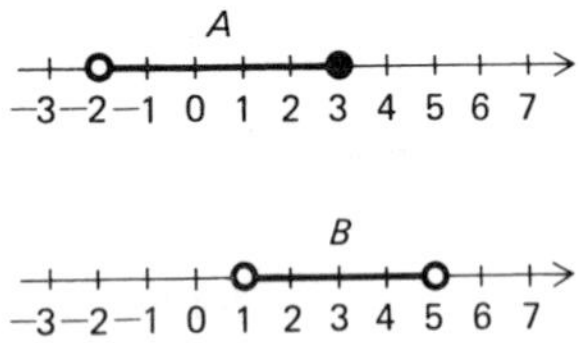

Fig. 10.3

5. Figure 10.4 shows the two parts of the range $A'$. Illustrate on the number line the range $A$.

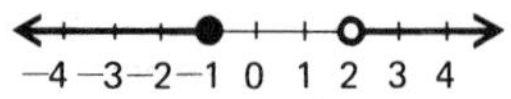

Fig. 10.4

6. The number lines shown in Fig. 10.5 illustrate two sets, $A$ and $B$. Use them to write down the ranges represented by

   (a) $A \cap B$     (b) $A \cup B$.

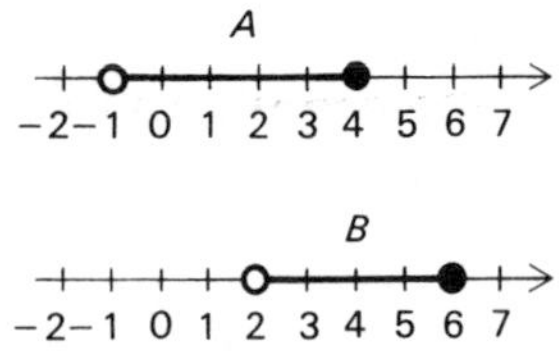

Fig. 10.5

7. The number lines shown in Fig. 10.6 illustrate the sets $A'$ and $B'$. Use them to write down the ranges illustrated by

   (a) $A' \cap B'$     (b) $A \cap B$.

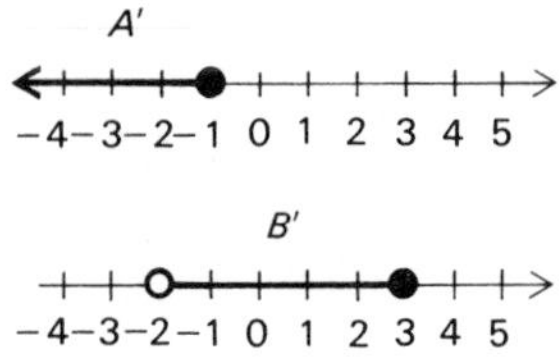

Fig. 10.6

8. The number lines shown in Fig. 10.7 illustrate the sets $E$ and $F$. Use them to write down the ranges illustrated by

   (a) $E \cap F$     (c) $E \cup F$.

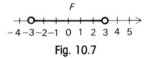

Fig. 10.7

Simplify:

9. $x + 3 < 8$

10. $x - 4 \geqslant -2$

11. $3x + 2 \geqslant 7$

12. $4(x - 6) < 3x$

13. $3 < 2(x + 1)$

14. $(x - 2) > 4(x + 2)$

158

15. $2(x-3) \geqslant 4x$

16. $\frac{1}{2}x - 5 \geqslant 3$

17. $\frac{1}{3}x - 4 < 3 - \frac{2}{3}x$

18. $-5x < -40$

19. $-2x > 5$

20. $3 - x < 3$

21. $-\frac{1}{3}x > -5$

22. $\dfrac{x+3}{2} > 4$

23. $\dfrac{x-3}{4} > \dfrac{x+2}{5}$

24. $\dfrac{x-1}{6} \leqslant \dfrac{1-x}{4}$

25. $\dfrac{x-2}{3} \geqslant \dfrac{2x+1}{5}$

26. $x(x-1) > x^2$

27. $2x(x+1) < 2x^2 - 3$

28. $3x^2 \leqslant (3x-1)(x-2)$

29. $(2x-1)(2x+3) > 4x^2$

30. $3x(x-1) \geqslant (3x-1)x + 3$

31. If $x \in \{1, 2, 3, 4, 5, 6\}$, find the solution sets to the following inequalities:
    (a) $(x-2)(x-4) < 0$  (b) $(x+2)(x-3) < 0$
    (c) $x(x-2) < 3$  (d) $3x^3 < 81$.

32. If $x$ is a positive integer, find the solution set to $x(x+1) \leqslant 6$.

33. Given that $f(x) = x^3 - 7$, find the set of integers such that $f(x) > 0$.

34. $x \in \{1, 2, 3, 4, 5, 6, 7, 8\}$. Find the solution sets to the following:
    (a) $x^2 + 14 \geqslant 9x$  (b) $x^2 > 80$  (c) $x(3-x) \geqslant 2$.

35. $x \in \{-2, -1, 0, 1, 2\}$. Find the solution sets to the following:
    (a) $x \leqslant 1$  (b) $x^2 > 0$  (c) $x^2 > 3$.

36. $x \in \{-4, -3, -2, -1, 0, 1, 2\}$. Find the solution sets to the following:
    (a) $x < -2$  (b) $2 - x < 3$  (c) $2 + x^2 > 3$.

## GRAPHICAL REPRESENTATION OF INEQUALITIES

An inequality is represented by an *area* on a graph. For example, all the points to the right of the line $x = 3$ satisfy the inequation $x > 3$ (Fig. 10.8). The *unwanted* region is shaded out, leaving the required area clear.

As $x > 3$, points *on* the vertical line $x = 3$ are *not* included; this exclusion is indicated by the dotted line. If points on the line are included, i.e. $x \geqslant 3$, then a solid, unbroken line is used instead.

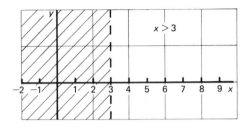

Fig. 10.8

If a number of inequalities are plotted on one graph, then the unshaded part will be limited to points which meet *all* the different inequalities.

**Example** Illustrate on one graph $x > 4$, $y > 2$ and $2x + y < 20$. Find the lowest value of $x + y$ subject to these inequalities, given that $x$ and $y$ are integers.

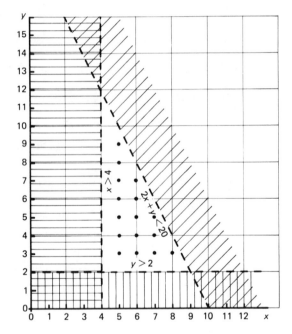

Fig. 10.9

First, plot the lines represented by the equations $x = 4$, $y = 2$ and $2x + y = 20$ (see Fig. 10.9). Find, for each line, which side is the required region. You can do this by testing whether the origin $(0, 0)$ does or does not satisfy the inequation. For example, $2x + y < 20$ is satisfied by $x = 0$, $y = 0$, so the origin and all points to the left of the line $2x + y = 20$ lie in the required region; points to the right of the line are excluded. Shade out the unwanted regions.

160

Within the unshaded region there are 16 points (indicated as dots) with integer coordinates: $(5,3), (5,4), (5,5), \ldots, (8,3)$. (Points on the line are *not* included in this case.) Given these choices, the least value of $x+y$ is $5+3=8$.

**EXERCISE 10b**

1. Write down the inequalities represented by the *unshaded* areas in Fig. 10.10:

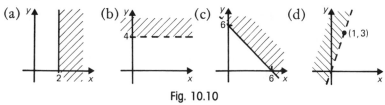

Fig. 10.10

2. Illustrate on *separate* diagrams, shading out the unwanted regions:

   (a) $x > 5$     (b) $y \leqslant 7$     (c) $x+y \leqslant 8$   (d) $x > 2y$.

3. Which area on the graph in Fig. 10.11 satisfies *both* the following inequalities:

   $$y \leqslant 1 \qquad x+y \geqslant 5.$$

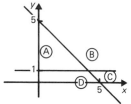

Fig. 10.11

4. Which area on the graph in Fig. 10.12 satisfies *all* the following inequalities:

   $$x \geqslant -2 \qquad y \leqslant 4 \qquad x+y \leqslant 5.$$

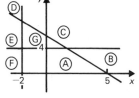

Fig. 10.12

5. Which area on the graph in Fig. 10.13 satisfies *all* the following inequalities:

   $$x \leqslant 4 \qquad y \geqslant 2 \qquad 3x \leqslant y.$$

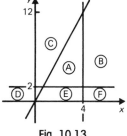

Fig. 10.13

6. Illustrate on a single graph the following inequalities:

   $$x \leqslant 10 \qquad y \leqslant 5 \qquad x+y \leqslant 12.$$

161

7. Illustrate on a single graph the inequalities:
$$x \geqslant 0 \qquad y \geqslant 0 \qquad x + y < 9 \qquad x + 2y < 12.$$

8. Illustrate on one graph the following inequalities:
$$x \leqslant 6 \qquad y \geqslant \tfrac{1}{2}x \qquad y \leqslant 2x.$$

9. Illustrate on one graph the following inequalities, shading out the unwanted region:
$$y > 0 \qquad y < 3x \qquad x + y < 4.$$
List the coordinates $(x, y)$ that satisfy all three inequalities, given that $x$ and $y$ are whole numbers.

10. Illustrate on one graph the following inequalities, shading out the unwanted regions:
$$x > 2 \qquad y > 3 \qquad \text{and} \qquad x + y < 10.$$
Assuming that $x$ and $y$ are both whole numbers, indicate on your graph the six points that simultaneously satisfy all three inequalities.

For each point find the value of $2x - y$ and hence the point which satisfies the inequalities and for which $2x - y$ is maximised.

11. Illustrate on one graph the following inequalities, shading out the unwanted regions:
$$x > 1 \qquad y < 11 \qquad \text{and} \qquad y > 3x.$$
Assuming that $x$ and $y$ are both whole numbers, indicate with a cross or a circle the five points that simultaneously satisfy all three inequalities.

For each point find the value of $x + y$ and hence the point which satisfies the inequalities and for which $x + y$ is minimised.

12. Using a scale of 1 cm to represent 1 unit on both axes, draw, for positive values only of $x$ and $y$, the graphs of the straight lines
$$2x + y = 22 \qquad 11x + 16y = 176 \qquad y = 2x.$$
Mark clearly on your graph paper all the points with coordinates $(x, y)$ such that $x$ and $y$ are whole numbers which satisfy simultaneously all the three inequalities
$$2x + y < 22 \qquad 11x + 16y > 176 \qquad y < 2x.$$
By listing the coordinates of these points, or otherwise, state the (whole-number) coordinates of the points which satisfy the inequalities above and are such that

(a) $x + y$ has its greatest value,

(b) $x^2 + y^2$ has its least value. (O & C)

13. A local cabinet maker has two designs: a standard version and a de luxe. In a week he makes $x$ de luxe and $y$ standard cabinets.

(a) The standard design takes 4 hours to build and the de luxe version takes 8 hours. Given that the cabinet maker works only 40 hours per week, show that

$$8x + 4y \leqslant 40$$

and hence that $\qquad 2x + y \leqslant 10.$

(b) He is under contract to produce at least four of the de luxe type and two of the standard type each week. Explain why $x \geqslant 4$ and $y \geqslant 2$.

(c) Illustrate the three inequalities on a graph, shading out the unwanted regions.

(d) Given that both $x$ and $y$ must be whole numbers, mark with a cross or a circle those points on your graph which satisfy all three inequalities.

(e) If the standard cabinet sells for £150 and the de luxe for £250 find the number of standard and de luxe cabinets the cabinet maker should build each week in order to maximise his income.

14. A manufacturer makes $x$ whichits and $y$ whatsits per week. Each whichit takes 3 machine hours and four units of raw materials to make; each whatsit takes 2 hours on the machine and one unit of raw materials.

(a) Show that the total machine time used is $3x + 2y$ hours.

(b) Show that the total of raw materials used is $4x + y$ units.

(c) If the manufacturer has only 42 machine hours per week and 36 units of raw materials, write down two inequalities that he must satisfy (other than $x \geqslant 0$ and $y \geqslant 0$).

(d) Illustrate these two inequalities on a graph, shading out the unwanted regions.

(e) The manufacturer is under contract to produce at least 7 whichits and 4 whatsits each week. Include the inequalities $x \geqslant 7$ and $y \geqslant 4$ on your graph.

(f) Mark with a cross or a circle those six points which satisfy all these inequalities. (Both $x$ and $y$ must be whole numbers.)

(g) Find, for each point, the manufacturer's possible profit given that he makes £50 on each whichit and £30 on each whatsit.

(h) What is the manufacturer's best possible profit?

15. A baker takes 1 hour to prepare a batch of pies and 2 hours to prepare a batch of cakes.

   (a) If she makes $x$ batches of pies and $y$ batches of cakes, how long must she work (in terms of $x$ and $y$)?

   (b) If the baker never works more than 10 hours in a day, write down an inequality that must be met by the baker.

   (c) The bakery has storage space for only nine batches of pies or cakes. Write down another inequality that must be met.

   (d) Illustrate these inequalities on a graph, shading out the unwanted regions.

   (e) The baker is contracted to supply a local café with 5 batches of pies every day. Explain why $x \geqslant 5$ and include this inequality on your graph.

   (f) Given that she makes £12 profit on each batch of pies and £18 on each batch of cakes, find the maximum profit the baker can make each day.

16. Instant coffee is sold in large jars costing £1.60 each and small jars costing £1 each. A customer receives tokens with his purchase of coffee, provided that he buys at least one large jar and more than two small jars. He can afford to spend up to £8 on coffee. He buys $y$ large and $x$ small jars.

   (a) Write down which two of the following inequalities are true:
   $$x \geqslant 2, \quad x > 2, \quad y \geqslant 1, \quad y > 1.$$

   (b) Prove that $5x + 8y \leqslant 40$.

   (c) If $x - y > 0$, does he buy more large or more small jars?

   (d) Draw a diagram showing all the constraints, including $x - y > 0$.

   (e) Indicate all the points on the diagram which satisfy the problem. (Use a cross or a circle.)

   (f) If he receives 5 tokens with a small jar and 7 tokens with a large jar, find the maximum number of tokens he could receive. (SUJB)

# 11 FURTHER GRAPHS

The graphs of equations involving powers of $x$ and $y$ (i.e. those not of the style $y = mx + c$) will *not* be straight lines. In particular, a quadratic equation (of the type $y = ax^2 + bx + c$) will have the shape shown in Fig. 11.1(a). If the $x^2$ term is negative, the graph will be the same shape, but upside down (see Fig. 11.1(b)).

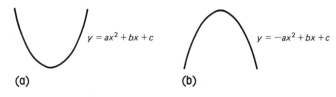

$y = ax^2 + bx + c$

$y = -ax^2 + bx + c$

(a)

(b)

**Fig. 11.1**

## PLOTTING THE GRAPH

To be sure of the exact path traced out by the function, it is necessary to find many coordinates that lie on the graph: two or three will *not* be enough.

**Example** Draw the graph of $y = x^2 - 2x - 8$ over the domain $-4 \leqslant x \leqslant +6$.

Putting $x = -4$ gives

$$\begin{aligned} y &= x^2 - 2x - 8 \\ &= (-4)^2 - 2(-4) - 8 \\ &= 16 + 8 - 8 \\ &= 16 \end{aligned}$$

So the point $(-4, 16)$ lies on the graph.

We must now repeat this for a series of values over the given domain. It is obviously simplest to use $x = -3, -2, -1$, etc., up to $+6$, and to set out the calculation of the $y$-coordinates as a table:

| $x$ | $-4$ | $-3$ | $-2$ | $-1$ | 0 | 1 | 2 | 3 | 4 | 5 | 6 |
|-----|------|------|------|------|---|---|---|---|---|---|---|
| $x^2$ | 16 | 9 | 4 | 1 | 0 | 1 | 4 | 9 | 16 | 25 | 36 |
| $-2x$ | $+8$ | $+6$ | $+4$ | $+2$ | 0 | $-2$ | $-4$ | $-6$ | $-8$ | $-10$ | $-12$ |
| $-8$ | $-8$ | $-8$ | $-8$ | $-8$ | $-8$ | $-8$ | $-8$ | $-8$ | $-8$ | $-8$ | $-8$ |
| $y$ | 16 | 7 | 0 | $-5$ | $-8$ | $-9$ | $-8$ | $-5$ | 0 | 7 | 16 |

From the table, we can see that the points $(-4, 16)$, $(-3, 7)$, $(-2, 0), \ldots, (6, 16)$ all lie on the graph $y = x^2 - 2x - 8$. The graph of these points, joined by a *smooth* curve is shown in Fig. 11.2.

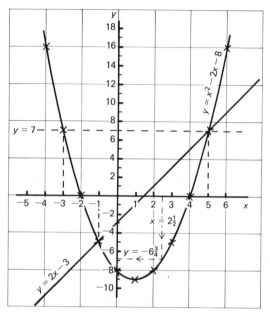

Fig. 11.2

The points $(-2, 0)$ and $(4, 0)$ where the graph crosses the $x$-axis, are of special importance for solving the equation $x^2 - 2x - 8 = 0$. They are called the *roots* of the equation. (We could have found them algebraically using the techniques described in Chapter 7.)

## READING THE GRAPH

We can read off points from the graph without further calculation. For example, at $x = 2\frac{1}{2}$ (reading down to the curve and along to the $y$-axis) we can see that $y = -6\frac{3}{4}$ (Fig. 11.3).

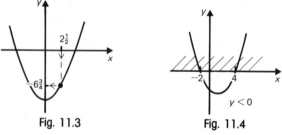

Fig. 11.3                    Fig. 11.4

Similarly, we can read off various inequalities from the graph. For example, $x^2 - 2x - 8$ is negative when the curve falls below the $x$-axis. So, reading off the graph, $x^2 - 2x - 8 < 0$ implies that $-2 < x < 4$ (Fig. 11.4).

In the same way, we can read off the ranges for which

$$x^2 - 2x - 8 > 2x - 3$$

The line $y = 2x - 3$ is already plotted on the graph in Fig. 11.2; the curve is above this line when $x < -1$ and when $x > 5$ (see Fig. 11.5).

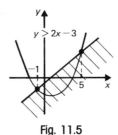

Fig. 11.5

## SOLVING RELATED EQUATIONS

Other equations can be solved using this graph of $y = x^2 - 2x - 8$ provided they can be rearranged to read $x^2 - 2x - 8 = \ldots$

**Example** Use the graph in Fig. 11.2 to solve the equation $x^2 - 2x - 15 = 0$.

If we add 7 to both sides of this new equation we get

$$x^2 - 2x - 15 + 7 = 0 + 7$$

i.e. $\qquad x^2 - 2x - 8 = 7$

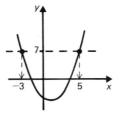

Fig. 11.6

From the graph (see also Fig. 11.6), we can see that $x^2 - 2x - 8 = 7$ at $x = -3$ and at $x = +5$.

**Example** Use the graph in Fig. 11.2 to solve the equation $x^2 - 4x - 5 = 0$.

Again, we must first rearrange the new equation to read $x^2 - 2x - 8 = \ldots$ So, we add $2x$ to both sides and subtract 3:

167

$$x^2 - 4x - 5 + 2x - 3 = 0 + 2x - 3$$

i.e. $$x^2 - 2x - 8 = 2x - 3$$

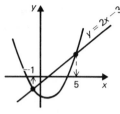

Fig. 11.7

If we plot the line $y = 2x - 3$ on the original graph (see Fig. 11.2), we find that it intersects with the original curve at $x = -1$ and at $x = +5$ (see also Fig. 11.7). These values are the solutions to the equation

$$x^2 - 2x - 8 = 2x - 3$$

and hence to the problem

$$x^2 - 4x - 5 = 0$$

## TANGENTS AND GRADIENTS

The gradient of a curve is continually changing. However, we can find its value at a particular point from the tangent drawn at that point.

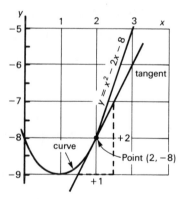

Fig. 11.8

Figure 11.8 shows the graph of $y = x^2 - 2x - 8$ for the limited domain $0 \leqslant x \leqslant 3$. The gradient of the curve at the point $(2, -8)$ is equal to the gradient of the tangent drawn at that point. Using the formula

$$\text{gradient} = \frac{\text{distance up}}{\text{distance along}} = \frac{+2}{+1} = 2$$

we see that the gradient of the tangent, and hence of the curve, at $(2, -8)$, is 2.

168

# MISCELLANEOUS EXERCISE 11

1. Complete the following table:

| x | −4 | −3 | −2 | −1 | 0 | 1 | 2 | 3 | 4 |
|---|---|---|---|---|---|---|---|---|---|
| $x^2$ | 16 | 9 | 4 | 1 | 0 | 1 | 4 | 9 | 16 |
| −4 | −4 | −4 | −4 | −4 | −4 | −4 | −4 | −4 | −4 |
| $y = x^2 - 4$ | 12 | 2 | 5 | −3 | −4 | −3 | 0 | 5 | 12 |

Draw the graph of $y = x^2 - 4$ for $-4 \leqslant x \leqslant 4$.
(a) What are the roots of the equation $x^2 - 4 = 0$?
(b) What is the minimum possible value of $x^2 - 4$?
(c) *Use your graph* to solve the equations
    (i) $x^2 = 8$      (ii) $x^2 = 10$.
(d) Draw on your graph the line $y = 3x$. What are the x-coordinates of the points of intersection with the curve? Show that these are the solution to the equation $x^2 - 3x - 4 = 0$.
(e) Draw another line on the graph that will enable you to read off the solutions to the equation $x^2 - 2x - 3 = 0$; write down these solutions.
(f) Draw the tangent to the curve at $(2, 0)$ and hence determine the gradient of the curve at that point.

2. Complete the following table and use it to draw the graph of $y = x^2 - x - 6$ over the domain $-4 \leqslant x \leqslant 5$.

| x | −4 | −3 | −2 | −1 | 0 | 1 | 2 | 3 | 4 | 5 |
|---|---|---|---|---|---|---|---|---|---|---|
| $x^2$ | +16 | +9 | | | | | 4 | 9 | 16 | 25 |
| −x | +4 | +3 | | | | | | −3 | | −5 |
| −6 | −6 | −6 | −6 | −6 | | | | −6 | −6 | −6 |
| y | 14 | 6 | | | | | | 0 | | 14 |

*Use your graph* to find
(a) the roots of the equation $x^2 - x - 6 = 0$
(b) the value of $y$ when $x =$
    (i) −1.2      (ii) +1.2      (iii) 2.4
(c) the values of $x$ when $y =$
    (i) 10      (ii) −5      (iii) 8

169

(d) the range of values of $x$ for which
   (i) $y < 0$       (ii) $y \leqslant 8$

(e) the range of values of $x$ for which
   (i) $y > 9$       (ii) $y > -2$

(f) the gradient of the curve at the points $(-1, -4)$ and $(2, -4)$ (you will need to draw the tangent at each point).

Solve the following equations by drawing appropriate lines on your graph:

(g) $x^2 - x - 6 = 3 - x$

(h) $x^2 - 3x = 4$.

3. Show that if $y = 9 - x^2$ then $y = -16$ when $x = +5$ *and* when $x = -5$. Construct a table of values of $y$ for $x = -5$, $-4, -3, -2, -1, 0, 1, 2, 3, 4, 5$ where $y = 9 - x^2$.

Draw the graph of $y = 9 - x^2$ over the given domain and use it to find

(a) the roots of the equation $9 - x^2 = 0$

(b) the value of $y$ when
   (i) $x = -2.8$     (ii) $x = +3.7$

(c) the values of $x$ when
   (i) $y = 2$        (ii) $y = 4.5$

(d) the range of values of $x$ for which $y > 0$

(e) the range of values of $x$ for which
   (i) $y < 3$        (ii) $y < -1$

(f) the gradient of the curve at the points $(-1, 8)$ and $(2, 5)$ (you will need to draw the tangent at each point).

Solve the following equations by drawing appropriate lines on your graph:

(g) $9 - x^2 = 5$

(h) $10 - 2x - x^2 = 2$.

Draw the line $y = 3x$ on your graph and hence solve the inequality $9 - x^2 < 3x$.

4. Copy and complete the table below for $y = 7x - x^3$.

| $x$ | $-3$ | $-2.5$ | $-2$ | $-1.5$ | $-1$ | $-0.5$ |
|---|---|---|---|---|---|---|
| $y$ | | $-1.875$ | | $-7.125$ | | $-3.375$ |

| $x$ | $0$ | $0.5$ | $1$ | $1.5$ | $2$ | $2.5$ | $3$ |
|---|---|---|---|---|---|---|---|
| $y$ | | $3.375$ | | $7.125$ | | $1.875$ | |

Draw the graph of $y = 7x - x^3$ for the range of values of $x$ from $-3$ to $3$, and from your graph determine for what values of $x$ in this range $7x - x^3 > 4$.

By drawing the appropriate straight line on your graph, find three solutions of the equation

$$6x - x^3 = 0. \qquad \text{(Ox)}$$

5. Construct a table of values of $y$ for $x = -1, -0.5, 0, 0.5, 1, 1.5, 2, 2.5,$ where

$$y = 20x^2 - x^3.$$

Plot the graph of $y = 20x^2 - x^3$, taking a scale of 4 cm to 1 unit on the $x$-axis and 2 cm to 10 units on the $y$-axis.

(a) Estimate from your graph the solutions of the equation
$$20x^2 - x^3 = 5.$$

(b) Estimate from your graph the solution of the equation
$$20x^2 - x^3 = 20.$$

(c) The equation $20x^2 - x^3 = k$ has just one solution. Find, from your graph, the set of values that $k$ can take. (O & C)

6. Functions f and g are defined by

$$f(x) = \frac{1}{x}, \qquad g(x) = 4 - x.$$

(a) Using a scale of 4 cm to 1 unit on each axis, plot and draw with the same axes the graphs of these two functions for $0.2 \leqslant x \leqslant 4.0$.

(b) From your graphs, estimate the two values of $x$ for which $f(x) = g(x)$.

(c) Write down an equation of which these two values are the roots and simplify it. (LU)

7. (a) If $y = x - 5 + \dfrac{10}{x}$, copy and complete the table below:

| $x$ | 1 | 1.5 | 2 | 3 | 4 | 5 | 6 |
|---|---|---|---|---|---|---|---|
| $y$ | | 3.17 | 2 | 1.33 | | | 2.67 |

(b) Taking 2 cm to represent 1 unit on the $x$-axis and 2 cm to represent 1 unit on the $y$-axis, draw the graph of $y = x - 5 + \dfrac{10}{x}$, for values of $x$ from $x = 1$ to $x = 6$.

(c) From your graph write down the range of values of $x$ for which $y$ is less than 2.5.

171

(d) On the same axes draw the straight line $x + y = 5$.

(e) By drawing a suitable parallel line estimate the value of $x$ on the graph of $y = x - 5 + \dfrac{10}{x}$, where the gradient of the tangent is $-1$. (AEB '81)

8. (a) If $y = 2^x$, calculate $y$ when $x = 0, 1, 2, 3, 4, 5, 6$.

(b) Draw the graph of $y = 2^x$ for values of $x$ lying between 0 and 6.

(c) Use the graph to find $N$, if $2^N = 20$.

(d) Find the gradient of the chord joining the point where $x = 1$ to the point where $x = 5$.

(e) Find the gradient of the curve at the point where $x = 4$. (SUJB)

9. Plot, on a single graph, the following curves:

(a) $y = x^2$       (b) $y = (x + 1)^2$     (c) $y = (x - 1)^2$.

What do you notice?

Now plot these curves on a second graph:

(d) $y = x^2 + 3$     (e) $y = (x + 1)^2 - 2$

(f) $y = (x - 1)^2 + 5$.

What do you notice?

Try to generalise: what would be the shape and position of the curve $y = (x - a)^2 + b$? How would changing the values of $a$ and $b$ alter the curve? Investigate further.

10. Plot on the same piece of graph paper the graphs of f($x$) and g($x$) where

$$f(x) = x^2 \quad \text{and} \quad g(x) = \pm\sqrt{x}$$

(a) When is f($x$) = g($x$)?

(b) What is the relationship between f($x$) and g($x$)?

(c) What transformation will map the graph of a function on to the graph of its inverse? Investigate further.

# 12 TRAVEL

## DISTANCE, SPEED AND TIME

Speed is defined as the ratio of distance travelled and time taken.

$$\text{speed} = \frac{\text{distance travelled}}{\text{time taken}}$$

The usual units are kilometres per hour (km/h), miles per hour (m.p.h.), or metres per second (m/s).

Re-arranging the speed formula gives:

$$\text{time taken} = \frac{\text{distance travelled}}{\text{speed}}$$

$$\text{distance travelled} = \text{speed} \times \text{time taken}$$

If a journey is full of starts and stops, fast and slow phases, then the speed is continually changing. We then talk of an *average speed* where

$$\text{average speed} = \frac{\text{total distance travelled}}{\text{total journey time}}$$

**Example** Driving through London, from Whitechapel to Mayfair, I occasionally reach 30 m.p.h.; however my journey is continually interrupted by red traffic lights, heavy traffic and other hold ups. The journey of 8 miles takes me one hour and twenty minutes. What is my average speed?

The speed of a car is usually given in miles per hour, so we need to convert 1 hour and 20 minutes to hours.

$$1 \text{ hour } 20 \text{ minutes} = 1 + \tfrac{20}{60} = 1\tfrac{1}{3} \text{ hours}$$

$$\text{average speed} = \frac{\text{distance travelled}}{\text{time taken}} = \frac{8}{1\tfrac{1}{3}} = 6 \text{ m.p.h.}$$

**EXERCISE 12a**   1. A train travels at constant speed covering 250 m in 7.5 s. Find its speed

(a) in metres per second, m/s.

(b) in kilometres per hour, km/h.

2. A spacecraft orbits the Earth travelling 13.5 kilometres every three seconds. What is its speed

   (a) in metres per second?

   (b) in kilometres per hour?

   How long would it take the spacecraft to travel from London to New York, a distance of approximately 5000 km?

3. In the United Kingdom there is a general speed limit of 70 m.p.h. on even the fastest roads. Given that a kilometre is $\frac{5}{8}$ths of a mile, what is this in km/h?

   The city speed limit in Spain is 50 km/h. What speed is this in miles per hour?

4. I cover the first six miles of my drive to work in twelve minutes and the remaining two miles in a further eight minute. What is my average speed?

5. A party of children travels by coach from school to Paris, via Dover and Calais. The distance from school to Dover is 350 miles and from Calais to Paris is 280 kilometres. Assuming an average speed of 50 miles per hour in England and 80 kilometres per hour in France:

   (a) calculate the travelling time from school to Dover;

   (b) calculate the travelling time from Calais to Paris;

   (c) calculate the journey time from school to Paris, given that the coach stops one hour at Dover, one hour at Calais, and takes two hours to cross the English Channel.
   (NREB)

6. One of the world's best women athletes can run 3000 metres in 8 minutes 10 seconds.

   (a) What is her average speed in kilometres per hour?

   (b) How long would it take her to run 100 metres at this speed. Why is this a very slow speed for the 100 metres race?

   (c) One of the world's very best women sprinters can run 100 metres in 10.9 seconds. How many kilometres per hour is this?

7. One of the more successful participants in last year's London Marathon (a distance of approximately 26 miles) completed the run 3 hrs and 28 minutes. What was his average speed?

8. A jogger usually runs for 40 minutes once a week over a distance of 5 miles. On one week's jog he stops for a rest for 8 minutes after running just 3 miles at his usual speed. How fast would he need to run in order to be back home at the usual time? Is this a speed he would be likely to manage?

9. Radio signals travel at the speed of light, i.e. at $3 \times 10^8$ m/s.

   (a) It takes a radar signal 2.56 seconds to travel to the Moon and back. Use this information to calculate the distance between the Moon and the Earth.

   (b) How long does it take light from the Sun to reach the Earth, given that the Sun is $1.5 \times 10^8$ km away?

10.

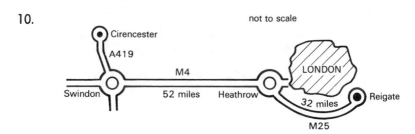

Fig. 12.1

   (a) A driver sets out from Cirencester and takes the A419 south in order to join the M4 motorway at Swindon. If this leg of the journey takes her 36 minutes travelling at an average speed of 35 m.p.h. how far is Cirencester from the motorway?

   (b) Once on the M4, the motorist increases her average speed to 65 m.p.h. How long will it take her to reach the M25 interchange at Heathrow, 52 miles away?

   (c) Road repairs and traffic jams on the M25 slow her down so that it takes a further 50 minutes to cover the 32 miles from Heathrow to Reigate. What is her average speed for this part of her journey?

   (d) For the whole journey from Cirencester to Reigate, calculate
      (i)   the total distance travelled,
      (ii)  the total time taken,
      (iii) the average speed in m.p.h.

175

11. The table shows the distance, in km, between the towns and cities named.

Distance table (km) between: ABERDEEN, BIRMINGHAM, CARDIFF, GLASGOW, LIVERPOOL, LONDON, NOTTINGHAM, OXFORD, PLYMOUTH, SOUTHAMPTON

```
645
776 160
224 464 592
522 144 264 340
784 176 248 630 315
592  80 245 442 157 197
744 104 168 563 246  91 152
955 330 256 776 443 336 410 288
845 205 189 664 344 125 253 104 244
```

(a) A student leaves Glasgow for Nottingham.
   (i) Write down the distance, in km, between the two cities.
   (ii) How far will she be from Nottingham after travelling non-stop for 3 hours at an average speed of 90 km/h?

(b) A lady travelled by car from Liverpool to Southampton and took 10 hours for the journey. This included 2 hours non-travelling time when she stopped for meals and rests.
   (i) What is the length, in km, of her journey?
   (ii) What average speed, in km/h, did she maintain whilst actually driving?

(c) On a non-stop journey from Plymouth to Birmingham a solicitor estimates that she can average 100 km/h.
   (i) What is the length, in km, of the journey?
   (ii) How long, in hours and minutes, should the journey take?

(d) Given that 8 km is approximately 5 miles, express the distance between Cardiff and Birmingham in miles.

(NWREB)

176

## DISTANCE–TIME GRAPHS

A journey can be illustrated graphically by plotting the distance travelled away from some starting point against the time taken. For example, Fig. 12.2 shows the distance–time graph for a journey of 12 km made by a cyclist. For the first 20 min, the cyclist makes good progress, covering a lot of ground quickly. Unfortunately, at A, he has a puncture, which he stops to repair. So for the next 15 min he does not travel any further: the portion AB of the distance–time graph is completely flat. Having made his repair, the cyclist continues his journey, but at a slower pace, until he arrives at C.

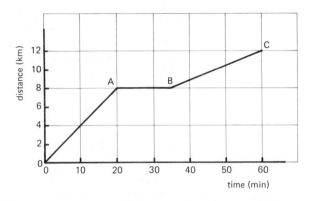

Fig. 12.2

The speed of the traveller can be found from the *slope* of the distance–time graph; the steeper the graph the faster the rate of travel. The cyclist in this example travels 8 km in the first 20 min of his journey, so his speed is $\dfrac{\text{distance}}{\text{time}} = \dfrac{8}{20} = 0.4$ km/min or $0.4 \times 60 = 24$ km/h. In the last 25 min of his journey he only covers another 4 km. So his speed is $\dfrac{4}{25} = 0.16$ km/min or $0.16 \times 60 = 9.6$ km/h.

More than one journey can be represented on the same graph. And a *return* journey is represented by a downward sloping graph (for, as time goes by, so the traveller gets nearer to his starting point).

**Example** Caroline sets out at 12 noon to drive from her lodgings in London to her parents' home in Chichester (a distance of 100 km). She drives at an average speed of 50 km/h. Her sister Susan decides to meet her. She sets out from Chichester at 12.30 p.m., cycling up

177

the London Road at 20 km/h for the first half hour. She rests for 20 min and then continues at the same speed. When do the sisters meet, and how far are they from Chichester?

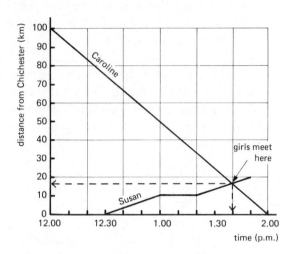

**Fig. 12.3**

Figure 12.3 shows the distance–time graph of the girls' journeys. Caroline's journey is shown as the *downward sloping* line, for she is *approaching* Chichester. It will take her 2 h to drive 100 km at 50 km/h. So she will arrive at Chichester at 2.00 p.m.

Susan's outward, slower journey is shown as the gently rising line. Her rest period is shown by the flat portion of the graph. From the graph, it is clear that they meet at 1.40 p.m., about 17 km from Chichester.

**EXERCISE 12b**

1. A boy sets out on a cycle ride. He cycles for half an hour at 20 km/h, stops for 10 minutes and then sets out again, this time at 15 km/h, for another 40 minutes. He stops for 15 min and then cycles home at a steady 20 km/h. How far is his complete journey? Illustrate the journey on a distance–time graph.

2. A motorist sets out on a journey of 100 km. He drives for the first half hour at an average speed of 40 km/h. Then he reaches the motorway and his speed increases to an average of 100 km/h. He drives for another half hour on the motorway, then stops for 15 min at a service station, before completing his journey by an 'A'-road at an average speed of 60 km/h. How long does the journey take him? Illustrate the journey with a distance–time graph.

3. Two trains, X and Y, set out at different times from the same station and for the same destination, D, passing through towns A, B and C along the way. The journeys are illustrated by the distance–time graph in Fig. 12.4. Describe, in words, the journeys of each train. When does the second train catch up with the first?

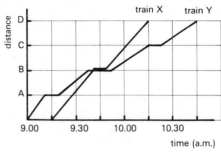

Fig. 12.4

4. Two men agree to meet at a point between their respective home-towns. Mr A sets out at 9.30 a.m. from Ayton, driving at a steady 60 km/h, half an hour after Mr B has left Beetown which is 120 km away. Mr B drives at 75 km/h but stops for 20 min on the way. Illustrate the men's journeys on a distance–time graph and use it to find the time at which the men meet and the distance of their rendezvous from Ayton.

5.

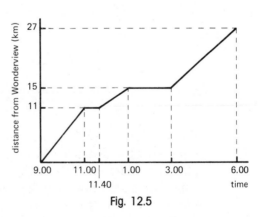

Fig. 12.5

The distance–time graph shown in Fig. 12.5 represents the progress made by a rambler journeying from Wonderview Youth Hostel to Longrest, 27 km away.

(a) What is the rambler's average speed for the whole journey?

(b) What is his fastest speed? How far did he walk at this speed?

(c) What is his slowest speed (not counting rest periods)?

6. The graph shows the distance of a motorist from his home at different times during the day. His journey from 11 a.m. to 3 p.m. was divided into four different parts:

A to B,     B to C,     C to D,     and D to E.

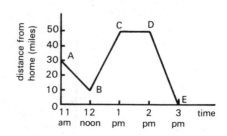

Fig. 12.6

(a) During which part of the journey was he travelling away from his home?

(b) During which part of his journey was he travelling at his greatest average speed?

(c) Assume each part of his journey was made by the shortest route.
   (i)  Calculate the distance he travelled from B to C.
   (ii) Calculate the total distance he travelled from A to E.

(WMEB)

7.

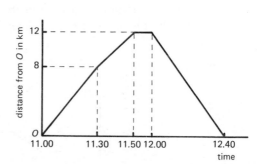

Fig. 12.7

The graph (Fig. 12.7) which consists of straight line segments represents the distance of a cyclist from his starting point (O) plotted against time. Draw the graph accurately on squared paper using scales of 1 cm for 5 minutes and 1 cm for 1 kilometre. Find the average speeds in km/h of the cyclist:

(a) between 11.00 and 11.30

(b) on his outward journey

(c) on his return journey.

At 11.30 a pedestrian was 12 km from O and walked towards O at a steady speed of 6 km/h. Plot the straight line graph of his path, and hence find the times of the two occasions when he met the cyclist.

(Ox)

**8.** A motorist travels at an average speed of 60 m.p.h. on a motorway.

At 1.00 p.m. he is at a point A on a motorway, and is travelling towards a service station B, which is 20 miles away. When he gets there he rests for 10 minutes before leaving the motorway to travel to C which is 40 miles *from* B, arriving there at 2.50 p.m. At C he joins another motorway and travels at 60 m.p.h. on to D, which is 50 miles *from* C.

D is therefore 110 miles from A.

(a) Draw a graph of the motorist's journey from A to D, using 6 cm to represent one hour and 2 cm to represent 10 miles.

At 2.00 p.m. a lorry driver leaves D to travel to C on the motorway, and passes the motorist at 3.00 p.m.

(b) Using the same graph paper, draw a graph of the lorry driver's journey.

(c) (i)  What time does the motorist arrive at D?
    (ii)  What is the motorist's speed when not on the motorway?
    (iii) What is the lorry driver's speed?
    (iv)  At what time does the lorry driver arrive at C?

(WJEC)

**9.** *ABCD* are four stations on a railway line. *B* is 40 miles from *A*, *C* is 80 miles from *A* and *D* is 120 miles from *A*. All trains travelling between *A* and *B* and between *C* and *D* travel at 60 miles per hour, but between *B* and *C* they can only travel at 40 miles per hour because of repairs being made to the track. All trains stop at *B* and *C* and wait at both stations for 6 minutes before proceeding on their way.

(a) (i)  Draw a graph of the train that starts from *A* at 12.00 noon and proceeds to *D*, using 6 cm to represent one hour (on the short side of the graph paper) and 2 cm to represent 10 miles (on the long side of of the graph paper).
    (ii)  Use your graph to find the time the train leaves *B*.

(b) (i)  On the same graph paper, draw a graph of the train that starts from *D* at 12.20 p.m. and proceeds to *A*.
    (ii)  Use your graph to find at what time this train ARRIVES at *B*.
    (iii) Use your graph to find when and where the two trains pass each other.

(WJEC)

10. A stone is thrown from the top of the Eiffel Tower and falls to the ground, accelerating all the time. Which of the following distance–time graphs is the most realistic? Justify your answer.

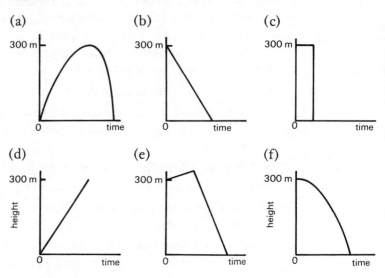

11. The distance–time graph showing the progress made by an athlete running a race might be any one of the following six possibilities:

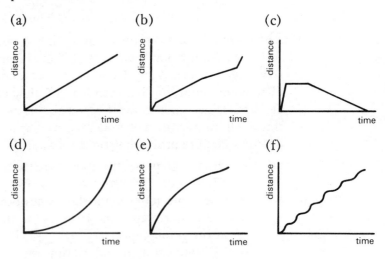

For each one, explain the meaning of the graph. Which would be the most realistic if the race were

(i)   a 100 m sprint

(ii)  a 3000 m circuit

(iii) a 40 km marathon?

12. A parachutist jumps out of an aeroplane. Explain the meaning of the following suggested graphs. Which one is the most realistic?

(a)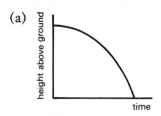

(b)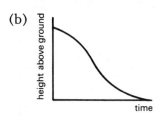

(c)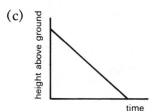

(d)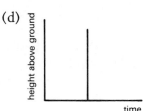

## VELOCITY–TIME GRAPHS

Instead of plotting the distance covered, we might instead plot a traveller's *speed* against time.

The total distance covered can be found from the area underneath the graph (see Fig. 12.8). The acceleration of the traveller at any time can be found from the slope of the graph.

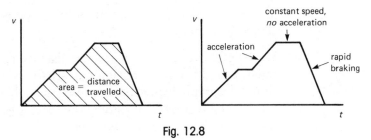

Fig. 12.8

*Note*: the average velocity $= \dfrac{\text{total distance covered}}{\text{total time taken}}$.

**Example** The velocity–time graph for a school race run by a young boy is shown in Fig. 12.9. Find

(a) his acceleration during each phase of the run,

(b) the length of the race,

(c) the boy's average speed over the whole race.

183

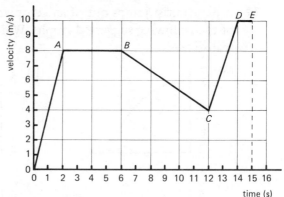

Fig. 12.9

(a) In the first 2 s the boy accelerates smoothly to 8 m/s.

$$\text{acceleration} = \frac{\text{increase in velocity}}{\text{time}} = \frac{8}{2} = 4 \text{ m/s}^2$$

For 4 s the boy maintains this pace, so he is not accelerating.

But for the next 6 s, from $B$ to $C$ on the graph, the boy tires and steadily loses speed.

$$\text{deceleration} = \frac{\text{decrease in velocity}}{\text{time}} = \frac{8-4}{6} = \frac{4}{6} = \frac{2}{3} \text{ m/s}^2$$

In the next phase, from $C$ to $D$ on the graph, the boy makes his final spurt. His speed increases from 4 m/s to 10 m/s in 2 s:

$$\text{acceleration} = \frac{10-4}{2} = \frac{6}{2} = 3 \text{ m/s}^2$$

In the final second, the velocity–time graph is flat, i.e. there is no acceleration.

(b) The length of the race, that is the distance run by the boy, can be found from the area underneath the graph. Figure 12.10 shows the graph divided into various triangular, rectangular and trapezoidal sections. By finding the area of each section and totalling them, we see the boy runs

$$8 + 32 + 36 + 14 + 10 = 100 \text{ m}$$

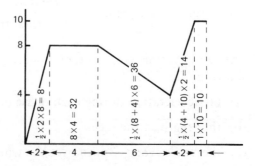

Fig. 12.10

184

(c) The boy's average speed $= \dfrac{\text{total distance run}}{\text{total time taken}} = \dfrac{100}{15}$

$= 6.67 \text{ m/s.}$

1. Figure 12.11 shows the velocity–time graph for a cycle ride.

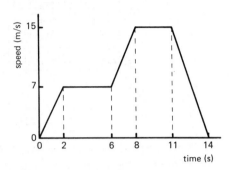

**Fig. 12.11**

(a) What is the cyclist's greatest speed?
(b) What is his greatest acceleration?
(c) How far does the cyclist ride?
(d) What is his average speed?

2.

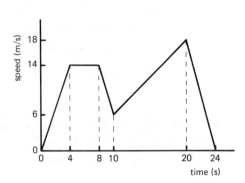

**Fig. 12.12**

Figure 12.12 shows the velocity–time graph for a certain journey.
(a) What is the greatest speed reached?
(b) What is the initial acceleration?
(c) What is the deceleration in the last phase of the journey?
(d) How long is the journey?
(e) What is the average speed?

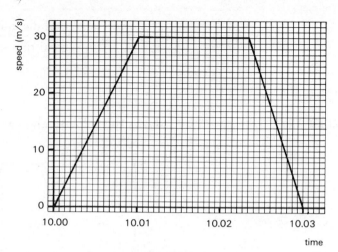

Fig. 12.13

The speed–time graph shows the speeds obtained by a train on a journey between two stations. Using the graph write down

(a) the fastest speed obtained by the train.

(b) the time the train arrived at its destination.

(c) the number of seconds it took the train to reach a speed of 20 m/s.

(d) the length of time the train travelled at its maximum speed.

Calculate

(e) the distance travelled at a constant speed,

(f) the distance between the two stations,

(g) the average speed of the train between the two stations.

(EAEB)

4. In the first 20 s of his journey, a motorist accelerates from rest to $v$ m/s, as shown in Fig. 12.14. How far, in terms of $v$, does he travel in this time?

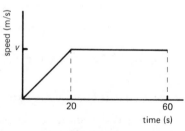

Fig. 12.14

The motorist continues at this speed; if he has travelled exactly 1 km in the first minute of his journey, calculate the value of $v$.

5. Figure 12.15 shows a sketch of the velocity–time graph for the first 80 s of a car journey. How far does the car travel in the first 10 s?

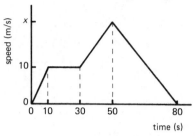

Fig. 12.15

If the car covers 1100 m in the 80 s, what is the value of $x$?

6.

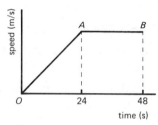

Fig. 12.16

The speed–time graph of a car during the first 48 seconds of its motion consists of two straight lines $OA$ and $AB$ (Fig. 12.16). The car starts from rest, travels 360 metres in the first 24 seconds and it then travels at a constant speed for the remaining 24 seconds.

Calculate

(a) the distance travelled in the first 12 seconds,

(b) the distance travelled in the last 24 seconds,

(c) the average speed for the 48 seconds.               (C)

7. A car is travelling at 36 km/h. What is this speed converted into m/s? The car accelerates from rest to 36 km/h in 5 s. It travels at this speed for 10 s before accelerating again to 108 km/h over a further 10 s. Sketch the velocity–time graph for these 25 s. How far does the car travel in this time?

8. A bus accelerates smoothly away from a bus-stop to 54 km/h in 20 s. It travels at this speed for 30 s, when the driver has to brake sharply, decelerating the vehicle from 54 km/h to 18 km/h in 2 s. The driver accelerates again, up to 36 km/h in

8 s and then slows gently to a halt, over a further 30 s, at the next bus-stop. Sketch the velocity–time graph for this journey (showing speeds in m/s). What is the distance between the two bus-stops?

9. A car accelerates from rest and readings are taken of the speed, in metres per second, and the time, in seconds.

| Speed | 0 | 5.2 | 10.1 | 14.2 | 17.1 | 18.9 | 20.2 | 21.1 | 21.7 | 22.0 | 22.2 |
|-------|---|-----|------|------|------|------|------|------|------|------|------|
| Time  | 0 | 1   | 2    | 3    | 4    | 5    | 6    | 7    | 8    | 9    | 10   |

Choose suitable scales to plot the readings on a graph, taking speed as the $y$-axis.

Use your graph to estimate:

(a)  the speed after 3.5 seconds;

(b)  the time when the speed is 8.0 m/s;

(c)  the rate at which the speed was changing (i.e. acceleration) at 6 seconds;

(d)  the distance travelled in the first ten seconds, to the nearest 5 m. (SUJB)

10. A particle moves along a straight line $AB$ so that, after $t$ seconds, the velocity $v$ m/s in the direction $AB$ is given by

$$v = 2t^2 - 9t + 5.$$

Corresponding values of $t$ and $v$ are given in the table below:

| $t$ | 0 | 1 | 2  | 3  | 4 | 5  | 6  | 7 |
|-----|---|---|----|----|---|----|----|---|
| $v$ | 5 |   | -5 | -4 | 1 | 10 | 23 |   |

Calculate the value of $v$ when $t = 1$ and the value of $v$ when $t = 7$.

Taking 2 cm to represent 1 second on the horizontal axis and 2 cm to represent 5 m/s on the vertical axis, draw the graph of

$$v = 2t^2 - 9t + 5 \quad \text{for the range } 0 \leqslant t \leqslant 7.$$

Use your graph to estimate

(a)  the values of $t$ when the velocity is zero,

(b)  the time at which the acceleration is zero.

(c)  the acceleration after 6 seconds. (C)

188

# 13 ANGLES AND PARALLELS

## ANGLES

A complete turn is divided into 360°. A quarter turn, or *right angle*, is 90°. An angle of less than 90° is called an *acute* angle. An angle between 90° and 180° is called *obtuse*. An angle greater than 180° is called a *reflex* angle.

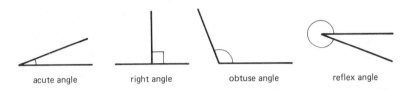

acute angle    right angle    obtuse angle    reflex angle

Fig. 13.1

Angles on a straight line add up to 180°; two angles that add up to 180° are said to be *supplementary*. For example, 73° and 107° are supplementary angles, and could be two angles on a straight line.

$73° \quad 107° \qquad 73° + 107° = 180°$

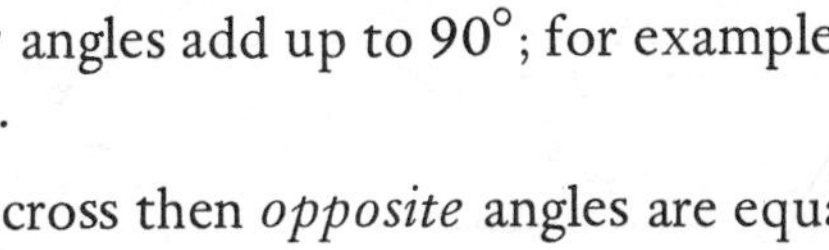

Fig. 13.2

*Complementary* angles add up to 90°; for example 23° and 67° are complementary.

When two lines cross then *opposite* angles are equal.

Fig. 13.3

Two lines that meet at right angles are said to be *perpendicular* to each other.

When a straight line cuts across two parallel lines then various angles are equal.

*Corresponding* angles are equal (Fig. 13.4).

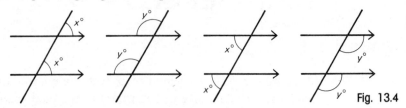

Fig. 13.4

*Alternate* angles are also equal (Fig. 13.5).

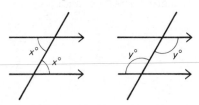

Fig. 13.5

1. Name the following types of angles:

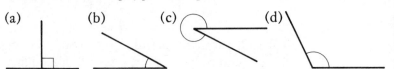

2. Give a reason for the angles shown being equal:

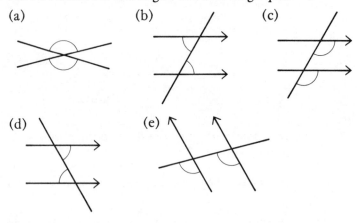

3. Work out the value of angle $x$ in each of the following, giving reasons for your answer:

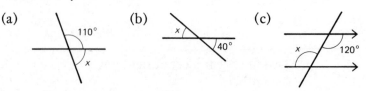

190

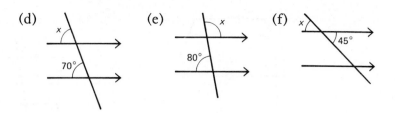

(d) $x$ 70°

(e) $x$ 80°

(f) $x$ 45°

4. Prove that the lines AB and CD in Fig. 13.6 are parallel. Give your reasons.

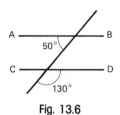

A ——— B
50°

C ——— D
130°

**Fig. 13.6**

In Questions 5 to 18, find the angles marked with letters. Be sure to give your reasons for every step.

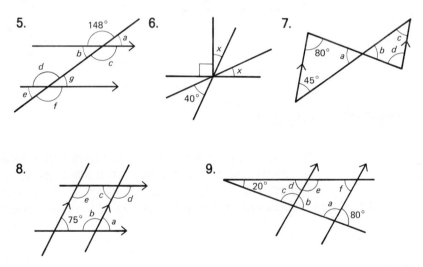

5.
148°
$a$
$b$
$c$
$d$
$g$
$e$
$f$

6.
$x$
$x$
40°

7.
80° $a$
$b$ $d$
$c$
45°

8.
$e$ $c$ $d$
75° $b$
$a$

9.
20° $c$ $d$ $e$ $f$
$b$ $a$
80°

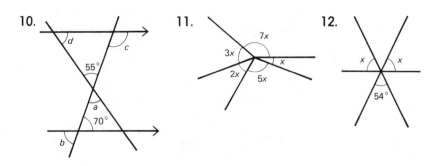

10.
$d$
$c$
55°
$a$
70°
$b$

11.
7$x$
3$x$
2$x$ 5$x$
$x$

12.
$x$ $x$
54°

**13.**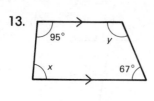

**14.**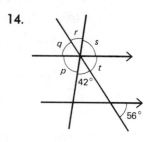

**15.**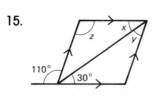

**16.**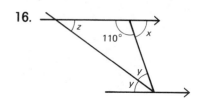

**17.**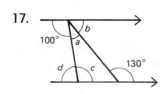

**18.**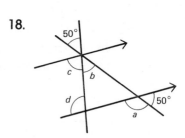

## SIMPLE CONSTRUCTIONS

Any work involving accurate construction requires a sharp, medium grade pencil, an efficient eraser, an undamaged ruler marked in millimetres, a pair of compasses and set-squares. Do *not* rub out the marks you make in the process of a correct construction.

### To draw one line parallel to another

(*i*)   Place the longest edge of the set-square along the given line (see Fig. 13.7).

(*ii*)  Place a ruler along another edge of the set square.

(*iii*) Slide the set-square down the edge of the ruler until it reaches the required position.

(*iv*)  Draw the parallel line.

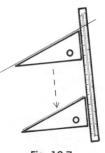

Fig. 13.7

## To bisect a line

(*i*) Set the compasses to a convenient radius, greater than half the length of the given line, AB.

(*ii*) Mark arcs, centred on A and B, above and below the line, in the middle region (Fig. 13.8(a)).

(*iii*) Draw a line through the points of intersection of these arcs. This line will bisect AB and be perpendicular to it (Fig. 13.8(b)).

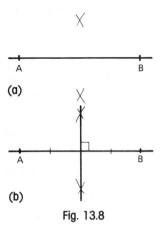

Fig. 13.8

## To construct a right angle at a point on a line

(*i*) Set the compasses to any convenient radius and mark two points, A and B, on the line on either side of the point, P (Fig. 13.9).

(*ii*) Bisect the line AB, following the procedures above.

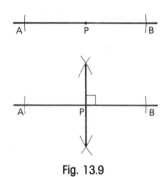

Fig. 13.9

## To bisect an angle

(*i*) Set the compasses to any convenient radius; mark arcs centred on O on both lines, as shown in Fig. 13.10(a) at A and B.

(*ii*) Draw an arc centred on A, and another centred on B, using the same radius, so that they intersect at C (Fig. 13.10(b)).

(*iii*) Draw the line OC which bisects the angle AOB (Fig. 13.10(c)).

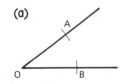

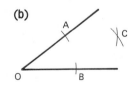

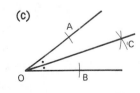

Fig. 13.10

193

**EXERCISE 13b** *In these constructions, use a pencil, ruler, set-square and compasses only. Use your protractor to* check *the accuracy of your drawing.*

1. Draw a line. Mark on it two points, A and B, 6 cm apart. Set a pair of compasses to a radius of 5 cm and draw above the line AB a wide arc, centred on A; change the radius to 7.5 cm and draw a second arc, centred on B, to intersect with the first at C. Draw the lines AC and BC to complete a triangle with sides 6 cm, 5 cm and 7.5 cm.

   Measure the three angles $\widehat{A}$, $\widehat{B}$ and $\widehat{C}$ with a protractor and check that they total 180°.

2. Follow the procedure of Question 1 to construct accurately a triangle with sides 7 cm, 5 cm and 4 cm.

3. Follow the procedure of Question 1 to construct an equilateral triangle with sides of 6 cm.

4. Construct an isosceles triangle with sides of 8 cm, 8 cm and 4 cm.

5. Construct an equilateral triangle with sides of any convenient length. Bisect one of the angles of the triangle to make an angle of 30°; bisect the 30° angle to make another angle of 15°.

6. Construct a right angle at any convenient point P on a line. Bisect the right angle to construct an angle of 45°.

7. Draw two lines, the second line parallel to the first and 4 cm from it. Set a pair of compasses to a radius of 5 cm and from a convenient point, A, on the first line mark a point B, 5 cm from A on the same line; now mark a third point, C, 5 cm from A on the *second* line. Join A to C. Complete the construction of a rhombus ABDC.

8. Construct a square of side length 6 cm.

9. Construct a parallelogram with sides 7 cm and 8 cm.

10. Construct a triangle of any convenient size. Bisect the three angles. These angle bisectors should all meet at a point.

    This point is the centre of the *inscribed circle* that is, the circle that is everywhere inside the triangle, just touching each side once. Draw the inscribed circle on your diagram.

11. Construct another triangle of any convenient size. Construct the perpendicular bisectors of the three sides. These, too, should meet at a point.

This point is the centre of the *circumcircle*, that is the circle that contains the triangle, passing through each of the three corners. Draw the circumcircle on your diagram.

12. Construct a third triangle of any convenient size. Bisect each side. Join the mid-point of each side to the corner opposite. These three lines (the *medians*) also meet at a single point.

13. (a) Draw a circle of radius 40 mm, with centre O.

(b) Mark in a diameter, PT, and construct another diameter perpendicular to the first. Label this diameter RV.

(c) Now bisect the two right angles, POR and POV.

(d) Construct the regular octagon PQRSTUVW.

14.

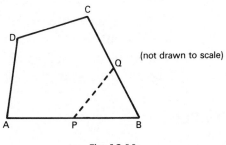

(not drawn to scale)

Fig. 13.11

A field is in the shape of a quadrilateral ABCD, where angle DAB = 80°, angle ABC = 65°, AB is 120 metres, BC is 90 metres and AD is 70 metres. There are stiles at P and Q, the mid-points of AB and BC, and a footpath runs from P to Q.

(a) By means of an accurate scale drawing (use a scale of 1 cm to 10 m) find the length of PQ.

(b) The farmer decides that there will be less damage to his crops in the adjoining fields if he moves the stile from P to A and re-routes this footpath along the bisector of angle DAB. Mark this new footpath on your diagram and show the position of the stile moved from Q. How long is the new footpath across the field? (ALSEB)

195

15.

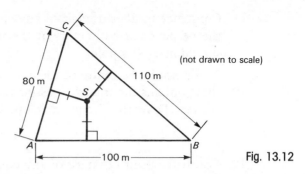

Fig. 13.12

(a) Triangle $ABC$ represents a field. A farmer placed a scare-crow, $S$, at the same perpendicular distance from each side of the field.

Make a scale drawing (with 1 cm representing 10 m) of the triangle $ABC$. To find the position of $S$ on your drawing, use the following steps.

(i) Construct $AD$ with each point on it equidistant from $AB$ and $AC$. ($D$ is on $BC$.)

(ii) Construct $BE$ with each point on it equidistant from $BA$ and $BC$. ($E$ is on $AC$.)

(iii) Mark $S$, the point at which $AD$ cuts $BE$.

Draw on your diagram the circle, centre $S$, which touches $AB$.

Use your drawing to write down an estimate of the perpendicular distance of $S$ from each side of the field.

(b) Calculate, in square metres, correct to two significant figures, the area of the field. (ALSEB)

## ANGULAR DIRECTION

Angles are used not only in the course of geometric problems and proofs but also as precise measures of direction, in which case certain conventions must be observed.

Mathematicians measure direction in an anticlockwise sense from the horizontal $x$-axis. For example, directions of $75°$, $110°$ and $330°$ are measured as illustrated in Fig. 13.13.

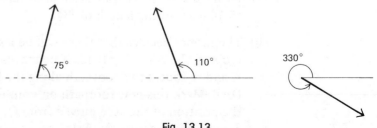

Fig. 13.13

If an angle is measured in the clockwise sense, then it is shown as a negative angle (see Fig. 13.14).

Fig. 13.14

# BEARINGS

Navigators measure direction as three-figure *bearings*, angles measured *clockwise* from north (see Fig. 13.15).

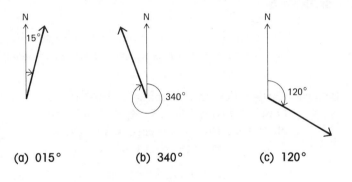

(a) 015°        (b) 340°        (c) 120°

Fig. 13.15

Alternatively, a navigator may measure from North or South in degrees east or west (Fig. 13.16).

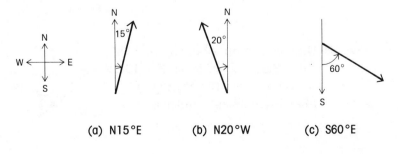

(a) N15°E        (b) N20°W        (c) S60°E

Fig. 13.16

In all, we have three formal ways of measuring a given direction.

Of course it would be inappropriate to use navigational bearings in the course of a mathematical problem or vice versa.

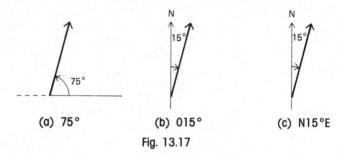

(a) 75°      (b) 015°      (c) N15°E

Fig. 13.17

A direction of 75° measured in a mathematician's way is equivalent to the navigator's bearing of 015° or N15°E (Fig. 13.17).

## BACK-BEARINGS

Given the bearings of a point B from a starting point A, then the bearing of A from B is known as the *back-bearing*.

**Example** Carlisle lies on a bearing of 334° from Penrith. From Fig. 13.18, it should be clear that the back-bearing, i.e. the bearing of Penrith from Carlisle, is

$$334° - 180° = 154°$$

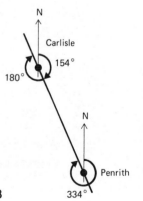

Fig. 13.18

**Example** Dundee lies on a bearing of 128° from Blairgowrie. From Fig. 13.19, we can see that the bearing of Blairgowrie from Dundee is

$$128° + 180° = 308°$$

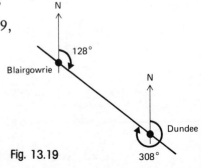

Fig. 13.19

1. Write as three-figure bearings the following directions (measured by the mathematicians' convention, anticlockwise from the $x$-axis):

   (a) 64°  (b) 72°  (c) 99°  (d) 195°  (e) 282°

   (f) 343°  (g) 210°  (h) 158°  (i) 285°  (j) 303°.

2. Write the following three-figure bearings as angles measured anticlockwise from the $x$-axis:

   (a) 050°  (b) 085°  (c) 125°  (d) 186°  (e) 222°

   (f) 333°  (g) 095°  (h) 189°  (i) 231°  (j) 282°.

3. Write the following directions as three-figure bearings:

   (a) N35°E  (b) N35°W  (c) S35°E  (d) S35°W.

4. Write as three-figure bearings the directions known as

   (a) due south  (b) south-east  (c) south-west

   (d) north-west  (e) north–north-west.

5. Fig. 13.20 (which is not drawn to scale) shows the five legs of an air-race starting and finishing at Paris. Copy and complete the table.

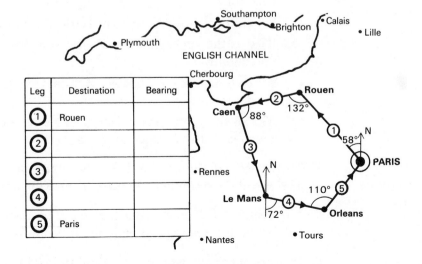

| Leg | Destination | Bearing |
|-----|-------------|---------|
| ① | Rouen | |
| ② | | |
| ③ | | |
| ④ | | |
| ⑤ | Paris | |

Fig. 13.20

6. The map, Fig. 13.21, shows some of the larger towns of Britain. It is drawn to scale. 1 cm represents 100 km.

Fig. 13.21

Use a ruler and protractor to answer the following:

(a) Which town on the map is approximately due West of Brighton?

(b) Which town is approximately 160 km from Leeds?

(c) What is the approximate distance from Inverness to Portsmouth?

(d) Which town is approximately 220 km from Cardiff on a bearing of 045°?

(e) What is the approximate bearing of Newcastle from Wells, and what is the distance between them?

7. The bearing of Kilmarnock from the centre of Dumfries is 318°. Find the bearing of Dumfries from Kilmarnock.

8. The bearing of Armagh from the centre of Londonderry is 147°. Find the bearing of Londonderry from Armagh.

9. The bearing of Newport from Cardiff is 049°. Find the bearing of Cardiff from Newport.

10. Plymouth lies on a bearing 234° from Exeter. Find the bearing of Exeter from Plymouth.

11. The bearing of Ipswich from Colchester is 039°; what is the bearing of Colchester from Ipswich?

12. The centre of Norwich is 26 km due west of the race-track at Great Yarmouth. The race-track, in turn, is 26 km due north of a light-house at Southwold. What is the bearing of the light-house from the centre of Norwich?

13.

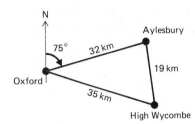

Fig. 13.22

Figure 13.22 (not drawn to scale) shows the distances between Oxford, High Wycombe and Aylesbury. Aylesbury lies on a bearing of 075° from Oxford. By drawing the triangle accurately to scale, use your protractor to find the bearing of High Wycombe:

(a) from Oxford

(b) from Aylesbury

Give your answers to the nearest degree.

14. Standing at the top of Snowdon, I can make out Conway Castle 30 km away on a bearing of 036°, and the cathedral at Bangor 15 km away on a bearing of 348°. By scale-drawing find, to the nearest whole number,

(a) the distance from Bangor to Conway,

(b) the bearing of Bangor from Conway.

15. Two aircraft set out simultaneously from Heathrow. One sets course for Paris on a bearing of 115° and travels at 330 km/h; the other sets course for Madrid on a bearing of 194° and travels at 420 km/h. By scale-drawing, find the distance between the two aircraft and the bearing of the first aircraft from the second after 20 min.

16. I run at 16 km/h for 15 min on a bearing of 342°, then walk for 20 min at 6 km/h on a bearing of 032°. I then jog for a further 30 min at 10 km/h on a bearing of 165°. Find, by scale-drawing, the course I must set to return directly to my starting point. How far will I have to travel, and how long will it take me at 10 km/h?

17. A party of explorers sets out from a point A to reach a point B which lies 120 km from A on a bearing of 330°. In order to avoid some difficult country the party first travels on a bearing of 030° for a distance of 60 km to a point P, and then on a bearing of 300° for a distance of 40 km to a point Q. By accurate drawing *on squared paper* or by calculation, find the bearing and distance of B from Q.

On their actual route the party average a speed of 4 km/h, whereas if they had travelled directly from A to B they would only have averaged a speed of 2 km/h. Calculate the time saved by taking the longer route. (O & C)

# 14 TRIANGLES

## TYPES OF TRIANGLE

A *scalene* triangle has no sides or angles equal (Fig. 14.1(a)).

An *isosceles* triangle has two sides and two angles equal (Fig. 14.1(b)). The line that cuts the third angle in half also cuts the base line in half, and meets it at right angles.

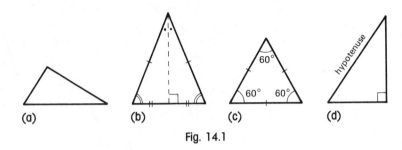

Fig. 14.1

An *equilateral* triangle has all sides equal and all angles equal to 60° (Fig. 14.1(c)).

A *right-angled* triangle contains one right angle and two acute angles (Fig. 14.1(d)). It may also be an isosceles triangle, but is never equilateral. The side opposite the right angle (the longest side) is called the *hypotenuse*.

The relationship between the different types of triangle can be shown on a Venn diagram (see Fig. 14.2).

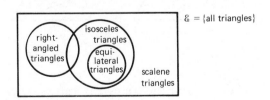

Fig. 14.2

## PROPERTIES OF TRIANGLES

For *all* triangles, the following conditions must hold:

(*i*)   The sum of the three interior angles is 180°.

203

(*ii*) The angle formed by extending one of the sides (the *exterior* angle) is equal to the sum of the two interior angles opposite.

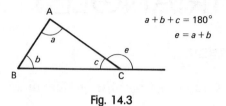

$$a + b + c = 180°$$
$$e = a + b$$

Fig. 14.3

(*iii*) The area $A$ of a triangle is given by

$$A = \tfrac{1}{2} \text{ base} \times \text{height}$$

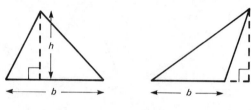

Fig. 14.4

There is nothing special about which way up a triangle is drawn; *any* side can be taken as the base simply by rotating the paper; the height will then be the perpendicular line through the opposite corner (Fig. 14.5).

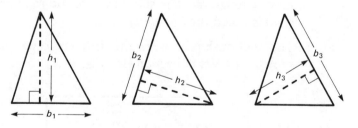

Fig. 14.5

If the area of the triangle is known, then it may be possible to deduce the length of the base or the height using

$$\text{base} = \frac{2 \times \text{area}}{\text{height}} \quad \text{or} \quad \text{height} = \frac{2 \times \text{area}}{\text{base}}$$

(*iv*) The sum of the lengths of any two sides is greater than the third.

**EXERCISE 14a**    1. Find the angles $x$, $y$ and $z$ in the following triangles:

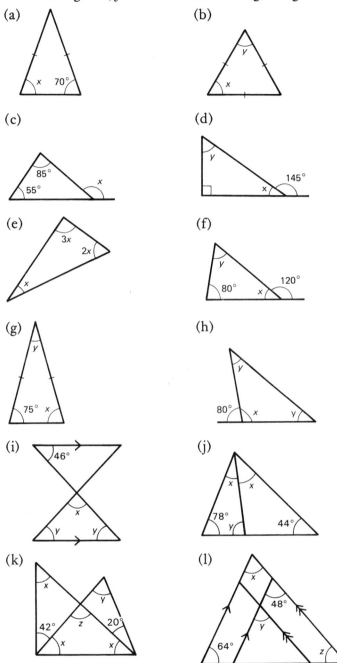

(a)

(b)

(c)

(d)

(e)

(f)

(g)

(h)

(i)

(j)

(k)

(l)

2. Find the area of a triangle of base length 5 cm and height 4 cm.

3. A triangle has area $18 \text{ cm}^2$ and height 3 cm. What is its base length?

4. A triangle has area 36 cm². If its base is 9 cm, what is its height?

5.

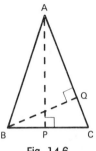

Fig. 14.6

In the triangle shown in Fig. 14.6, BC = 9 cm, BQ = 6 cm. Find the lengths of AP and AC, given that the area of the triangle is 54 cm².

6.

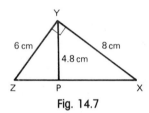

Fig. 14.7

In the triangle XYZ, $\hat{Y} = 90°$, XY = 8 cm and YZ = 6 cm. If YP = 4.8 cm, find the length of XZ.

7.

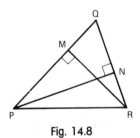

Fig. 14.8

In triangle PQR (Fig. 14.8), PQ = 12 cm, MR = 6 cm and PN = 9 cm. Find the length of QR.

8. Fig. 14.9 shows a rectangle ABCD in which $F\hat{C}D = 23°$. Find $x$ and $y$.

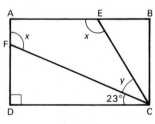

Fig. 14.9

## SIMILAR TRIANGLES

If two triangles are the same basic shape, but one is an enlargement of the other, they are said to be *similar*. Any pair of triangles with two corresponding angles equal must be similar. The lengths of corresponding sides of similar triangles are proportional to each other. For example, triangles ABC and DEF in Fig. 14.10 are similar.

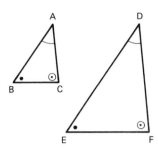

Fig. 14.10

$$\hat{A} = \hat{D}; \quad \hat{B} = \hat{E}; \quad \hat{C} = \hat{F}$$

and
$$\frac{AB}{DE} = \frac{AC}{DF} = \frac{BC}{EF} = k \quad \text{(the scale factor)}$$

The **area** scale factor is $k^2$ **(not $k$)**

$$\text{area } \triangle DEF = k^2 \times \text{area ABC}$$

**Example** Two triangles, ABC and XYZ (Fig. 14.11), are similar. If XY = 20 cm, find the lengths of the other two sides of XYZ.

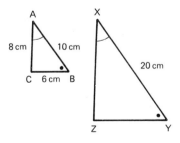

Fig. 14.11

Since $\dfrac{XY}{AB} = \dfrac{20}{10} = 2$ it follows that $\dfrac{YZ}{BC} = \dfrac{ZX}{CA} = 2$ (because $\triangle ABC$ is similar to $\triangle XYZ$), i.e. the other sides of XYZ are twice the length of the corresponding sides in ABC. Thus YZ = 12 cm and ZX = 16 cm.

207

**Example** Two lines, AB and CD, are parallel (Fig. 14.12). The diagonals, AD and CB, meet at X. Prove that the triangles AXB and CXD are similar. If $CD = 6$ cm, $AB = 4$ cm, $CX = 4\frac{1}{2}$ cm and $AX = 2$ cm, find BX and DX. If the area of triangle AXB is 4 cm², write down the area of $\triangle CXD$.

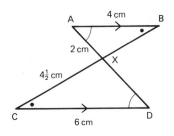

Fig. 14.12

$\hat{A} = \hat{D}$ (alternate) and $\hat{B} = \hat{C}$ (alternate).

So because the two triangles have two equal corresponding angles, AXB and DXC must be similar.

Redraw the triangles to make the correspondence between them clear. (Triangle AXB must be rotated by 180° to make obvious the correspondence between sides AX and DX, and between sides XC and BX — see Fig. 14.13).

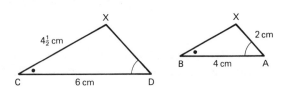

Fig. 14.13

$$\frac{CD}{BA} = \frac{6}{4} = \frac{3}{2}$$

Thus the scale factor, $k = \frac{3}{2}$. Hence

$$\frac{CX}{BX} = \frac{4\frac{1}{2}}{BX} = \frac{3}{2} \quad \text{giving} \quad BX = \frac{4\frac{1}{2} \times 2}{3} = 3 \text{ cm}$$

and $\quad \dfrac{DX}{AX} = \dfrac{DX}{2} = \dfrac{3}{2} \quad \text{giving} \quad DX = 2 \times \dfrac{3}{2} = 3 \text{ cm}$

Now if the scale factor is $\frac{3}{2}$, then the area factor is $(\frac{3}{2})^2 = \frac{9}{4}$. So if the smaller triangle has an area of 4 cm², then the larger one, $\triangle CXD$, has an area $\frac{9}{4} \times 4 = 9$ cm².

## PARALLEL DIVISION

From similar triangles we can deduce that a line parallel to one of the sides of a triangle will divide any lines it crosses, including the two sides, in the same ratio.

$$\frac{AP}{PB} = \frac{AQ}{QD} = \frac{AR}{RC}$$

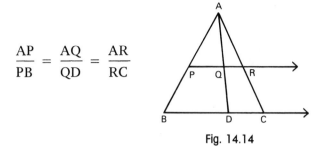

Fig. 14.14

## OTHER SHAPES

Similarity can be established with shapes other than triangles. The corresponding lengths will be related by a scale factor $k$, the areas by $k^2$ (*not k*) and, in the case of similar *objects*, the *volumes* will be related by $k^3$ (see Chapter 19).

**EXERCISE 14b**　1. Triangles ABC and PQR are similar. Given the lengths shown in Fig. 14.15, find the scale factor and hence calculate the lengths $x$ and $y$.

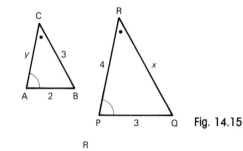

Fig. 14.15

2.

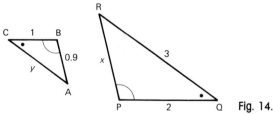

Fig. 14.16

The two triangles, ABC and PQR, shown in Fig. 14.16, are similar. First, redraw the triangles so that the positions of corresponding sides match each other. Find the scale factor and hence calculate $x$ and $y$.

In Questions **3** to **14**, the pairs of triangles are similar. In each case find the scale factor and calculate the lengths $x$ and $y$. (Remember, it may be necessary to redraw the triangles so that the positions of corresponding sides match each other.)

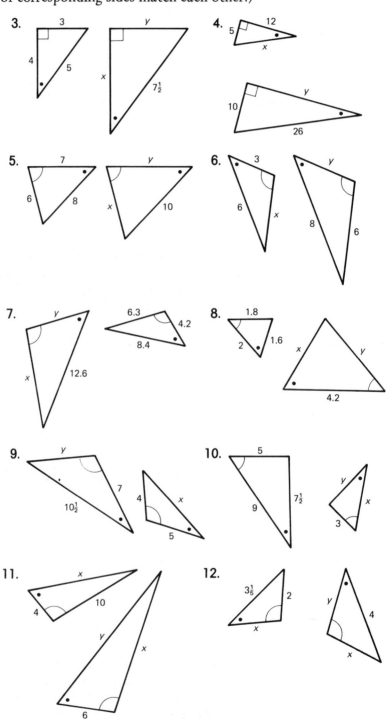

**3.**

**4.**

**5.**

**6.**

**7.**

**8.**

**9.**

**10.**

**11.**

**12.**

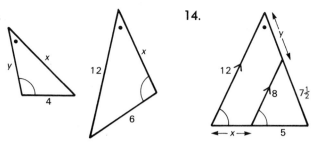

**13.**  **14.**

**15.** A triangle ABC as shown is divided by a line MN parallel to BC such that AM : MB = 4 : 5.

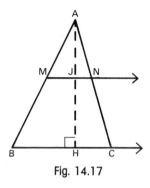

Fig. 14.17

(a) Prove that triangle ABC and AMN are similar.

(b) If AB is 18 cm, find MB.

(c) If AN is 6 cm, find NC.

(d) If MN crosses the line AH at J write down the ratio AJ : JH.

**16.** The scale factor between two similar triangles is 1 : 3. What is the ratio of their areas?

**17.** Two similar triangles have areas in the ratio 16 : 9. What is the ratio of the lengths of their corresponding sides?

**18.**

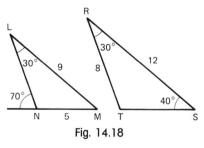

Fig. 14.18

Prove that the triangles LMN and RST in Fig. 14.18 are similar, with a scale factor of 3 : 4. Find the lengths of LN and ST. Find the area of triangle RST, given that the area of LMN is 18 square units.

**19.**

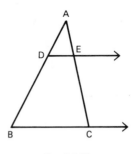

Fig. 14.19

Prove that triangles ADE and ABC, shown in Fig. 14.19, are similar. If AD = 3 cm, AE = $2\frac{3}{4}$ cm, DB = 6 cm and BC = 6 cm, find the lengths of DE and EC.

Given that the area of ADE is $2\frac{3}{4}$ cm² find the area of ABC. Hence show that the area of the quadrilateral, DBCE is 22 cm².

**20.**

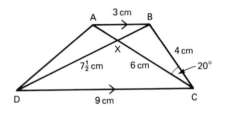

Fig. 14.20

Figure 14.20 shows a trapezium, ABCD, with AB‖CD. Prove that the triangles ABX and DXC are similar. Calculate the lengths of AX and BX.

**21.**

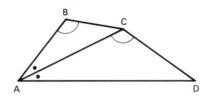

Fig. 14.21

In the quadrilateral ABCD shown in Fig. 14.21, the diagonal AC bisects BÂD and AB̂C = AĈD. If AB = 8 cm, BC = 6 cm and AC = 12 cm, find the lengths of CD and AD.

The area of triangle ACD is 90 cm²; what are the areas of the triangle ABC and the quadrilateral ABCD?

# CONGRUENT TRIANGLES

Congruent triangles are the same shape (as are similar triangles) but they are also the same *size* as each other. (Congruent triangles can be considered a special case of similar triangles in which the scale factor, $k$, is one.) There are four conditions that will prove a pair of triangles to be congruent.

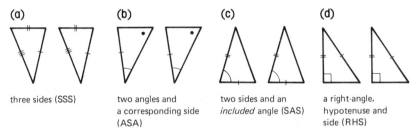

(a) three sides (SSS)

(b) two angles and a corresponding side (ASA)

(c) two sides and an *included* angle (SAS)

(d) a right-angle, hypotenuse and side (RHS)

Fig. 14.22

**Example** Use congruent triangles to prove that the bisector of the odd angle of an isosceles triangle meets the opposite side at its mid-point and at right angles. (A 'bisector' cuts a line or an angle in half.)

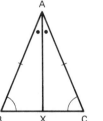

Fig. 14.23

In triangles BAX and CAX (Fig. 14.23), $\widehat{BAX} = \widehat{CAX}$ (AX is the angle bisector), $\widehat{B} = \widehat{C}$ ($\triangle ABC$ is an isosceles triangle) and AX is a common side. Thus triangles BAX and CAX are congruent (by condition (b) in Fig. 14.22 – ASA).

Hence BX = CX, so X is the mid-point of BC. Also, $\widehat{BXA} = \widehat{CXA}$ but $\widehat{BXA} + \widehat{CXA} = 180°$ (angles on a straight line), so $\widehat{BXA} = \widehat{CXA} = 90°$.

**EXERCISE 14c**  1. Give reasons for the following pairs of triangles to be congruent:

(a)

(b)

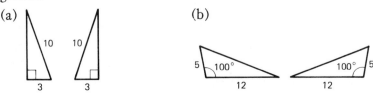

213

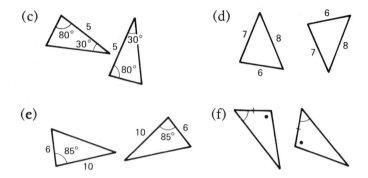

2. OAB and OCD are two triangles drawn within a circle, centre O, as shown in Fig. 14.24. Prove that the triangles are congruent.

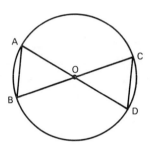

Fig. 14.24

3. A rectangle, ABCD, is divided by the diagonal AC and then by diagonal BD. Prove that triangle ABC is congruent to triangle BCD. Hence deduce that the diagonals of a rectangle are equal in length.

4.

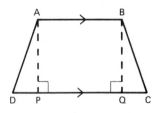

Fig. 14.25

In Fig. 14.25, ABCD is an isosceles trapezium, with AB∥CD and AD = BC. AP and BQ are drawn perpendicular to DC. Prove that triangles APD and BCQ are congruent and hence deduce that $\hat{D} = \hat{C}$.

**5.**

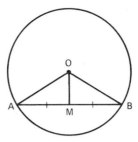

Fig. 14.26

AB is a chord of a circle, and the mid-point of the chord, M, is joined to the centre O of the circle (Fig. 14.26). Prove that triangles OAM and OBM are congruent and hence deduce that OM cuts AB at right angles.

**6.**

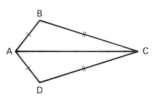

Fig. 14.27

Figure 14.27 shows a kite, ABCD, with AB = AD and CB = CD. Show that triangles ABC and ADC are congruent, and hence deduce that $\hat{B} = \hat{D}$.

**7.**

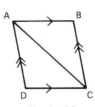

Fig. 14.28

ABCD is a parallelogram, cut by the diagonal AC, as shown in Fig. 14.28. By proving that triangles ABC and ADC are congruent, deduce that, in a parallelogram

(a) opposite sides are equal

(b) opposite angles are equal.

**8.**

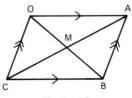

Fig. 14.29

The parallelogram OABC shown in Fig. 14.29 is divided into four triangles by its diagonals OB and AC. The diagonals meet at M. Show that triangles OMA and CBM are congruent and so deduce that M is the mid-point of OB.

9.

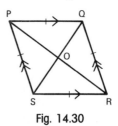

Fig. 14.30

PQRS is a rhombus, that is PQ∥RS, QR∥SP and all four sides are equal (Fig. 14.30). Show that the four triangles OPQ, OQR, ORS and OSP are all congruent. Hence deduce that the diagonals, PR and SQ, cut at right angles.

10.

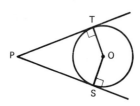

Fig. 14.31

Two lines are drawn from a point P to touch a circle, centre O, at T and S (see Fig. 14.31). The radius OT meets PT at right angles, and the radius OS meets PS at right angles. Use congruent triangles to prove that PT = PS.

## MISCELLANEOUS EXERCISE 14

1.

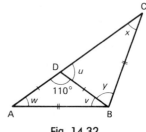

Fig. 14.32

ABC is an isosceles triangle with AB = BC. D is a point on AC such that AD = DB and $A\hat{D}B = 110°$. Calculate the sizes of the angles marked, $u, v, w, x, y$.　　　　(WJEC)

**2.**

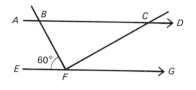

Fig. 14.33

ABCD and EFG are two parallel straight lines with BF and FC two transversals (Fig. 14.33). $B\hat{F}E = 60°$ and $B\hat{C}F : F\hat{C}D = 1:5$.
Calculate the value of $A\hat{B}F$, $B\hat{C}F$, $C\hat{F}G$ and $B\hat{F}C$.　　(WJEC)

**3.**

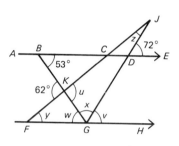

Fig. 14.34

ABCDE and FGH are two parallel straight lines with transversals BKG, FKCJ and GDJ (Fig. 14.34). $J\hat{D}E = 72°$, $K\hat{B}C = 53°$ and $B\hat{K}F = 62°$. Calculate the size of the angles marked $u, v, w, x, y$ and $z$.　　(WJEC)

**4.**

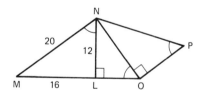

Fig. 14.35

Triangles LMN, LNO and NOP in Fig. 14.35 are all similar. Write down the ratios

(a) MN : NO : NP

(b) area LMN : area LNO : area NOP.

**5.** ABCD is a square of area 64 cm². M, N, P and Q are the midpoints of the sides. The diagonal AC meets MQ at R, as shown in Fig. 14.36.

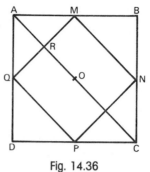

Fig. 14.36

Calculate the area of the following triangles:

(a) ABC       (b) BMN       (c) ARQ.

6. Each of the following diagrams shows a rectangle ABCD with S and T as the mid-points of BC and CD respectively.

In each of the following write down the fraction of the whole rectangle which is shaded. Give each answer in its simplest form.

(a) 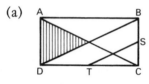       (b)

(c) 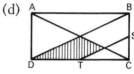       (d)

Fig. 14.37           (WMEB)

7.

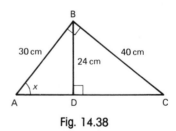

Fig. 14.38

In triangle ABC (Fig. 14.38), $\widehat{B} = 90°$. A perpendicular is dropped from B to a point D on AC, as shown. Show that triangles ABC, ABD and BDC are all similar to each other.

Use similarity to find the lengths AD and DC, given that AB = 30 cm, BC = 40 cm and BD = 24 cm.

218

8. Two lines, AB and CD, intersect at X such that $AX = CX$ and $BX = DX$. Prove that $AC \| DB$.

9.

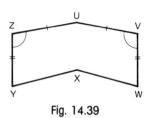

Fig. 14.39

UVWXYZ is an irregular hexagon, as shown in Fig. 14.39. $UV = UZ$; $VW = YZ$; $U\hat{Z}Y = U\hat{V}W$. Prove that $UY = UW$. If, further, $X\hat{U}W = X\hat{U}Y$, show that $WX = XY$, and that UX is a line of symmetry.

10. P, Q and R are three points on a circle, centre O, such that $PQ = QR$. Prove that $O\hat{Q}P = O\hat{Q}R$.

11.

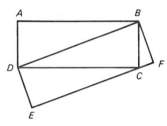

Fig. 14.40

$ABCD$ and $BDEF$ are rectangles (Fig. 14.40). $ECF$ is a straight line. Prove that
(a) angle $ADB$ = angle $CDE$;
(b) triangles $ABD$, $ECD$, $FBC$ are similar;
(c) the rectangles are equal in area;
(d) $\dfrac{EC}{CF} = \dfrac{AB^2}{AD^2}$. (Ox)

12.

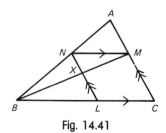

Fig. 14.41

In the diagram (Fig. 14.41), $NM$ is parallel to $BC$, and $NL$ is parallel to $AC$. Prove that $\triangle ANM$ is similar to $\triangle NBL$.

219

Given that $\dfrac{AN}{NB} = \dfrac{2}{3}$, calculate the numerical value of the ratios

(a) $\dfrac{\text{area of } \triangle ANM}{\text{area of } \triangle NBL}$

(b) $\dfrac{NM}{BC}$

(c) $\dfrac{\text{area of trapezium } BNMC}{\text{area of } \triangle ABC}$

(d) $\dfrac{NX}{MC}$.

(C)

13.

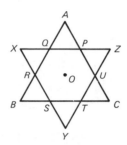

Fig. 14.42

The diagram (Fig. 14.42) shows a six-pointed star which is formed by drawing an equilateral triangle on each side of the regular hexagon $PQRSTU$. The centre of the hexagon is $O$.

(a) Prove that $\triangle XYZ$ is congruent to $\triangle ABC$.

(b) Show that the area of the six-pointed star is twice the area of the hexagon $PQRSTU$.

(c) If $OA$ is drawn from $O$ perpendicular to $QP$ to meet $QP$ at $N$, find the value of the ratio $\dfrac{ON}{OA}$.

(d) Find the value of the ratio

$$\dfrac{\text{area of circle } AXBYCZ}{\text{area of circle inscribed in hexagon } PQRSTU}.$$

(The inscribed circle is that which touches each side of the hexagon.)

(LU)

14.

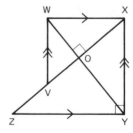

Fig. 14.43

In Fig. 14.43, $VW \parallel XY$ and $WX \parallel YZ$. $W\hat{O}X = X\hat{Y}Z = 90°$.

(a) Show that the six triangles OVW, OWX, OXY, OYZ, XYZ and VWX are all similar to each other.

(b) If $OY = 48$ cm and $OZ = 64$ cm, find the area of triangle XYZ and the length of OV.

220

# 15 QUADRILATERALS AND OTHER POLYGONS

Any four-sided figure is a *quadrilateral*. For any quadrilateral the sum of the interior angles is 360° (Fig. 15.1).

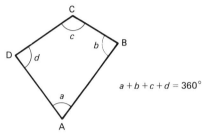

$$a + b + c + d = 360°$$

Fig. 15.1

Some quadrilaterals have special properties — usually because one pair (or both pairs) of sides are parallel.

## TRAPEZIUMS

A trapezium has *one* pair of parallel sides (see Fig. 15.2). The area of a trapezium is the *average* of the parallel sides × the perpendicular distance between them.

$$A = \left(\frac{a + b}{2}\right) \times h$$

An *isosceles* trapezium has one pair of parallel sides and the other pair of sides equal in length (Fig. 15.3). The upper pair of interior angles are equal and so are the lower pair. Moreover, an upper and a lower angle add up to 180°, and the diagonals are equal in length.

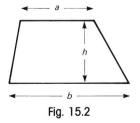

Fig. 15.2

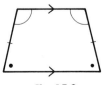

Fig. 15.3

221

# PARALLELOGRAMS

A parallelogram is a quadrilateral with *both* pairs of sides parallel (Fig. 15.4). Its properties are:

- opposite sides are parallel
- opposite sides are equal in length
- opposite angles are equal
- the diagonals bisect each other
- each diagonal bisects the area (into two congruent triangles)
- the area of a parallelogram is given by

$$A = \text{base} \times \text{perpendicular height}$$

Fig. 15.4

## Rectangles

A rectangle is a special parallelogram in which adjacent sides are at right angles to each other (Fig. 15.5). The properties of a rectangle are those of a parallelogram *plus*

- the diagonals are of equal length.

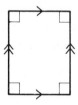

Fig. 15.5

## Rhombuses

A rhombus (Fig. 15.6) is a special parallelogram in which all sides are equal in length. Its properties are those of a parallelogram *plus*

- the diagonals cut at right angles
- the diagonals bisect the interior angles

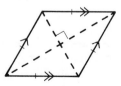

Fig. 15.6

# Squares

A square is a parallelogram that is both a rectangle *and* a rhombus (Fig. 15.7). It has all the properties of those shapes. Its area is, of course, the square of one side.

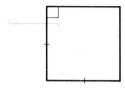

**Fig. 15.7**

The Venn diagram in Fig. 15.8 illustrates the relationships between these special parallelograms.

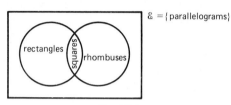

**Fig. 15.8**

# KITES

A kite has *no* parallel sides but has two pairs of adjacent sides of equal length (Fig. 15.9).

The diagonals of a kite meet at right angles.

The area of a kite can be found by multiplying together the lengths of the two diagonals and dividing by 2.

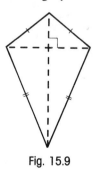

**Fig. 15.9**

# CYCLIC QUADRILATERALS

Any figure that fits exactly inside a circle is called *cyclic*. *All* triangles are cyclic, but *not* all quadrilaterals are. For a

223

quadrilateral to be cyclic, its opposite angles must add up to 180°
(Fig. 15.10).

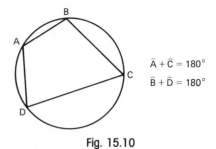

$$\hat{A} + \hat{C} = 180°$$
$$\hat{B} + \hat{D} = 180°$$

Fig. 15.10

All rectangles, squares and isosceles trapeziums are cyclic. Parallelograms and ordinary trapeziums are not. A kite may or may not be
cyclic; if it is, then it must contain two right angles opposite each
other, as shown in Fig. 15.11.

**Cyclic**

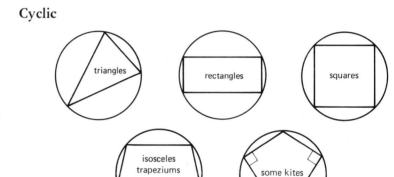

**Non-cyclic**

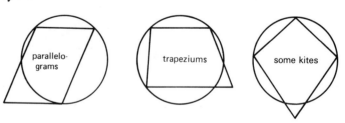

Fig. 15.11

**EXERCISE 15a** In Questions 1 to 9, find the angles marked $x$ and $y$.

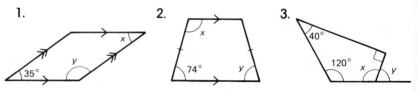

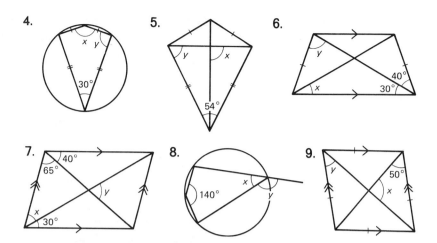

10. The table gives the characteristics of special quadrilaterals that have opposite sides equal and parallel. In each case, write down the type of quadrilateral. (WJEC)

| Diagonals | Adjacent sides | Name of quadrilateral |
|---|---|---|
| unequal | unequal | |
| equal | unequal | |
| unequal | equal | |
| equal | equal | |

11. Find the areas of the following quadrilaterals:

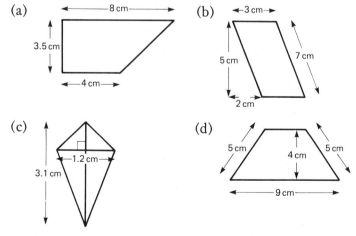

12. A parallelogram has an area of 18 cm²; its base is 6 cm long. What is the height of the parallelogram? Is it possible to find the slant height of the parallelogram from this information?

13. A quadrilateral is formed by joining the points A(2, 1), B(8, 4), C(8, 7) and D(5, 7). Plot the points A, B, C and D and identify the type of quadrilateral. Calculate the area ABCD.

14.

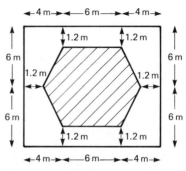

Fig. 15.12

In Fig. 15.12, which is not drawn to scale, the shaded area represents a flower bed surrounded by a path. Find the area of the flower bed. (Ox)

15.

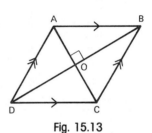

Fig. 15.13

The diagonals of a parallelogram ABCD meet at right angles at O (Fig. 15.13).

Use congruent triangles to prove that AD = AB, and hence that ABCD is a rhombus.

16. If, in Fig. 15.13, AO = OD, prove that ABCD is a square.

17.

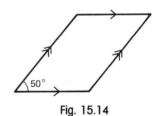

Fig. 15.14

A parallelogram includes an angle of 50° as shown in Fig. 15.14. Prove that the parallelogram cannot be cyclic.

18. Prove that a cyclic rhombus must be a square.

**19.**

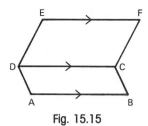

Fig. 15.15

Figure 15.15 shows two parallelograms, ABCD and CDEF, that share the side CD. Copy the diagram and add the diagonals AF and BE. Prove that these diagonals bisect each other.

**20.** In a quadrilateral, PQRS, it is known that PQ∥RS. If the diagonal PR bisects the angle SPQ and other diagonal, SQ, bisects angle PSR, prove that PQRS is a rhombus.

**21.** & = {all quadrilaterals}, P = {parallelograms}, C = {cyclic quadrilaterals}. Name and draw a member of

(a) $P \cap C$     (b) $P' \cap C$     (c) $P' \cap C'$

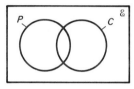

Fig. 15.16

Figure 15.16 shows a Venn diagram with sets P and C. Copy the diagram and add to your figure the sets S = {squares} and K = {kites}.

**22.** How many squares can be found on a chess board? (There are considerably more than 64!)

**23.**

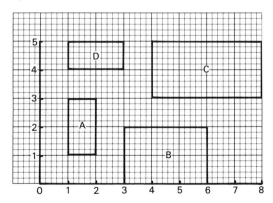

Fig. 15.17

(a) Which rectangle is congruent to A?

(b) Which rectangle is similar but not congruent to A?

(ALSEB)

227

## OTHER POLYGONS

A five-sided figure is called a *pentagon*; a six-sided figure is a *hexagon*; an eight-sided figure is an *octagon*. Many-sided figures are referred to in general as *polygons*. A *regular* polygon is one with all its sides equal in length and its angles equal to one another.

The sum of all the exterior angles of a polygon is 360° (Fig. 15.18).

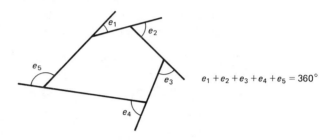

$$e_1 + e_2 + e_3 + e_4 + e_5 = 360°$$

Fig. 15.18

The sum of all the interior angles depends upon the number of sides, $n$, and is $(2n - 4)$ right angles. If the polygon is regular, then each of the $n$ equal angles must be $\dfrac{2n - 4}{n}$ right angles.

**Example**  Find the interior angle of a regular decagon.
A decagon has ten sides; hence $n = 10$. Each angle is

$$\frac{(2 \times 10) - 4}{10} \times 90° = \frac{16}{10} \times 90° = 144°$$

**EXERCISE 15b**  1. A farmer walks around the perimeter of his field, starting from the gate at G (Fig. 15.19). Given the angles on the diagram, through what angle must he turn at F?

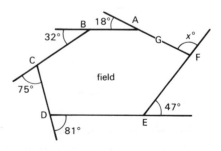

Fig. 15.19

228

2. Fig. 15.20 shows three regular figures — a square, a regular pentagon and a regular hexagon. What does the description *regular* mean?

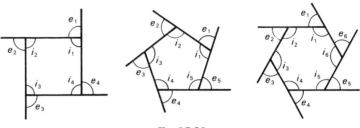

Fig. 15.20

What can you say about the exterior angles (marked *e* in the diagrams) of any regular polygon?

Given that the sum of the exterior angles of any polygon is 360°, write down the values of the exterior angles for each of the figures shown and hence deduce the values of their interior angles (marked *i* in the diagrams).

What would be the exterior angle of

(a) a regular octagon (8 sides),

(b) a regular nonagon (9 sides),

(c) a regular decagon (10 sides).

What would be the value of the interior angles of these shapes?

Write down the values of the exterior and interior angles of a regular shape with *n* sides.

3. Figure 15.21 shows an irregular pentagon ABCDE divided into three triangles ABC, ACD and ADE. What is the sum of the interior angles of each triangle? Deduce the sum of the interior angles of the pentagon.

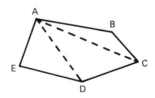

Fig. 15.21

4. Draw an irregular hexagon and divide it into triangles like the pentagon in Question 3. How many triangles are there? Deduce the sum of the interior angles of the hexagon.

5. What is the sum of all seven interior angles of a heptagon? If the heptagon is regular, what is the size of each angle?

6. What is the sum of all eight interior angles of an octagon? If the octagon is regular, what is the size of each angle?

7. By what name is a regular quadrilateral better known?

8.

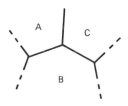

Fig. 15.22

Figure 15.22 shows the meeting point of three regular polygons, A, B and C, that form part of an interlocking pattern. A and B have the same number of sides.

(a) If A and B both have eight sides, how many sides has C?

(b) If C has ten sides, how many sides each have A and B?

9. The interior angles of an irregular pentagon are in the ratio $3:4:5:7:8$. What are its interior angles, in degrees?

10. The interior angles of an irregular hexagon are in the ratio $4:3:2:4:3:4$.

(a) What are its interior angles?

(b) What is the ratio of its *exterior* angles?

11. The interior angles of a straight-sided shape make a total of $1980°$. How many sides does it have?

12. A regular figure has an interior angle equal to $156°$. How many sides does it have?

13. The diagram (Fig. 15.23) which is not drawn to scale, shows two regular hexagons joined along the line PS. Calculate the size, in degrees, of angle PQR.

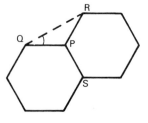

Fig. 15.23                                    (EMREB)

14. How many diagonals has an $n$-sided polygon? Investigate. Can you find the general formulae.

# 16 SYMMETRY

## LINE SYMMETRY

If a figure can be drawn on paper in such a way that if the paper is folded in half the two halves of the figure exactly cover each other, then the shape is symmetric. The line of fold is called the *axis of symmetry*. For example, a kite can be folded down the middle; the two halves cover each other exactly (Fig. 16.1).

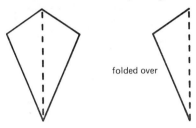

folded over

Fig. 16.1

Alternatively, we might imagine a mirror has been placed along the axis of symmetry. The image in the mirror looks exactly like the hidden half; with the half still showing, we can still 'see' the original shape (Fig. 16.2).

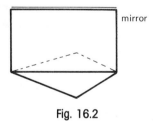

mirror

Fig. 16.2

It follows that irregular figures with no equal sides or angles cannot possibly have symmetry.

The kite shown in Fig. 16.1 has one axis of symmetry. An isosceles triangle also has one axis of symmetry, whereas an equilateral triangle has three axes of symmetry (see Fig. 16.3).

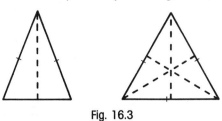

Fig. 16.3

Fig. 16.4

Trapeziums generally have no axes of symmetry, although an isosceles trapezium has one (Fig. 16.4). Parallelograms generally have no axes of symmetry either, although a rectangle has two, a rhombus has two (the diagonals) and a square (being both a rhombus and a rectangle) has four (Fig, 16.5).

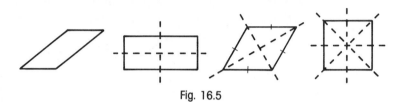

Fig. 16.5

## PLANE SYMMETRY

Three-dimensional objects may also display reflection symmetry. But as they are objects, they cannot be reflected in a line: they *must* be reflected in a plane mirror — hence *plane symmetry* — that would 'slice' through their centre. For example, the pyramid shown in Fig. 16.6 has plane symmetry.

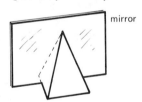

Fig. 16.6

## ROTATIONAL SYMMETRY

If a shape can be turned round and yet appear not to have been changed in any way, it is said to have *rotational symmetry*. For example, an equilateral triangle could be turned around its centre by $120°$ and appear to be in the same position (Fig. 16.7(a)). Of course, if we label the corners A, B and C, then the change is apparent (Fig. 16.7(b)).

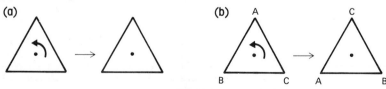

Fig. 16.7

232

We could rotate the triangle through 120° twice more (making three possible turns) before the triangle resumes its original position. Thus an equilateral triangle is said to have *rotational symmetry of order three* (Fig. 16.8).

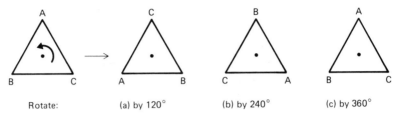

Fig. 16.8

Parallelograms (including rectangles and rhombuses) can be rotated by 180° and appear unchanged. Again, if we label the corners, the change is apparent, as in Fig. 16.9. A shape that can be turned through 180° and still look the same is said to have *point symmetry*. Notice that a second turn of 180° (i.e. a total turn of 360°) restores the parallelogram to its original position. Thus the parallelogram has rotational symmetry of order two (Fig. 16.10).

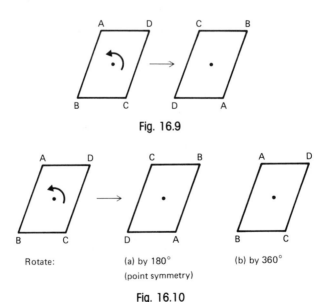

Fig. 16.9

Fig. 16.10

A square has rotational symmetry of order four (Fig. 16.11). Kites and trapeziums have no point symmetry (they are clearly 'upside down' when rotated by 180° — see Fig. 16.12). However, they appear unchanged if rotated by 360° (as does any figure) so they have rotational symmetry of order one.

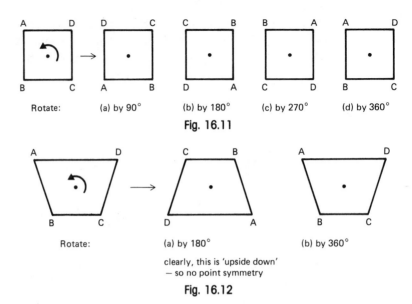

Rotate:    (a) by 90°    (b) by 180°    (c) by 270°    (d) by 360°

**Fig. 16.11**

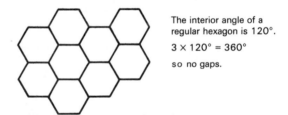

Rotate:    (a) by 180°    (b) by 360°

clearly, this is 'upside down'
— so no point symmetry

**Fig. 16.12**

## TESSELLATIONS

Polygons that fit together to fill the page without gaps are said to *tessellate*.

For example, regular hexagons fit together to form a *tessellation*:

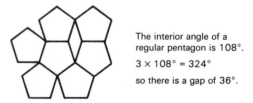

The interior angle of a regular hexagon is 120°.

$3 \times 120° = 360°$

so no gaps.

**Fig. 16.13**

However, regular pentagons do not:

The interior angle of a regular pentagon is 108°.

$3 \times 108° = 324°$

so there is a gap of 36°.

**Fig. 16.14**

All quadrilaterals (including irregular ones) will tessellate and so will all triangles, since it is always possible to fit them together to make an angle of 360°.

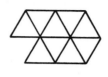

Fig. 16.15

It is also possible to tessellate some three dimensional shapes.

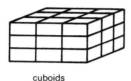

cuboids

hexagonal prisms

Fig. 16.16

## MISCELLANEOUS EXERCISE 16

1. Copy the following figures and show with broken lines any axes of symmetry.

(a)   (b)   (c)   (d)

(e)   (f)   (g)   (h)

(i)   (j)   (k)   (l)

2. Which of the figures in Question 1 have rotational symmetry (other than rotation by 360°)? For each shape write down its order of rotational symmetry.

3. Which shapes in Question 1 have point symmetry?

4. Name and draw two quadrilaterals with exactly one axis of symmetry.

5. Name and draw two quadrilaterals with exactly two axes of symmetry.

6. A quadrilateral has two pairs of equal sides but no axis of symmetry. What must it be?

235

7. A quadrilateral has two pairs of equal sides and two axes of symmetry. What must it be?

8. In the drawings below, lines of symmetry are shown as broken lines. Copy and complete the figures.

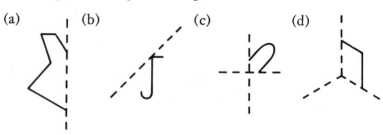

(a)  (b)  (c)  (d)

9.

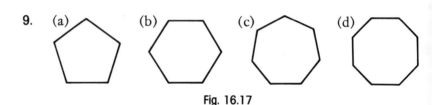

(a)  (b)  (c)  (d)

Fig. 16.17

Figure 16.17 shows the outlines of
(a) a regular pentagon
(b) a regular hexagon
(c) a regular heptagon
(d) a regular octagon.

For each shape:
(i) copy the outline and mark on it, as a broken line, all the axes of symmetry.
(ii) write down the number of sides, the number of axes of symmetry, and the order of rotational symmetry.
(iii) Which of these shapes have point symmetry?
(iv) Which will tessellate?

10. (a) From the word

E X A C T

write down all the letters that have
(i) a vertical line of symmetry
(ii) a horizontal line of symmetry
(iii) point symmetry.

(b)

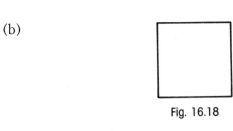

Fig. 16.18

Draw all the lines of symmetry for this square (Fig. 16.18) in the plane of the paper. (AEB '81)

11. Why do ambulances have these letters painted on the front?

ƎƆИA⅃UꓭMA

Which letters of the word AMBULANCE have
(a) a vertical line of symmetry
(b) a horizontal line of symmetry
(c) point symmetry?

12. The sets $C$, $P$ and $S$ are given as follows:
$$C = \{\text{cyclic quadrilaterals}\}$$
$$P = \{\text{quadrilaterals with point symmetry}\}$$
$$S = \{\text{quadrilaterals with exactly two axes of symmetry}\}$$
Name and draw a shape that is a member of
(a) $C \cap S$    (b) $C \cap S'$    (c) $C' \cap P$    (d) $C \cap P$
(e) $P \cap S$.

13. How many planes of symmetry has a
(a) cube    (b) cuboid    (c) cone?

14. Why is it only possible to tessellate polygons whose interior angles may be combined to make an angle of $360°$?

15. Draw any irregular quadrilateral of your own design. Show that it tessellates. (You may find a piece of tracing paper helpful.)

16. Repeat question 15 for any triangle.

17. Show that regular octagons do not tessellate.

18. Show, by drawing the shapes several times and using a cardboard template if necessary, that each of the following will tessellate.

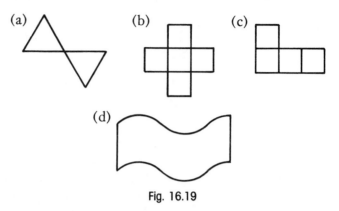

Fig. 16.19

19. Which of the following will tessellate?

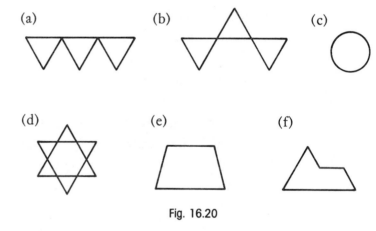

Fig. 16.20

20. It is said that only three regular polygons tesselate. Investigate.

21. Do these irregular pentagons tessellate? How might you tell *without* drawing them out? Will the lengths of the sides matter? Investigate.

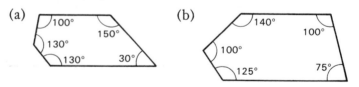

# 17 PYTHAGORAS' THEOREM AND TRIGONOMETRY

The longest side in a right-angled triangle is always opposite the right-angle; it is called the *hypotenuse*.

## PYTHAGORAS' THEOREM FOR RIGHT-ANGLED TRIANGLES

The square of the hypotenuse of a right-angled triangle is equal to the sum of the squares of the other two sides.

$$a^2 + b^2 = c^2$$

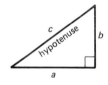

Fig. 17.1

Remember, Pythagoras' theorem *only* applies to *right-angled triangles*: it is *not true* of other triangles.

The reverse or *converse* also applies: if $a^2 + b^2 = c^2$ then the triangle must be right-angled.

**Example** Find the hypotenuse of a right-angled triangle with sides of length 3 cm and 5 cm (Fig. 17.2).

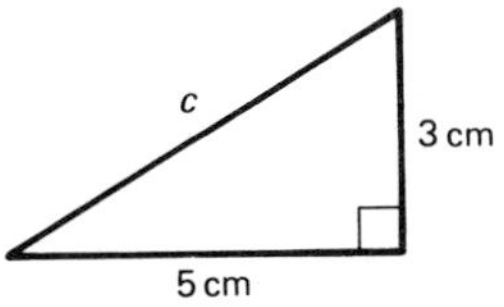

Fig. 17.2

$$a^2 + b^2 = 3^2 + 5^2$$
$$= 9 + 25$$
$$= 34 \ = c^2$$

So
$$c = \sqrt{34} = 5.83 \text{ cm}$$

239

**Example** A right-angled triangle has a hypotenuse of length 13 cm and a second side of length 5 cm. What is the length of the third side?

**Fig. 17.3**

Using Pythagoras' theorem (refer also to Fig. 17.3):

$$a^2 + b^2 = c^2$$
$$5^2 + b^2 = 13^2$$
$$25 + b^2 = 169$$

So
$$b^2 = 169 - 25 = 144$$
$$b = 12 \text{ cm}$$

The third side is 12 cm long.

**EXERCISE 17a**    1. Use Pythagoras' theorem to find the length of the side marked $x$ in the following triangles:

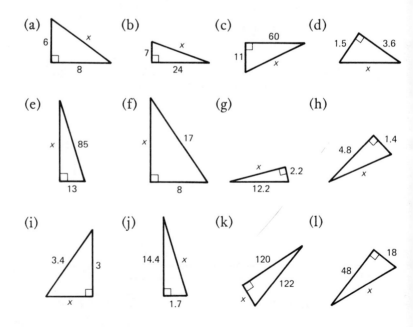

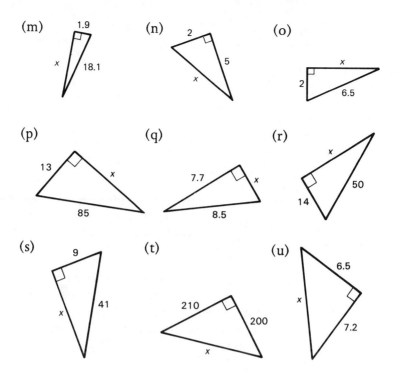

2. A rectangle ABCD has side lengths AB = 6.3 cm and AD = 8.4 cm. Find the length of the diagonal AC.

3. A square has sides of 5 cm. Find, to three significant figures, the length of the diagonals.

4. The diagonals of a rectangle are 6.5 cm long. If one pair of sides are 2.5 cm long, how long are the other two sides?

5.

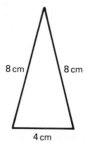

Fig. 17.4

An isosceles triangle has sides 8 cm, 8 cm and 4 cm (Fig. 17.4). Use Pythagoras' theorem to find its height, and hence find its area, to 3 s.f.

**6.**

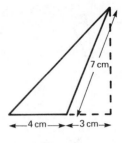

Fig. 17.5

A triangle ABC has sides of length 4 cm and 7 cm as shown in Fig. 17.5. If it overhangs its base by 3 cm, find its area to the nearest square centimetre.

7. A tent pole is supported by two guy ropes, one each side. If the pole is 1 m high and the ropes are each 150 cm long when fully stretched, how far from the foot of the pole must they be fixed into the ground? Give your answer to the nearest centimetre.

8. A dustbin is 1 m high and 60 cm across. What is the length, in centimetres, of the longest stick that can be put in it, if the lid is to fit on top?

9. Copy the diagram in Fig. 17.6. Mark in the lengths $a$ and $b$ indicated.

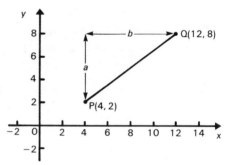

Fig. 17.6

Use Pythagoras' theorem to find the length of the line PQ.

10. Plot the following pairs of points on graph paper. (You will need a range from −10 to +10 on the horizontal axis and from −10 to +15 on the vertical axis.) Join each pair of points with a straight line.

Use Pythagoras' theorem to calculate the length of each line.

(a) A(5, 6) and B(8, 10)

(b) C(4, 1) and D(9, 13)

(c) E(2, 0) and F(10, 15)

(d) G(3, −10) and H(10, 14)

(e) J(−5, −10) and K(15, 11)

(f) L(−8, −7) and M(0, 8)

11.

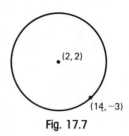

Fig. 17.7

A circle is drawn on graph paper. If its centre is at the point (2, 2) and it passes through the point (14, − 3) (see Fig. 17.7), what is its radius?

12. A quadrilateral ABCD is formed by joining the points A(− 5, − 3), B(4, 9), C(19, 9) and D(10, − 3). Prove that the four sides are of equal length and hence that ABCD is a rhombus.

13.

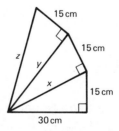

Fig. 17.8

Calculate the distances $x$, $y$ and $z$ in Fig. 17.8. Give your answers in centimetres to 1 d.p.

14. Fig. 17.9 shows the framework of a rectangular wooden gate.

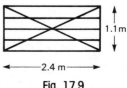

Fig. 17.9

Calculate the length of wood required to build it.

**15.** By substituting $p = 2, 3, 4, \ldots$ and $q = 1, 2, 3, \ldots$ extend the following table. What do you notice about the three last columns?

| $p$ | $q$ | $2pq$ | $p^2 - q^2$ | $p^2 + q^2$ |
|---|---|---|---|---|
| 2 | 1 | 4 | 3 | 5 |
| 3 | 1 | 6 | 8 | 10 |
| 3 | 2 | 12 | 5 | 13 |
| 4 | 1 | 8 | 15 | 17 |
| 4 | 2 | 16 | . | . |
| 4 | 3 | 24 | . | . |
| 5 | 1 | . | . | . |
| . | 2 | . |   |   |
| . | . | . |   |   |
| . | . | . |   |   |
|   | . |   |   |   |

Show algebraically that $(p^2 - q^2)^2 + (2pq)^2 = (p^2 + q^2)^2$.

## SINES, COSINES AND TANGENTS

All right-angled triangles with a second angle, say $x$, in common must be similar to each other (see Chapter 14) though they may be quite different in size (Fig. 17.10).

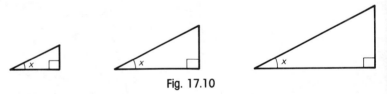

Fig. 17.10

The ratios of corresponding sides in all such right-angled triangles will be equal. Taking the side next to the angle $x$ as the 'adjacent', the other side as the 'opposite', and the longest side the hypotenuse we can define three ratios:

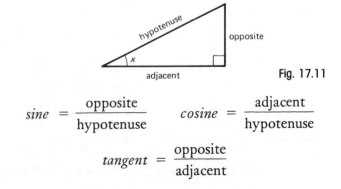

Fig. 17.11

$$sine = \frac{opposite}{hypotenuse} \qquad cosine = \frac{adjacent}{hypotenuse}$$

$$tangent = \frac{opposite}{adjacent}$$

We write for short:

$$\sin x = \frac{o}{h} \qquad \cos x = \frac{a}{h} \qquad \tan x = \frac{o}{a}$$

These ratios must be memorised. It might help to run the letters, $s = \dfrac{o}{h}$, $c = \dfrac{a}{h}$, $t = \dfrac{o}{a}$, together to make the word SOH-CAH-TOA (pronounced 'so-car-toe-ah'), reputedly the name of an Indian Chief!

The actual value of these ratios depends upon the angle $x$; for different values of $x$, the ratios will be different.

For any given angle the values of the sine, cosine and tangent can be found from a scientific calculator. For example, $\sin 30° = 0.5$. This means that, in any *right-angled* triangle that contains an angle of $30°$ (and therefore a $60°$ angle, too), the side opposite the $30°$ angle is half the length of the hypotenuse (see Fig. 17.12).

So if the opposite side is 1 cm long, the hypotenuse is 2 cm; if the opposite side is 2 cm, the hypotenuse is 4 cm; if the opposite side is $2\frac{1}{2}$ cm, the hypotenuse is 5 cm, and so on.

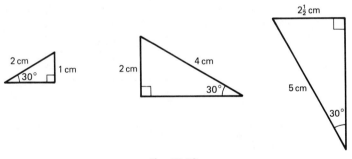

Fig. 17.12

# SOLUTION OF RIGHT-ANGLED TRIANGLES

**Example** In the right-angled triangle ABC in Fig. 17.13, $\widehat{A} = 30°$ and AB = 8 cm. Find the length of BC.

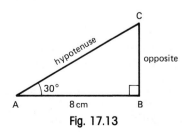

Fig. 17.13

245

To find the length of the opposite side, i.e. BC, given the length of the adjacent side, AB, we need to use the ratio that links the two, i.e.

$$\text{tangent} = \frac{\text{opposite}}{\text{adjacent}}$$

Thus
$$\tan 30° = \frac{o}{a} = \frac{BC}{AB}$$

From a calculator, $\tan 30° = 0.577\,35$; we also know that $AB = 8$ cm. So, substituting these values in the equation above gives:

$$0.577\,35 = \frac{BC}{8}$$

$$BC = 8 \times 0.577\,35 = 4.6188$$

Rounding off, $\quad BC = 4.62$ cm $\quad$ (3 s.f.)

**Example** Find the angle CAB in the triangle ABC (Fig. 17.14), given that $\hat{B} = 90°$, $AC = 13$ cm and $BC = 5$ cm.

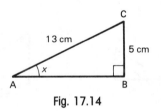

Fig. 17.14

BC is opposite the angle CAB, and AC is the hypotenuse, so we shall use the sine:

$$\sin x = \frac{o}{h} = \frac{BC}{AC} = \frac{5}{13} = 0.384\,62$$

Using the *inverse* sine function on the calculator, we get

$$x = 22.620°$$
$$= 22.6° \quad (3\text{ s.f.})$$

*Notes:*

(*i*)  When using one of these ratios, define it anew *every time* you use it. Do not skip steps, but write the full process, e.g.

$\sin x = \dfrac{o}{h} = \dfrac{BC}{AC} = \dfrac{5}{13}$, etc. This will help you to understand

and solve the problem.

(*ii*) Avoid, if you can, using your answers to earlier parts of a problem in subsequent calculations (you may be carrying forward a complete mistake). When this is not possible use the *unrounded* figures, i.e. all five (or more) figures you are using on your calculator.

(*iii*) The *angle of elevation* is the angle between the horizontal and the line of sight for an observer on the ground of some object above him. The equivalent for an object below him is called an *angle of depression.*

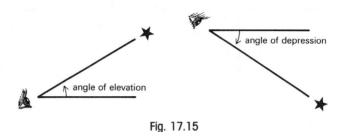

Fig. 17.15

**EXERCISE 17b**   1.  Find the lengths of the sides marked $x$ in the following:

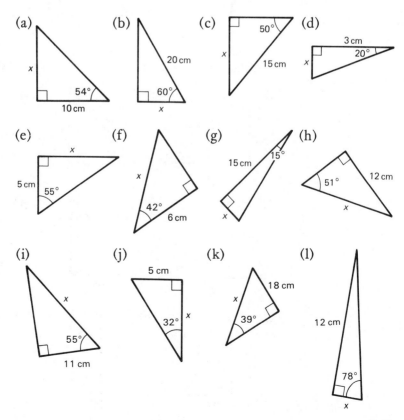

247

2. Find the angles marked $x$ in the following:

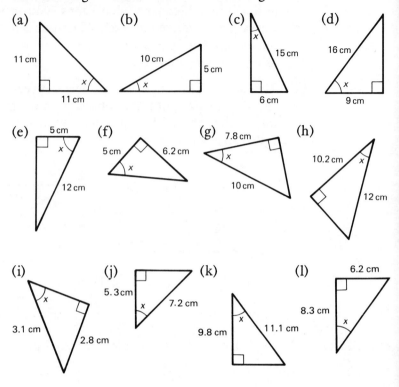

(a)

11 cm
11 cm
$x$

(b)

10 cm
5 cm
$x$

(c)

$x$
15 cm
6 cm

(d)

16 cm
$x$
9 cm

(e)

5 cm
$x$
12 cm

(f)

5 cm
6.2 cm
$x$

(g)

7.8 cm
$x$
10 cm

(h)

10.2 cm
$x$
12 cm

(i)

$x$
3.1 cm
2.8 cm

(j)

5.3 cm
$x$
7.2 cm

(k)

$x$
9.8 cm
11.1 cm

(l)

6.2 cm
8.3 cm
$x$

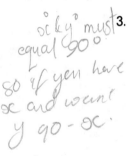
3. Find the lengths and angles indicated in the following:

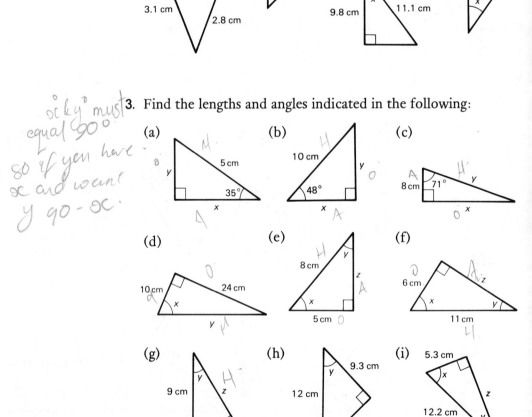

(a)

$y$
5 cm
35°
$x$

(b)

10 cm
$y$
48°
$x$

(c)

8 cm
71°
$y$
$x$

(d)

10 cm
24 cm
$x$
$y$

(e)

8 cm
$y$
$z$
$x$
5 cm

(f)

6 cm
$z$
$x$
$y$
11 cm

(g)

9 cm
$y$
$z$
$x$
6 cm

(h)

12 cm
$y$
9.3 cm
$x$
$z$

(i)

5.3 cm
$x$
$z$
12.2 cm
$y$

248

4.

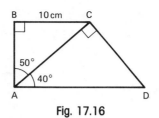

Fig. 17.16

In Fig. 17.16, $\widehat{ABC} = \widehat{ACD} = 90°$. BC = 10 cm. Find the lengths of AC and CD, giving your answers to 3 s.f.

5.

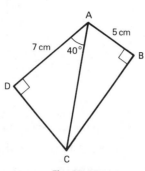

Fig. 17.17

A quadrilateral ABCD has right angles at B and D (Fig. 17.17). Given that $\widehat{DAC} = 40°$, AD = 7 cm and AB = 5 cm, find

(a) the length of the diagonal AC,

(b) $\widehat{ACB}$.

6.

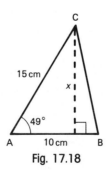

Fig. 17.18

In triangle ABC, $\widehat{CAB} = 49°$, AB = 10 cm and AC = 15 cm (Fig. 17.18). Find the height, $x$, of the triangle and hence its area.

7. In triangle XYZ, $\widehat{ZXY} = 25°$, XY = 14.2 cm and XZ = 9.8 cm. Find the area of XYZ.

8. In the parallelogram PQRS, PQ = 4.9 cm, QR = 5.6 cm and $\widehat{PQR} = 38°$. Find the perpendicular distance between the sides PS and QR and the area of the parallelogram.

9. In Fig. 17.19, ABCDE, angles BAE, BCD and DBE are right angles. BC = 12 m, CD = 5 m, BD = 13 m and AE = 3 m.

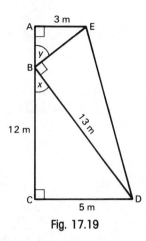

Fig. 17.19

(a) Calculate the size, in degrees, of the angle marked $x$.

(b) What is the size, in degrees, of the angle labelled $y$?

(c) Calculate the length of AB.

(d) Find the area of the trapezium ACDE.          (NWREB)

10. The plans of the sails of a boat are shown in Fig. 17.20, but are not drawn to scale.

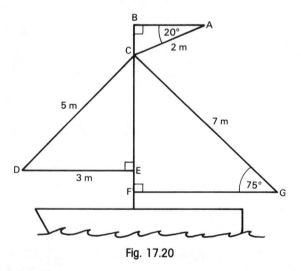

Fig. 17.20

Calculate, giving all final answers to one decimal place,

(a) the length AB,

(b) the length CF,

(c) the angle CDE.          (YHREB '84)

250

11. A man stands 25 m from a tall building and measures the angle of elevation of the top as 36°. What is the height of the building?

12. Standing at the top of a vertical cliff, a man spots a buoy out at sea. He knows this buoy to be 250 m from the beach and he observes the angle of depression to be 10.5°. How high is the cliff?

13. A 5 m ladder rests against a wall, with the foot of the ladder 1.2 m from the bottom of the wall. What angle does the ladder make with the ground and how far off the ground is the top?

14. An observer in a sailing dinghy 50 m out from the shore notices that the angle of elevation of the cliff top is 60° and that of a climber making his way up the vertical rock-face is exactly half, i.e. 30°. Show that the climber is *not* simply half-way up, but still has two-thirds of his climb to complete.

## DROPPING A PERPENDICULAR

If a triangle does not contain a right angle, then neither Pythagoras' theorem nor sines, cosines and tangents can be simply applied to it. Sometimes, however, it is possible to solve a problem by dividing the triangle into two right-angled portions by dropping a perpendicular from one corner to the side opposite.

**Example** In triangle ABC (Fig. 17.21), $\widehat{A} = 37°$, $\widehat{B} = 63°$, AC = 5 cm. Find the base length AB.

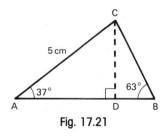

Fig. 17.21

Since the angles in a triangle must add up to 180°, we know that angle C must be given by

$$\widehat{C} = 180° - 37° - 63° = 80°$$

There is no right angle in this triangle. However, if we drop a perpendicular from C to meet the base AB at D, we create two right-angled triangles that we *can* solve.

251

In triangle ACD

$$\cos 37° = \frac{a}{h} = \frac{AD}{AC}$$

So $\qquad$ AD $= AC \times \cos 37° = 5 \times 0.798\,64 = 3.9932$ cm

Similarly

$$\sin 37° = \frac{o}{h} = \frac{CD}{AC}$$

So $\qquad$ CD $= AC \times \sin 37° = 5 \times 0.601\,82 = 3.0091$ cm

Then in triangle CDB

$$\tan 63° = \frac{o}{a} = \frac{CD}{DB}$$

So $\qquad$ DB $= \dfrac{CD}{\tan 63°} = \dfrac{3.0091}{1.9626} = 1.5332$ cm

Now, $\qquad$ AB $=$ AD $+$ DB $= 3.9932 + 1.5332 = 5.5264$

$\qquad\qquad\qquad = 5.53$ cm (3 s.f.)

**EXERCISE 17c**   1. Find the lengths indicated in the following triangles:

(a)
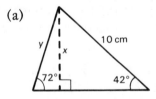

(b)
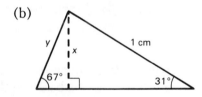

(c)
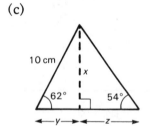

(d)
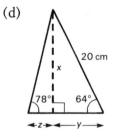

(e)
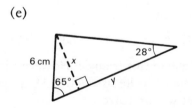

(f)
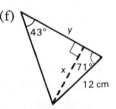

252

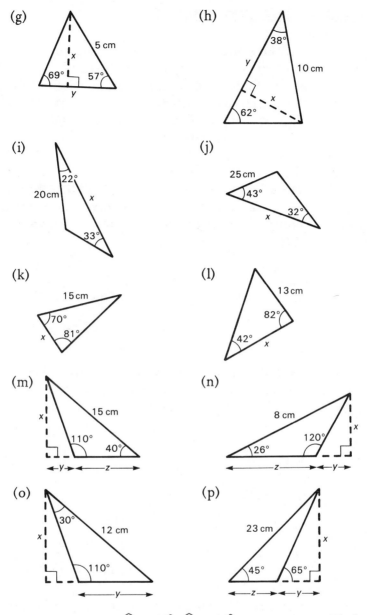

(g)

5 cm

$x$

69°    57°

$y$

(h)

38°

$y$

10 cm

$x$

62°

(i)

22°

20 cm

$x$

33°

(j)

25 cm

43°

$x$    32°

(k)

15 cm

70°

$x$    81°

(l)

13 cm

82°

42°    $x$

(m)

$x$

15 cm

110°

40°

$y$    $z$

(n)

8 cm

120°

26°

$z$    $y$

$x$

(o)

30°

$x$

12 cm

110°

$y$

(p)

23 cm

45°    65°

$z$    $y$

$x$

2. In triangle ABC, $\widehat{A} = 64°$, $\widehat{B} = 54°$, $AC = 10$ cm. Find the base length AB and the area of the triangle.

3. In triangle XYZ, $\widehat{X} = 32°$, $\widehat{Y} = 45°$, $XZ = 2$ m. Find the base length XY and the area of the triangle.

4. In triangle PQR, $\widehat{P} = 38°$, $\widehat{Q} = 32°$, $PR = 5$ m. Find the area of PQR.

5. Triangle EFG is obtuse-angled, with $\widehat{F} = 132°$. If $EF = 6$ cm, $FG = 4$ cm, find the height of G above the base line EF, and hence the area of the triangle.

253

## PROBLEMS IN THREE DIMENSIONS

The three dimensions — length, breadth and height — are all perpendicular to each other, and problems set in three dimensions mainly involve finding right-angled triangles within the more complicated three-dimensional structure. It is good practice to keep one 'master' diagram to represent the full structure and show extracted right-angled triangles separately.

**Example** Figure 17.22 represents a wedge of cheese. It is cut with wire vertically through the diagonal CF, so that the wire passes through the cheese down the edge CD (which is also vertical) and finally through the diagonal DF. Calculate the length DF and the angle CFD.

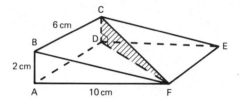

Fig. 17.22

To find DF, consider the triangle DAF which lies flat on the horizontal table (Fig. 17.23).

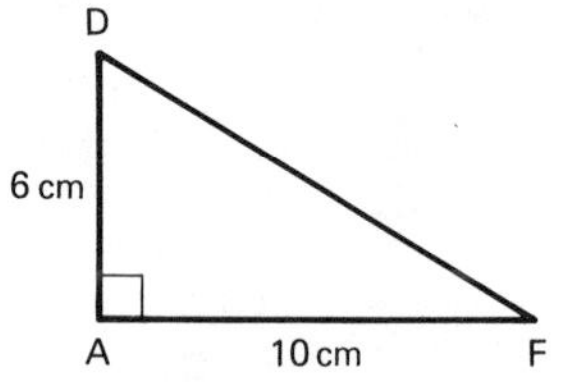

$$D\hat{A}F = 90°$$

$$DA = BC = 6\,cm$$

$$AF = 10\,cm$$

Fig. 17.23

Using Pythagoras' theorem:

$$DF^2 = DA^2 + AF^2$$

$$= 6^2 + 10^2 = 136$$

$$DF = \sqrt{136} = 11.662 = 11.7\,cm \quad (3\,s.f.)$$

To find $C\hat{F}D$, consider the triangle CDF which stands upright, in the vertical plane (Fig. 17.24).

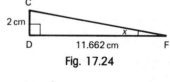

Fig. 17.24

$$C\hat{D}F = 90°$$

$$DF = 11.662\,cm \quad (from\ above)$$

$$CD = BA = 2\,cm$$

$$\tan x = \frac{o}{a} = \frac{CD}{DF} = \frac{2}{11.662} = 0.171\,50$$

Hence $\qquad x = 9.73°$ (3 s.f.)

**EXERCISE 17d**

1. Calculate the length of the diagonal AC (Fig. 17.25) that divides the bottom of a shoe box measuring 36 cm × 15 cm × 12 cm. Hence find the length of the diagonal AG and the angle GAC.

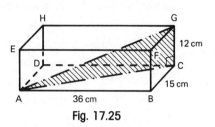

**Fig. 17.25**

2. A pyramid, 4 m high, stands on a 2 m square base, ABCD (Fig. 17.26). Its topmost point, O, is directly above the centre, M, of the square. Find the distance AM (halfway along the diagonal of the square) and hence find the slant height, OA, of the pyramid, and the angle OAM.

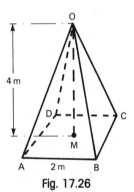

**Fig. 17.26**

3. The apex, O, of a pyramid with square base ABCD lies vertically above the centre, M, of the square. Each of the triangular faces is equilateral, with sides of 6 m. E is the mid-point of BC. Calculate

(a) the height OM,

(b) the angle BOM,

(c) the angle EOM,

(d) the angle between the faces BOC and AOD.

**4.**

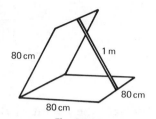

Fig. 17.27

A trapdoor, 80 cm square, is held in the open position by a supporting bar of 1 m length, as shown in Fig. 17.27. Find the angle the bar makes with the opened trapdoor and the angle the door makes with the horizontal.

5. A vertical radio mast is sited 1 km due north of an observer at O, who notes the angle of elevation of the top of the mast to be 5°. Another observer is at P, 1.4 km due east of O. Find

(a) the height of the radio mast,

(b) the bearing of the radio mast from P,

(c) the distance of the radio mast from P,

(d) the angle of elevation of the top of the mast to the observer at P.

6.

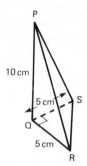

Fig. 17.28

A pointed, triangular-based arrow head, PQRS, measures 10 cm × 5 cm × 5 cm (as shown in Fig. 17.28). Given that P lies directly above Q and that SQR = 90°, calculate the lengths

(a) SR          (b) PR.

Find also the angle between the face PRS and the horizontal plane QRS.

## SINE AND COSINE RULES

For triangles without a right angle, two formulae apply.

(i) $$\frac{a}{\sin \widehat{A}} = \frac{b}{\sin \widehat{B}} = \frac{c}{\sin \widehat{C}}$$     (the *sine rule*)

(ii)    $a^2 = b^2 + c^2 - 2bc \cos \widehat{A}$    (the *cosine rule*)

where $a$ is the length of the side opposite the corner A (i.e. BC); $b$ is the length of the side opposite B; and $c$ the length of the side opposite C (Fig. 17.29).

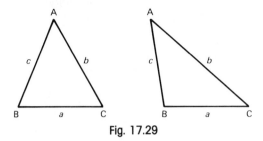

Fig. 17.29

The cosine rule also applies to the other sides:

$$b^2 = a^2 + c^2 - 2ac \cos \widehat{B} \qquad \text{and} \qquad c^2 = a^2 + b^2 - 2ab \cos \widehat{C}$$

Furthermore, the cosine rule can be rearranged to give a required angle when all three sides of the triangle are known:

$$\cos \widehat{A} = \frac{b^2 + c^2 - a^2}{2bc}$$

The sine and cosine rules apply not only to acute-angled triangles but also to obtuse-angled triangles (i.e. those that contain an angle of more than 90°).

Notice that Pythagoras' theorem is a special case of the cosine rule. If $\widehat{C} = 90°$ then $\cos \widehat{C} = 0$ so

$$c^2 = a^2 + b^2 - 2ab \cos \widehat{C}$$

becomes

$$c^2 = a^2 + b^2 \qquad\qquad \text{Pythagoras' theorem}$$

**Example** In the triangle ABC (Fig. 17.30), AC = 10 cm, BC = 12 cm and $\widehat{C} = 110°$.

(a) Use the cosine rule to find the length of AB.

(b) Use the sine rule to find $\widehat{A}$.

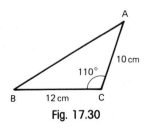

Fig. 17.30

(a) To find AB ($= c$):

$$c^2 = a^2 + b^2 - 2ab \cos \hat{C}$$
$$= 12^2 + 10^2 - 2 \times 12 \times 10 \cos 110°$$

The cosine of an obtuse angle is negative. Using a calculator we find $\cos 110° = -0.342\,02$.

So, 
$$c^2 = 144 + 100 - 240 \times (-0.342\,02)$$
$$= 326.08$$

Hence

$$AB = \sqrt{326.08} = 18.058 = 18.1 \text{ cm} \quad (3 \text{ s.f.})$$

(b) To find $\hat{A}$:

$$\frac{a}{\sin \hat{A}} = \frac{c}{\sin \hat{C}}$$

Rearranging:

$$\frac{a \sin \hat{C}}{c} = \sin \hat{A}$$

Hence

$$\sin \hat{A} = \frac{12 \sin 110°}{18.058} = \frac{12 \times 0.939\,69}{18.058} = 0.624\,44$$

and so $\hat{A} = 38.6°$ (3 s.f.)

**EXERCISE 17e**

1. (a) Use your calculator to find the values of
   (i) $\sin 105°$ (ii) $\cos 125°$ correct to 2 decimal places.

   (b) Using your calculator to help, draw up a table showing the value, to 2 decimal places, of $\sin x°$ and of $\cos x°$ for values of $x$ ($0 \leqslant x \leqslant 360$) in steps of $15°$.

   Your table should look something like this:

   | $x$ | $15°$ | $30°$ | $45°$ | $60°$ | $75°$ | $90°$ | $105°$ | ... | $345°$ | $360°$ |
   |---|---|---|---|---|---|---|---|---|---|---|
   | $\sin x°$ | | | | | | | | | | |
   | $\cos x°$ | | | | | | | | | | |

   Plot as accurately as you can the graphs of
   (i) $y = \sin x°$
   (ii) $y = \cos x°$.

258

(c) Use your graphs of $\sin x$ and $\cos x$ to answer the following:
  - (i)   what are the maximum and minimum values of $\sin x$ and $\cos x$?
  - (ii)  find two values of $x$ for which $\sin x = 0.6$.
  - (iii) find two values of $x$ for which $\cos x = -0.7$.
  - (iv)  for what range of values of $x$ is $\sin x < 0$?
  - (v)   for what range of values of $x$ is $\cos x < 0$?
  - (vi)  for what values of $x$ does $\sin x = \cos x$?

2. Use the sine rule to find the given angles and sides of the following triangles:
  - (a) $\hat{A} = 43°$, $BC = 12$ m, $AB = 11$ m. Find $\hat{C}$
  - (b) $\hat{B} = 62°$, $AC = 9$ cm, $BC = 8$ cm. Find $\hat{A}$
  - (c) $\hat{C} = 54°$, $AB = 7$ mm, $CA = 4.1$ mm. Find $\hat{B}$
  - (d) $\hat{A} = 67°$, $BC = 11.1$ m, $\hat{B} = 32°$. Find $AC$
  - (e) $\hat{Q} = 110°$, $RP = 8$ cm, $\hat{R} = 21°$. Find $PQ$
  - (f) $\hat{X} = 20°$, $ZY = 3$ cm, $XY = 8$ cm. Find $\hat{Z}$.

3. Use the cosine rule to find the missing side in these triangles:
  - (a) $\hat{A} = 32°$, $AB = 54$ mm, $AC = 45$ mm
  - (b) $\hat{B} = 67°$, $BC = 34$ cm, $BA = 41$ cm
  - (c) $\hat{C} = 27°$, $CA = 73$ cm, $CB = 48$ cm
  - (d) $\hat{P} = 111°$, $PQ = 4$ cm, $PR = 5.3$ cm
  - (e) $\hat{Y} = 123°$, $YZ = 4.1$ cm, $YX = 7.2$ cm.

4. Use the cosine rule to find the interior angles of these triangles, in which all three side lengths are known:
  - (a) $AB = 32$ cm, $BC = 45$ cm, $CA = 38$ cm
  - (b) $PQ = 4.2$ mm, $QR = 2.8$ mm, $RP = 3.5$ mm
  - (c) $MN = 3$ cm, $NO = 11$ cm, $OM = 9$ cm
  - (d) $RS = 8.2$ km, $ST = 16.3$ km, $TR = 11.5$ km.

5. Find all the missing sides and angles in the following triangles:
  - (a) $AB = 13$ cm, $AC = 11$ cm and $\hat{C} = 65°$
  - (b) $AB = 15$ cm, $BC = 13$ cm and $\hat{A} = 48°$
  - (c) $XY = 12$ cm, $YZ = 9.8$ cm and $\hat{Y} = 103°$
  - (d) $PQ = 17$ mm, $QR = 34$ mm and $\hat{Q} = 110°$
  - (e) $RS = 3.81$ m, $ST = 5.32$ m and $TR = 6.4$ m
  - (f) $MN = 4.4$ km, $NO = 5.6$ km and $OM = 7.5$ km.

1. On a clean sheet of paper, draw a fine, straight line and mark off any convenient length.

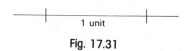

Fig. 17.31

Taking this length to be one unit, use only a straight edge, a compass and Pythagoras' theorem, draw lengths of:

(a) $\sqrt{2}$    (b) $\sqrt{5}$    (c) $\sqrt{3}$   and   (d) $\sqrt{10}$ units.

2. A submarine leaves Port P and travels due east for 30 kilometres to point A. It then changes course to a bearing of 030° and travels a distance of 20 kilometres to B, finally travelling due north to C for 25 kilometres.

The diagram (Fig. 17.32) which is not drawn to scale, represents the three stages of the journey.

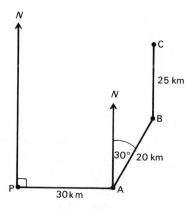

Fig. 17.32

(a) Consider the part of the journey from A to B. Calculate how far east and how far north the submarine travels.

(b) Using your answers to part (a) and any other information which is given find
   (i)  how far north C is from P,
   (ii) how far east C is from P.

(c) Using Pythagoras' Theorem calculate the distance from P to C.

(d) Calculate the bearing of C from P.          (YHREB '84)

3. Auldville is 23 km from Coaltown on a bearing of 121°. Bincester is 40 km west of Auldville.

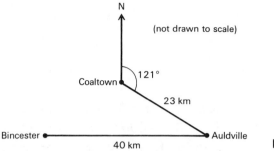

Fig. 17.33

Calculate (giving answers to 3 significant figures):
(a) how far Auldville is south of Coaltown;
(b) how far Auldville is east of Coaltown;
(c) how far Bincester is west of Coaltown;
(d) how far Bincester is from Coaltown;
(e) the bearing of Bincester from Coaltown. (ALSEB)

4. The diagram (Fig. 17.34), which is not drawn to scale, illustrates the journey of a ship which sails from a port A on a bearing of 040° for 10 miles to a port B. At B it alters course and sails on a bearing of 300° for 20 miles to a port C.

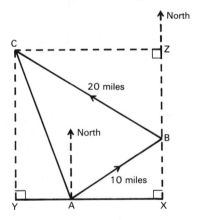

Fig. 17.34

(a) On graph paper make a scale drawing of the journey taking 1 cm to represent 2 miles.
(b) Using your scale drawing find
    (i) the distance from A to C to the nearest mile,
    (ii) the bearing of C from A to the nearest degree.
(c) By calculation find
    (i) the distance CZ,
    (ii) the distance AX,
    (iii) how far C is west of A. (NWREB)

261

**5.**

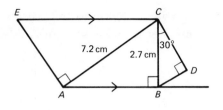

Fig. 17.35

The line $AB$ (Fig. 17.35) is parallel to the line $EC$, and angles $EAC$, $ABC$ and $BDC$ are right angles. $B\widehat{C}D = 30°$, and the lengths of $AC$ and $BC$ are 7.2 cm and 2.7 cm respectively. Calculate

(a) angle $ACB$,

(b) the length of $BD$,

(c) the length of $EA$. (Ox)

**6.** $AB$ is a building 16 metres high and $MT$ a vertical mast, with $BT$ representing level ground (Fig. 17.36).

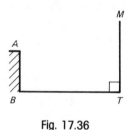

Fig. 17.36

The angle of elevation of the top of the mast from the top of the building is $16.7°$ and the angle of depression of the bottom of the mast from the top of the building is $21.8°$.

(a) Make a sketch showing clearly the angles of elevation and depression given above.

(b) Calculate
  (i)   the length of $BT$ (to the nearest metre),
  (ii)  the height of the mast (by using your answer to (i)),
  (iii) the angle of elevation of the top of the mast from the bottom of the building. (WJEC)

**7.** The diagram (Fig. 17.37) represents a quadrilateral $PQRT$ in which angles $QRT$, $PUQ$ and $PSR$ are right angles, angle $PTS$ is $39°$, $QR = PU = US = 11$ m and $RS = 8$ m.

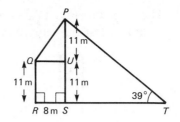

**Fig. 17.37**

Calculate

(a) angle $PQU$,

(b) the length of $PT$,

(c) the length of $RT$,

(d) the area of $PQRT$,

(e) angle $PTQ$. (JMB)

8. Six equal billiard balls fit exactly into an equilateral triangular wooden frame ABC. The sides of the frame just touch the balls.

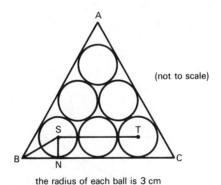

(not to scale)

the radius of each ball is 3 cm

**Fig. 17.38**

S and T are the centres of two balls. N is the point of contact of the ball centre S with the side BC of the frame.

(a) (i) Write down the size of angle ABC.
   (ii) Calculate the size of angle BSN.
   (iii) Calculate the length of BN, correct to three significant figures.

(b) (i) Write down the length of ST.
   (ii) Calculate the length of BC, correct to three significant figures. (WMEB)

9. The diagram (Fig. 17.39) shows a lighthouse and two buoys, A and B, respectively 50 m due north and 80 m due east of it.

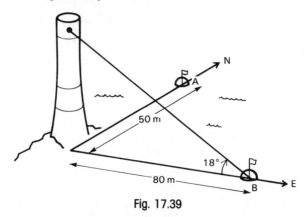

Fig. 17.39

The angle of elevation from B of the beacon at the top of the lighthouse is 18°. Find

(a) the distance between the two buoys,

(b) the bearing of B from A,

(c) the height of the lighthouse beacon above sea-level,

(d) the angle of elevation of the beacon from A.

10. The diagram (Fig. 17.40) (which is not drawn to scale) shows a helicopter landing area painted on the level deck of a ship.

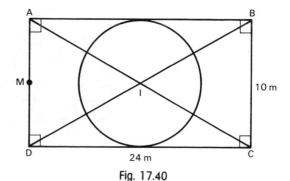

Fig. 17.40

Point I is the centre of both the circle and the rectangle ABCD.

$$AB = DC = 24\,m \qquad AD = BC = 10\,m$$

(a) Calculate the area of the circle.

(b) (i) Calculate the length of DB.
    (ii) Calculate the size of angle DBC.

(c) A helicopter H is hovering 20 m above M, the mid-point of AD. Calculate
    (i) the length of MI,
    (ii) the size of angle HIM. (EMREB)

11.

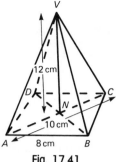

Fig. 17.41

The diagram (Fig. 17.41) shows a pyramid with a rectangular base *ABCD* and vertex *V*.

The slant edges *VA*, *VB*, *VC* and *VD* are all equal and the diagonals of the base intersect at *N*.

$AB = 8$ cm, $AC = 10$ cm and $VN = 12$ cm.

(a) Calculate *BC*.

(b) Calculate *VC*.

(c) Write down the tangent of the angle between *VN* and *VC*.

(C)

12.

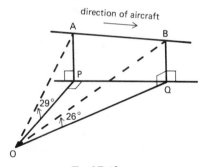

Fig. 17.42

O is the position of an observer on the horizontal plane OPQ (Fig. 17.42). The observer is watching an aircraft which is flying due east at a constant speed of 400 km/h and at a constant height of 2000 m.

When the aircraft is at A, it is due north of O and its angle of elevation from O is 29°.

Calculate the distance OP.

Later, when the aircraft is at B, its angle of elevation from O is 26°. Calculate the bearing of the aircraft from O at this instant.

Find the distance AB and hence deduce the time, in seconds to the nearest second, between the two observations.

(AEB '81)

# 18 CIRCLES

## CIRCUMFERENCE AND AREA

The circumference and the area of a circle depend upon the radius, $r$, of the circle and the constant, $\pi$. The circumference is given by

$$\text{circumference} = 2\pi r$$

and the area is given by

$$\text{area} = \pi r^2$$

$\pi$ is an irrational number. It cannot be written as an exact value for it continues for ever: a non-terminating, non-recurring decimal. Suitable working approximations are 3.142, 3.1416 or $\frac{22}{7}$, though (if you have one) use the $\pi$ key on your calculator.

**Example** Find the circumference and the area of a circle of radius 4 cm.

$$\text{circumference} = 2\pi r = 2 \times 3.1416 \times 4 = 25.13 \text{ cm}$$
$$\text{area} = \pi r^2 = 3.1416 \times 4^2 = 50.27 \text{ cm}^2$$

## Arcs

An *arc* is part of the circumference of a circle, and is $\dfrac{x}{360}$ of its length, where $x$ is the angle at the centre (Fig. 18.1).

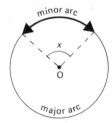

Fig. 18.1

$$\text{length of arc} = \frac{x}{360} \times \text{length of circumference}$$

$$= \frac{x}{360} \times 2\pi r$$

266

# Sectors

The area of a *sector* (part of the circle shaped rather like a slice of pie) is $\dfrac{x}{360}$ of the whole area, where $x$ is the angle at the centre.

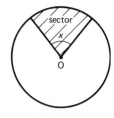

Fig. 18.2

$$\text{area of sector} = \frac{x}{360} \times \text{area of circle}$$

$$= \frac{x}{360} \times \pi r^2$$

**Example** What is the length of an arc and the area of a sector of this circle formed by two radii at an angle of 72°?

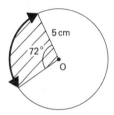

Fig. 18.3

The circumference of the circle is given by

$$2\pi r = 2 \times 3.1416 \times 5 = 31.416 \text{ cm}$$

The area of the circle is

$$\pi r^2 = \pi \times 5^2 = 3.1416 \times 25 = 78.540 \text{ cm}^2$$

The arc length is

$$\frac{72}{360} \times 31.416 = 6.2832 = 6.28 \text{ cm} \quad (3 \text{ s.f.})$$

The area of the sector is

$$\frac{72}{360} \times 78.540 = 15.708 = 15.7 \text{ cm}^2 \quad (3 \text{ s.f.})$$

# Chords

A straight line joining two points on the circumference is called a *chord*. The longest chord that it is possible to draw is the *diameter*, which passes through the centre of the circle and is twice the radius (Fig. 18.4).

267

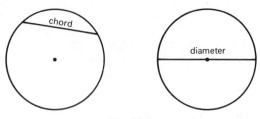

Fig. 18.4

A chord cuts the circle into *segments*, that is, portions of the circle shaped rather like a piece of an orange (Fig. 18.5).

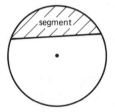

Fig. 18.5

The perpendicular bisector of a chord passes through the centre of the circle.

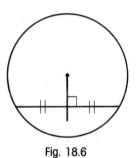

Fig. 18.6

## Tangents

A *tangent* to a circle is a line that just touches it. The tangent forms a right angle with a radius drawn from the centre to the point of contact (Fig. 18.7).

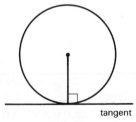

Fig. 18.7

If two tangents touch the circle at points T and S, and themselves meet at a third point, P, then PT = PS (Fig. 18.8) and PO is an axis of symmetry.

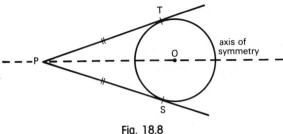

**Fig. 18.8**

**EXERCISE 18a** *Throughout this exercise take π as 3.1416 or use the π key on your calculator.*

1. Find the area and perimeter of the shapes shown.

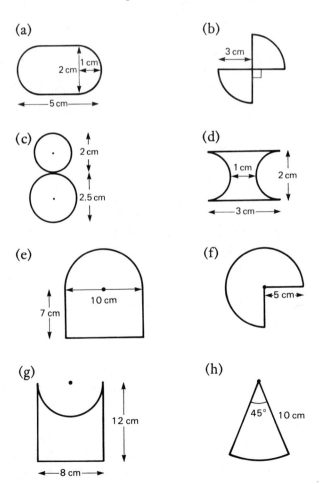

2. Find the area of the shaded parts shown.

(a)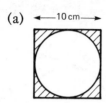

(b)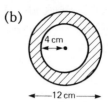

(c)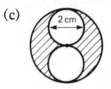

(d)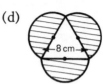

(e)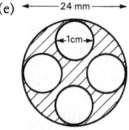

(f)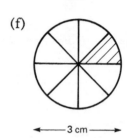

(g)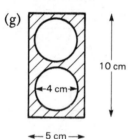

(h)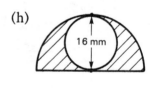

3. Find the arc length and area of a sector of a circle if
   (a) the radius is 5 cm and the centre angle is 72°
   (b) the radius is 8 cm and the centre angle is 135°
   (c) the radius is 15 cm and the centre angle is 156°.

4. Find the radius of a circle that has a circumference of
   (a) 15.7 cm       (b) 169.6 cm       (c) 78.5 cm
   (d) 37.3 cm       (e) 39.8 cm        (f) 42.7 cm.

5. Find the radius of a circle that has an area of
   (a) 78.5 cm²      (b) 706.9 cm²      (c) 125 700 cm²
   (d) 31.4 cm²      (e) 112 cm²        (f) 72.3 cm².

6. A bicycle wheel has a radius of 32 cm. How far will it have travelled when it has made 100 revolutions? How many revolutions will the wheel complete in a journey of 1 km?

270

7. The wheels of a car revolve 750 times for every kilometre travelled. What is their radius (to the nearest centimetre)?

8. The circumference of a circle is 785.5 mm. What is its area in cm²?

9.

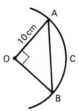

Fig. 18.9

Figure 18.9 shows part of a circle, radius 10 cm. If AÔB = 90°, find the area of

(a) triangle AOB    (b) sector AOB    (c) segment ACB.

10. Find the area of a segment between the minor arc of a circle and a chord 10 cm long if the radius of the circle is

(a) 10 cm        (b) 13 cm        (c) 7 cm

(d) 8 cm         (e) 12 cm        (f) 20 cm.

11.

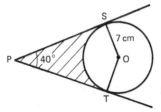

Fig. 18.10

Two tangents drawn from a point, P, meet a circle, centre O, at S and T (Fig. 18.10). If the radius of the circle is 7 cm and TP̂S = 40°, find the shaded area.

# FOUR COMMON CIRCLE THEOREMS

## Centre angle double that at circumference

The angle at the centre of a circle is double the angle at the circumference that stands on the same arc (Fig. 18.11).

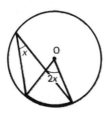

Fig. 18.11

The theorem is also true for the reflex angle at the centre (Fig. 18.12).

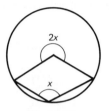

Fig. 18.12

## Angles on the same arc are equal

Angles at the circumference that stand on the same arc are equal.

Fig. 18.13

## Angles on a diameter are 90°

Angles at the circumference that stand on a diameter are right angles.

Fig. 18.14

## Opposite angles of a cyclic quadrilateral make 180°

Opposite angles of a cyclic quadrilateral add up to 180°.

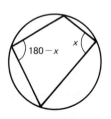

Fig. 18.15

272

The *converse* of this also applies, i.e. any quadrilateral known to have opposite angles that add up to 180° is cyclic.

It follows that the exterior angle of a cyclic quadrilateral is equal to the interior opposite angle.

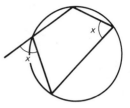

Fig. 18.16

*Note*: When finding angles in a circle, remember that any triangle with two sides equal to the radius is isosceles.

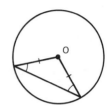

Fig. 18.17

**Example** $\widehat{ACB} = 30°$, $\widehat{ABD} = 100°$ (see Fig. 18.18). Find
(a) $\widehat{ADB}$　　(b) $\widehat{DAB}$.

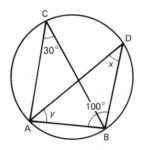

Fig. 18.18

(a) $\widehat{ADB} = \widehat{ACB} = 30°$ (angles on the same arc, AB).

(b) In triangle ADB, $\widehat{ABD} = 100°$, $\widehat{ADB} = 30°$. But

$$\widehat{DAB} + \widehat{ABD} + \widehat{ADB} = 180° \quad \text{(sum of angles in a triangle)}$$

Therefore

$$\widehat{DAB} = 180° - 100° - 30° = 50°$$

273

**Example** ABCD is a cyclic quadrilateral; O is the centre of the circle; $\hat{ADC} = 140°$ (Fig. 18.19). Find

(a) $\hat{ABC}$      (b) $\hat{AOC}$      (c) $\hat{OAC}$.

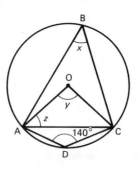

Fig. 18.19

(a) $\hat{ADC} + \hat{ABC} = 180°$ (opposite angles of a cyclic quadrilateral). So

$$\hat{ABC} = 180° - \hat{ADC} = 180° - 140° = 40°$$

(b) $\hat{AOC} = 2 \times \hat{ABC}$ (angle at centre is twice that at circumference). Therefore

$$\hat{AOC} = 2 \times 40° = 80°$$

(c) OA is a radius of the circle and so is OC. Thus OA = OC and triangle OAC is isosceles. Hence $\hat{OAC} = \hat{OCA}$. But, as $AOC = 80°$, $\hat{OAC} + \hat{OCA} = 100°$ (sum of angles in a triangle). Therefore

$$\hat{OAC} = \tfrac{1}{2} \times 100° = 50°$$

**EXERCISE 18b** Find the angle $x$ in each of the following and give a reason for your answer.

1.
2.
3.
4.

5.
6.
7.
8.

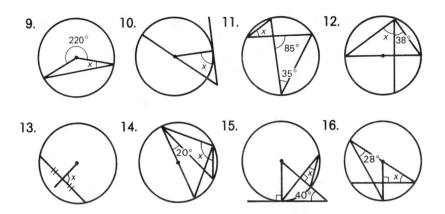

9. 220°  x
10. x
11. x  85°  35°
12. x  38°

13. x
14. 20°  x
15. x  40°
16. 28°  x

In Questions 17 to 29 find the angles indicated *x*, *y* and *z*. Give a reason for each step in your calculations.

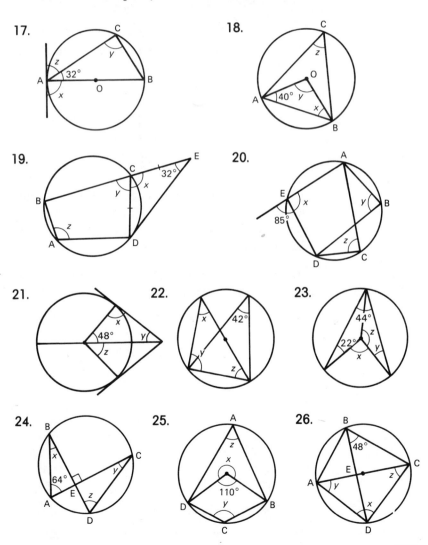

17. C  y  z  32°  A  O  B  x

18. C  z  O  A  40°  y  x  B

19. E  C  32°  y  x  B  z  A  D

20. A  E  x  y  B  85°  z  D  C

21. x  48°  z  Y

22. x  42°  y  z

23. 44°  z  22°  x  y

24. B  x  64°  C  y  E  z  A  D

25. A  z  x  110°  D  y  B  C

26. B  48°  E  C  A  y  z  x  D

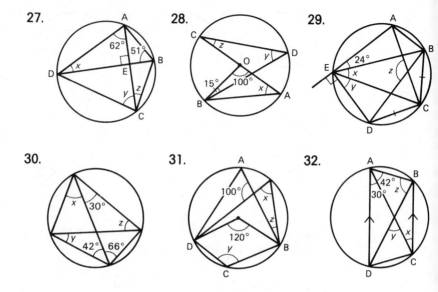

33. AC and BD are diameters of a circle. Show that the quadrilateral ABCD is a rectangle.

34.

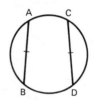

Fig. 18.20

AB and CD are two non-parallel chords of the same circle such that AB = CD (Fig. 18.20). Copy the diagram, adding lines, AC, BD, AD and BC. If the diagonals of the quadrilateral ABCD meet at X, prove that

(a) triangles ABX and CXD are congruent

(b) triangle AXC is isosceles

(c) AC‖BD, and hence that ABCD is an isosceles trapezium.

35.

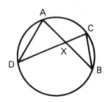

Fig. 18.21

Two chords of a circle, AB and CD, intersect at X (Fig. 18.21). Use angles on the same arc to prove that triangles AXC and DXB are similar. Hence show that AX×BX = CX×DX.

Use this result, known as the *intersecting chords theorem*, to find

(a) DX when AX = 3 cm, BX = 12 cm and CX = 9 cm

(b) CX when  AX = 15 cm,  BX = 5 cm  and  DX = 6 cm

(c) The length of the chord AB if  AX = 4 cm,  CX = 5 cm
and  DX = 8 cm.

36.

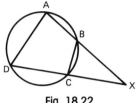

Fig. 18.22

ABCD is a cyclic quadrilateral. AB and DC are extended to a
point X where they intersect (Fig. 18.22). Prove that triangles
AXD and CXB are similar, and hence show that
AX × BX = CX × DX.

Use this result to find

(a) DX if  AX = 18 cm,  BX = 10 cm  and  CX = 15 cm

(b) CX if  AX = 20 cm,  BX = 18 cm  and  DX = 18 cm

(c) The length of the chord AB if  AX = 24 cm,  CX = 30 cm
and  DX = 6 cm.

## ALTERNATE SEGMENT THEOREM

If a tangent and a chord meet on the circumference of a circle,
then the angle between them is equal to the angle that stands on
the chord in the alternate (opposite) segment (see Fig. 18.23).

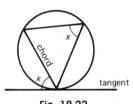

Fig. 18.23

**Example** In Fig. 18.24, we can use the alternate segment theorem to find

$$x = \widehat{ATU} = 70°$$

and $$y = \widehat{BAT} = 60°$$

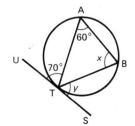

Fig. 18.24

277

**Example** A tangent touches a circle at T. A chord of the circle, AB, is parallel to the tangent (Fig. 18.25). Prove that the triangle TAB is isosceles.

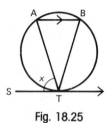

Fig. 18.25

Let the angle $S\widehat{T}A$ be $x$. Then $T\widehat{B}A = x$ (alternate segment theorem). But also $T\widehat{A}B = x$ (alternate angles). So in triangle TAB, $T\widehat{A}B = A\widehat{B}T$, and hence TAB is isosceles.

**EXERCISE 18c** Find the angle marked $x$ in the following. Give a reason for each step in your calculation.

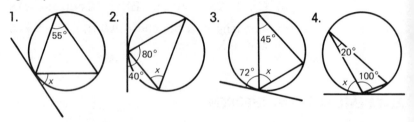

Find the angles marked $x$, $y$ and $z$ in Questions 5 to 13. Be sure to give a reason for every step in your calculations.

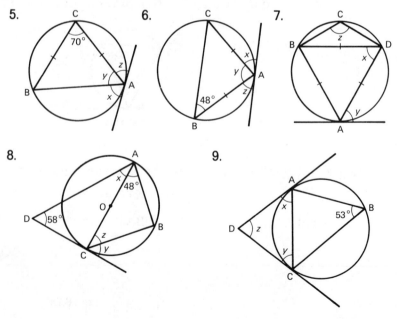

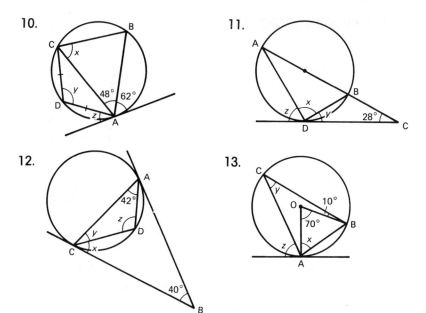

**14.** Two circles, one inside the other, as shown in Fig. 18.26 have a common tangent at their point of contact, E. Prove that AB∥CD.

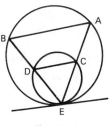

**Fig. 18.26**

**15.** A tangent is drawn from a point X to touch a circle, centre O, at T. P is any point on the circumference of the circle. Prove that angle TOP is twice angle XTP.

**16.**

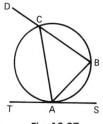

**Fig. 18.27**

In Fig. 18.27, TAS is a tangent to the circle. BCD is a chord, extended to D outside the circle, as shown. Prove that DĈA = CÂS.

## MISCELLANEOUS EXERCISE 18

1.

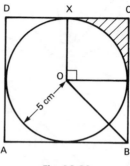

Fig. 18.28

The diagram (Fig. 18.28) shows a circle, radius 5 cm, drawn to touch the sides of a square ABCD.

(a) What type of figure is OXCB?

(b) State the length of AB, in cm.

(c) Find the area of the circle, in cm², and use it to calculate the shaded area.

(d) Find the circumference of the circle, in cm, and use it to find the perimeter of the shaded part.

(e) Using Pythagoras' Theorem, calculate the distance OB. Give your answer correct to 2 decimal places.     (SEREB)

2.

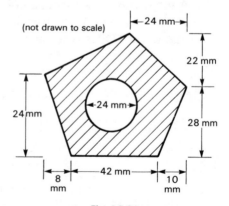

Fig. 18.29

Find the area of the shaded part in Fig. 18.29.

**3.**

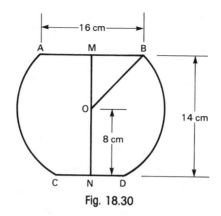

Fig. 18.30

The diagram (Fig. 18.30) above represents the section of a goldfish bowl.

O is the centre of the circular part, AB (mid-point M) is the top and CD (mid-point N) the bottom of the bowl.

(a) If AB = 16 cm, ON = 8 cm and the height of the bowl is 14 cm, write down, or calculate, in cm,

    (i)   the length MB,
    (ii)  the length OM,
    (iii) the radius OB,
    (iv) the length ND.

(b) If water is poured into the bowl to a depth of 12 cm calculate

    (i)   the height above O of the water surface,
    (ii)  the radius, in cm, of the water surface,
    (iii) the area, in cm$^2$, of the water surface,
    (iv) your answer to (iii) correct to two significant figures.

(YHREB '85)

4. In the sector OAB (Fig. 18.31), O is the centre of the circle and the angle AOB = 45°. The radius of the circle is 12 cm and C and D are both 4 cm from O.

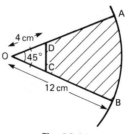

Fig. 18.31

Calculate the shaded area ABCD. Give your answer to the nearest square centimetre.

**5.**

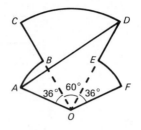

Fig. 18.32

The diagram (Fig. 18.32) represents a badge made from sectors of two circles with a common centre $O$.

The radius $OA = 5$ cm, and the radius $OC = 9$ cm.

$$A\hat{O}B = E\hat{O}F = 36° \quad \text{and} \quad C\hat{O}D = 60°.$$

Give all your answers correct to 3 significant figures.

(a) Find the length of the arc $EF$.

(b) Gold braid, of negligible width, is sewn round the perimeter $OABCDEFO$ of the badge. Calculate the length of gold braid used.

(c) Calculate the area of cloth used for the sector $OCD$.

(d) A thin straight silver wire runs from $A$ to $D$. Calculate its length. (C)

**6.** A satellite is in orbit 20 km above the ground. How much further than the circumference of the Earth does it travel in each revolution?

**7.** What is the largest possible area of a rectangle drawn inside a circle of 5 cm radius? Investigate.

**8.** Use a tin or other round object to draw a circle of any convenient size. (Do not use a pair of compasses.) Investigate ways of *accurately* pin-pointing the centre of the circle.

**9.** In Fig. 18.33 (not drawn accurately) TA and TB are tangents to the circle centre O, touching the circle at A and B respectively. $A\hat{O}B = 130°$. Calculate the sizes of the angles marked $a, b, c$ and $d$.

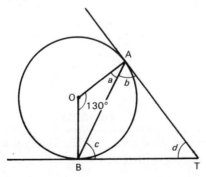

Fig. 18.33          (LREB)

10.

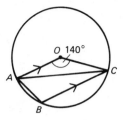

Fig. 18.34

In the diagram (Fig. 18.34), $O$ is the centre of the circle, $AO$ is parallel to $BC$ and $A\hat{O}C = 140°$. Calculate the value of

(a) $A\hat{C}B$     (b) $A\hat{B}C$.                                                    (C)

11.

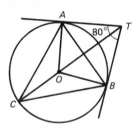

Fig. 18.35

In the diagram (Fig. 18.35), $TA$ and $TB$ are tangents to a circle, centre $O$. $TOC$ is a straight line and $A\hat{T}B = 80°$. Calculate

(a) $A\hat{B}T$,     (b) $A\hat{O}B$,     (c) $A\hat{C}O$.                              (C)

12.

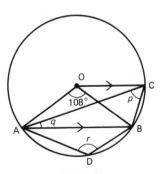

Fig. 18.36

In the diagram (Fig. 18.36), the points A, D, B and C are on the circumference of the circle, centre O. Given that OC is parallel to AB and that the angle AOB = 108°, calculate

(a) $p$          (b) $q$          (c) $r$.                              (AEB '81)

13.

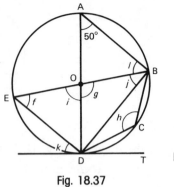

Fig. 18.37

Fig. 18.37

ABCDE are points on a circle, centre O (Fig. 18.37). DT is the tangent to the circle at D. $D\widehat{A}B = 50°$. Calculate, but do not prove, the value of the angles marked $f, g, h, i, j, k, l$.

(WJEC)

14.

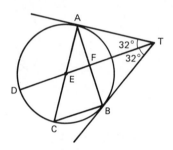

Fig. 18.38

TA and TB are tangents to a circle ABCD from an external point T. E is the centre of the circle, AC is a diameter and $A\widehat{T}B = 64°$. DEFT is a straight line bisecting $A\widehat{T}B$ (Fig. 18.38). Find (but do not prove) the size of angles $C\widehat{A}T, A\widehat{B}C, T\widehat{A}B,$ $C\widehat{A}B, A\widehat{F}E, A\widehat{E}F, A\widehat{D}E$ and $B\widehat{C}D$. (WJEC)

# 19 THREE-DIMENSIONAL FIGURES

## COMMON THREE-DIMENSIONAL FIGURES

Some three-dimensional figures — cubes, cylinders and cones, for example — are very well known to you.

Some others that are also common are shown below:

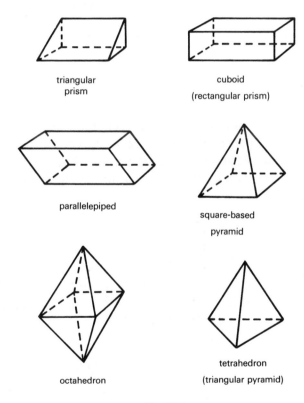

triangular
prism

cuboid
(rectangular prism)

parallelepiped

square-based
pyramid

octahedron

tetrahedron
(triangular pyramid)

Fig. 19.1

A *regular* figure is one in which all the faces are the same shape and size (for example, a cube).

Any three-dimensional figure with a polygon base, parallel sides, and unchanging cross-section is a *prism*. (A cuboid, for example, is a rectangular prism.)

Similarly, any three-dimensional figure with a polygon base and triangular faces meeting at a point is a *pyramid*. (A tetrahedron, for example, is a triangular pyramid.)

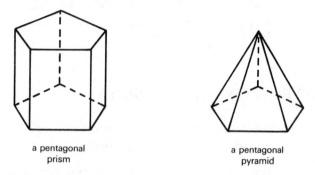

a pentagonal
prism

a pentagonal
pyramid

**Fig. 19.2**

## NETS

If we were to try to construct these three-dimensional shapes from stiff paper we would first need to draw out a *net* which could be cut out and folded to the required shape. Fig. 19.3 shows possible nets for a cuboid, a regular tetrahedron and a square-based pyramid.

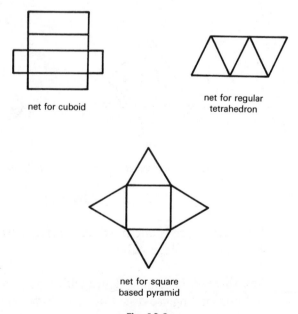

net for cuboid

net for regular
tetrahedron

net for square
based pyramid

**Fig. 19.3**

**EXERCISE 19a**    1. Copy and complete the following table:

| Figure | | Number of faces F | Number of vertices (corners) V | Number of edges E | F + V |
|---|---|---|---|---|---|
| Cube | | 6 | 8 | 12 | |
| Triangular prism | | 5 | 6 | | |
| Tetrahedron | | 4 | | | |
| Square-based pyramid | | | | | |
| Cuboid | | | | | |
| Pentagonal prism | | | | | |
| Hexagonal pyramid | | | | | |

What is the relationship between $F + V$ and $E$? Does the pattern hold for other three-dimensional shapes?

2.

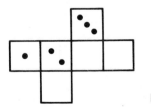

Fig. 19.4

Fig. 19.4 shows a net of an ordinary die. The number of dots on opposite faces add up to seven. Copy the diagram and mark in the dots on the three blank faces.

3. What shapes can be formed from these nets?

(a)                        (b)

(c)                        (d)

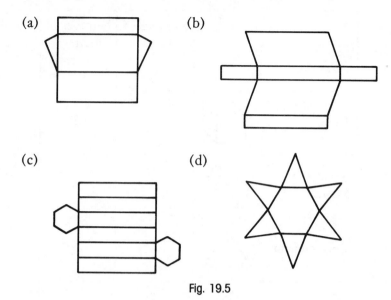

Fig. 19.5

4. Sometimes it is possible to draw several nets for one shape. For example, either of the two nets shown in Fig. 19.6 could be used to construct a square box with no top.

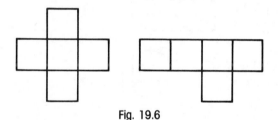

Fig. 19.6

There are six more possibilities (all completely different from each other: reflections or rotations of the same shape do not count). Try to find them all.

5. A net for a cube must consist of six squares. Fig. 19.7 shows two different possibilities.

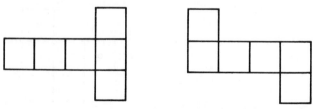

Fig. 19.7

Try to find all nine of the remaining possibilities. (Again, reflections and rotations of the same shape do not count.)

288

6. How many blocks have been used to construct the shapes in Fig. 19.8?

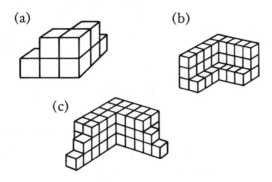

(a)          (b)

(c)

Fig. 19.8

7. Fig. 19.9 shows three different shapes that can be made with four cubes. Try to find others. (Again, reflections and rotations of the same basic shape do not count.)

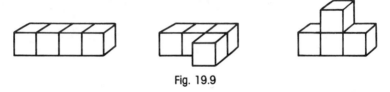

Fig. 19.9

8. How many different shapes can you make with five cubes? There are twenty-nine altogether.

## VOLUMES

The volume, $V$, of prisms and all solids with sides perpendicular to the ends, can be generalised by

$$V = \text{base area} \times \text{height}$$

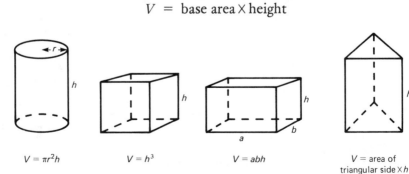

$V = \pi r^2 h$      $V = h^3$      $V = abh$      $V = $ area of triangular side $\times h$

cylinder      cube      cuboid      triangular prism

Fig. 19.10

For pyramids, i.e. figures with *sloping sides*, the volume is given by

$$V = \tfrac{1}{3} \text{ base area} \times \text{vertical height}$$

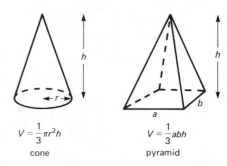

$$V = \frac{1}{3}\pi r^2 h$$
cone

$$V = \frac{1}{3}abh$$
pyramid

**Fig. 19.11**

The sphere is a special case:

$$V = \tfrac{4}{3}\pi r^3$$

where $r$ is its radius (Fig. 19.12).

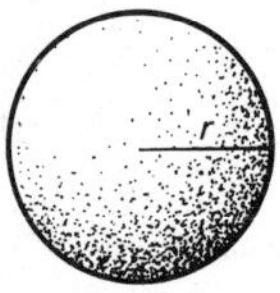

**Fig. 19.12**

## SURFACE AREAS

For straight-sided figures, it is best to work out the area of the separate sides and add them together to find the total surface area of the shape.

The curved surface area of a cylinder is given by

$$A = \text{base circumference} \times \text{height} = 2\pi rh$$

The curved surface area of a cone is given by

$$A = \pi rl$$

where $l$ is the *slant height*.

**Fig. 19.13**

The circular tops and bottoms may also be required as part of the total surface area of the cylinder or cone, so check.

The curved surface area of a sphere is given by $4\pi r^2$.

**Example** Find the volume and the surface area of an open-topped cylindrical water tank 0.5 m in radius and 1 m high.

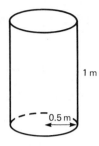

1 m

0.5 m

Fig. 19.14

The volume $V$ is given by

$$V = \pi r^2 h$$
$$= \pi (0.5)^2 \times 1$$
$$= 3.1416 \times 0.25 \times 1$$
$$= 0.785 \text{ m}^3 \quad (3 \text{ s.f.})$$

The area of the curved surface is given by

$$2\pi r h = 2 \times \pi \times 0.5 \times 1$$
$$= 3.1416 \text{ m}^2$$

The area of the circular bottom is

$$\pi r^2 = 3.1416 \times (0.5)^2$$
$$= 0.785\,40 \text{ m}^2$$

Total surface area $= 3.1416 + 0.785\,40 = 3.9270$
$$= 3.93 \text{ m}^2 \quad (3 \text{ s.f.})$$

**Example** Find the total surface area of a cone with *slant* height of 20 cm and sides inclined at 30° to the base.

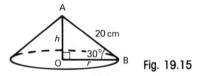

A

$h$

20 cm

30°

O    $r$    B    Fig. 19.15

First we need to find the radius of the cone and its vertical height, using trigonometry. In the triangle OAB (formed from half of the vertical cross-section of the cone)

$$\cos 30° = \frac{\text{adjacent}}{\text{hypotenuse}} = \frac{\text{radius}}{\text{slant height}}$$

Hence, the radius, $r$, is given by

$$r = \cos 30° \times \text{slant height} = 0.866\,03 \times 20 = 17.321 \text{ cm}$$

The curved surface area of the cone is given by

$$\pi r l = 3.1416 \times 17.321 \times 20$$
$$= 1088.31 \text{ cm}^2$$

The area of the circular base is given by

$$\pi r^2 = 3.1416 \times (17.321)^2$$
$$= 942.53 \text{ cm}^2$$

So the total surface area of the cone is

$$1088.3 + 942.5 = 2031 \text{ cm}^2 \text{ (to the nearest whole number)}$$

**EXERCISE 19b**  *Throughout this exercise take $\pi$ as 3.1416 or use the $\pi$ key on your calculator.*

1. Find the volume and curved surface area of a cylinder of radius 6 m and height 10 m.

2. Find the volume and total surface area of a cube of sides 2 m.

3. Find the volume of a cone of radius 4 cm and height 6 cm. What is the slant height of this cone? Find also its total surface area (including the base).

4. Find the volume of the pyramid shown in Fig. 19.16 given that it is 10 cm high and the base is square with sides of 5 cm.

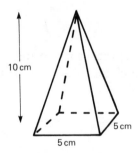

Fig. 19.16

5. Find the volume and surface area of a sphere of radius 10 cm.

6. Find the volume and total surface area (including the top and base) of a cylinder of radius 8 cm and height 20 cm.

7. Find the volume and surface area of a closed rectangular-based water tank with sides 2 m, 1 m and height 1.5 m.

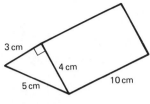

Fig. 19.17

Find the volume and surface area of a triangular prism that is 10 cm long and has sides 3 cm, 4 cm and 5 cm as illustrated in Fig. 19.17.

9.

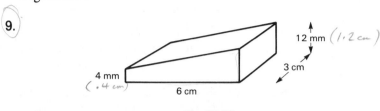

Fig. 19.18

A plastic door-wedge has a trapezium cross-section, as shown in Fig. 19.18. If the wedge is 3 cm wide, find the volume of plastic required to manufacture it, in cm³.

10. Which has the greater volume, a sphere of radius 2 cm or a cube of side length 3 cm? Which has the greater surface area? Justify your answers.

11. Show that the surface area of a closed cylinder of radius 10 cm and height 20 cm is exactly equal to that of a cone of radius 15 cm and height 20 cm.

12. A wigwam has an irregular base covering 2.6 m² of ground. If it is 2 m high, what is its volume?

13. The luggage space of a popular modern motor car is found to be 1.6 m long. If the manufacturers claim the car's luggage capacity to be 2.4 m³, what must the area of the cross-section be?

14.

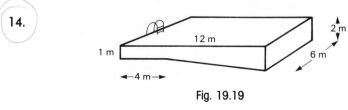

Fig. 19.19

Figure 19.19 shows the design of a swimming pool. What is the area of its cross-section? If the pool is 6 m wide, what volume of water could it contain?

**15.**

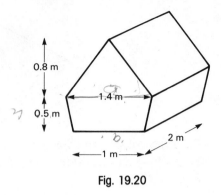

Fig. 19.20

Figure 19.20 shows the design of a tent. What is the area of this cross-section? If the tent is 2 m long, what is its volume?

**16.** Fig. 19.21 shows a thick, lead pipe. Find the area of the cross-section and hence the volume of lead used to manufacture 1 m of the pipe.

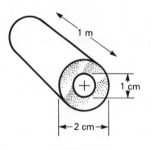

Fig. 19.21

**17.** Fig. 19.22 shows a steel girder. What is the area, in cm², of its cross-section?

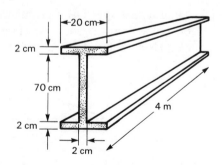

Fig. 19.22

Given that the girder is 4 m long, find the volume, in m³, of steel used to make it.

18.

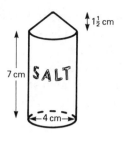

Fig. 19.23

A salt cellar consists of a cylindrical base, 7 cm high and 4 cm in diameter, and a conical cap $1\frac{1}{2}$ cm high (see Fig. 19.23). Find its volume.

19. Water flows through a 2 cm diameter pipe at 3 cm/s. What is the volume of a 3 cm length of pipe? Hence deduce the rate of flow of water, in $cm^3/s$.

20. Oil gushes through a pipeline at 0.4 m/s. If the diameter of the pipe is 0.2 m find the volume of a 0.4 m length of pipe and so deduce the rate of oil flow in $m^3/s$.

How long, to the nearest minute, would it take to fill a rectangular oil tank 4 m by 6 m by 2 m at this rate?

21. Fuel flows through a pipe at a speed of 0.1 m/s. If the radius of the fuel-line is 1 cm find the volume of fuel contained in a 0.1 m section and hence deduce the rate of flow of fuel in $m^3/s$.

# SIMILAR OBJECTS

A three-dimensional object is said to be similar to another if it is the same shape but different in size.

Suppose the height and other linear dimensions (such as radius) of the larger object are $k$ times those of the smaller one. We call $k$ the *linear scale factor*. The *area* and *volume* scale factors are not $k$ but $k^2$ and $k^3$. That is:

*measurements of larger object* $= k \times$ *measurements of smaller object*

*surface area of larger object* $= k^2 \times$ *surface area of smaller object*

*volume of larger object* $= k^3 \times$ *volume of smaller object*

**Example** A manufacturer of baked beans sells his product in various sizes of cylindrical tin. The small tin is 6 cm tall and has a radius of 3 cm; the 'jumbo' size is similar in shape to the small can but it is 12 cm tall and has a radius of 6 cm. Find the volume of the small can and the area of the label stuck on to its curved side. Find, too, the volume of the larger can and the area of its label.

Fig. 19.24

The volume of the small can is

$$V = \pi r^2 h = 3.1416 \times 3^2 \times 6$$
$$= 169.65 \text{ cm}^3$$

The area of the label is

$$A = 2\pi r h = 2 \times 3.1416 \times 3 \times 6$$
$$= 113.10 \text{ cm}^2$$

To find the volume and curved surface area of the 'jumbo' can, we could repeat these calculations from scratch, but it is easier to use the similarity of the cans' shapes.

$$\text{linear scale factor} = \frac{\text{height of larger can}}{\text{height of smaller can}} = \frac{12}{6} = 2$$

Thus   the area of the 'jumbo' label $= 2^2 \times$ area of small label

$$= 4 \times 113.10$$
$$= 452.40 \text{ cm}^2$$

the volume of the 'jumbo' can $= 2^3 \times$ volume of small can

$$= 8 \times 169.65$$
$$= 1357.2 \text{ cm}^3$$

**EXERCISE 19c** *Throughout this exercise take π as 3.1416 or use the π key on your calculator.*

1. Three cubes, A, B and C, have side lengths 1 cm, 2 cm and 3 cm. For each of the cubes find

   (a) the surface areas          (b) the volume.

Write down, in their lowest terms, the ratios

(c) side length A : side length B : side length C

(d) area A : area B : area C

(e) volume A : volume B : volume C.

2. Three spheres, P, Q and R, have radii 1 cm, 2 cm and 3 cm. Find

(a) the surface area        (b) the volume

of the three spheres, leaving $\pi$ in your answers.

Write down, in lowest terms, the ratios

(c) radius P : radius Q : radius R

(d) area P : area Q : area R

(e) volume P : volume Q : volume R.

3. Three cones, X, Y and Z, are all similar. The first has radius 1 cm and height 2 cm, the second has radius 2 cm and height 4 cm and the third has radius 3 cm and height 6 cm. Find the volumes of the three cones leaving $\pi$ in your answers. Write down, in lowest terms, the ratio

volume X : volume Y : volume Z

4. A piece of metal is melted down and moulded into 24 model elephants. How many similar models of twice the height might have been made from the same piece of metal?

5. A gold ingot is melted down and moulded into 120 gold medallions. How many similar medallions of half the radius might have been made from the same ingot?

6. A piece of black plastic is used to produce 100 12-inch diameter 'long-playing' gramophone records. How many similar 7-inch 'singles' could have been made with the same quantity of plastic?

7. A piece of cloth is cut to produce 8 patterned shapes. How many similar shapes of half the width could have been cut from the same piece of cloth?

8. 1600 ball-bearings of radius 0.5 cm have the same volume as $n$ larger ball-bearings with radius 2 cm. Find $n$.

9. Find the volume and surface area of a sphere of radius 3 cm. *Write down* the volume and surface area of a sphere of radius 30 cm.

10. Find the volume of a 9 cm high pyramid with a square base of side length 5 cm. *Write down* the volume of a similar pyramid 36 cm high.

11. A small water tank in my house holds 5 litres. The man next door has a similar tank, made and installed by the same people, but its sides are twice as long and it is twice as high as mine. How much water does it hold?

12. A small sherry glass holds 80 ml. The large wine goblet in the same set is 1.4 times the height of the sherry glass. How much wine does it hold?

13.

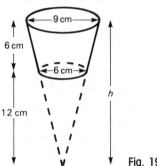

Fig. 19.25

An ice-cream tub consists of the top part of a cone (Fig. 19.25). The diameter at the top of the tub is 9 cm; at the bottom the diameter is 6 cm; it is 6 cm high. Find

(a) the height of the complete cone, $h$,

(b) the volume of the complete cone,

(c) the volume of the bottom part of the cone,

(d) the volume of the tub.

14.

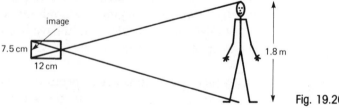

Fig. 19.26

A man is 1.8 m tall. Someone is to take his picture using an old-fashioned pin-hole camera. If the camera is 7.5 cm tall and 12 cm deep (Fig. 19.26), how far from the camera must the man stand if his head and feet are to be included in the picture?

The man is holding a scroll, 30 cm by 21 cm. What are the dimensions of the scroll's image on the back of the camera?

**15.**

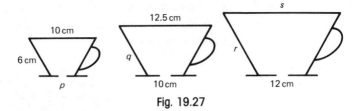

Fig. 19.27

Figure 19.27 shows the cross-sections of three similar coffee filter cones.

(a) Calculate the lengths $p$, $q$, $r$ and $s$.

(b) If the filter for the smallest size is made from 160 cm² of paper, how much paper is needed to make the filter for
   (i) the medium size     (ii) the large size?

(c) The largest size holds 756 cm³ of liquid. What is the volume of
   (i) the medium size     (ii) the small size?

## MISCELLANEOUS EXERCISE 19

*Throughout this exercise take π as 3.1416 or use the π key on your calculator.*

1. Twenty-seven cubes are stacked together, $3 \times 3 \times 3$ to make a larger cube, as shown.

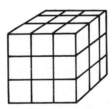

Fig. 19.28

If the six faces of the larger cube are painted red, how many of the smaller cubes will be painted

   (a) on four faces

   (b) on three faces

   (c) on exactly two faces

   (d) on just one face

   (e) on no faces at all?

2. Repeat Question 1 for
   (a) sixty-four cubes stacked to make larger cube, $4 \times 4 \times 4$
   (b) one hundred and twenty-five cubes stacked $5 \times 5 \times 5$
   (c) $n^3$ cubes stacked to make a large cube, $n \times n \times n$.

3. As part of an army assault course, a wall is built from 1 foot cubic blocks to enclose completely a square of length equal to the height of the wall.

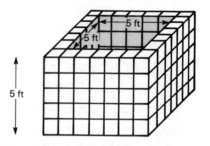

Fig. 19.29

(a) How many blocks would it take to build the 5 foot wall enclosing the 5 foot square illustrated in Fig. 19.29?

(b) How many blocks would it take to build a similar enclosure 8 feet high?

(c) How many blocks would it take to built a similar enclosure $n$ feet high?

4. The diagram shows the net of a solid.

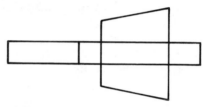

Fig. 19.30

(a) For this solid, state
   (i)   the number of faces F,
   (ii)  the number of vertices (corners) V,
   (iii) the number of edges E.

(b) Calculate $F + V - E$.                                    (EMREB)

5.

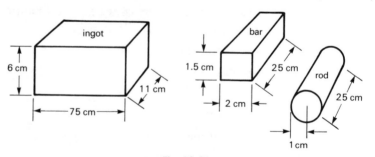

Fig. 19.31

A steel ingot 75 cm long, 11 cm wide and 6 cm deep is to be melted down and cast into steel bars 25 cm long, 2 cm wide and 1.5 cm deep.

300

(a) Calculate
    (i)   the volume of the ingot in cm³,
    (ii)  the volume of one bar in cm³,
    (iii) the number of bars that can be made from the ingot.

(b) If the ingot was instead cast into cylindrical rods with cross sections of radius 1 cm and length 25 cm, calculate how many rods could be made from the ingot.

(c) If the steel weighs 8.2 g per cm³, calculate
    (i)   the weight of one bar in g,
    (ii)  the weight of the ingot in kg.               (SEREB)

6. A local firm makes metal tubes for bicycles, exhaust pipes, etc. The diagrams below show how a cylindrical metal tube is formed by rolling a rectangular sheet ABCD so that AB meets DC. The ends AB and DC are then welded together to form a cylinder of height AB.

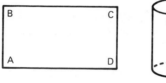

Fig. 19.32

(a) Find the length AD of sheet metal which is necessary to make a tube with a radius of 3 cm.

(b) Calculate the area of metal required to produce a tube with a radius of 6 cm and a height of 1.2 m. Give your answer in cm².

(c) A sheet of metal ABCD with AB = 1 m and AD = 200 mm is made into a cylindrical tube as shown above. Calculate the diameter of the tube in mm.

(d) A metal tube is 1.2 m high and is made of metal 2 mm thick. The external radius of the tube is 3.2 cm. A cross-section of the tube is shown below. Calculate the volume of metal used to make the tube, giving your answer in cm³.

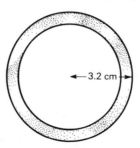

Fig. 19.33                                              (NREB)

7. Fig. 19.34 shows a vertical cross-section of a grain storage tank which is in the shape of a cylinder (height 20 m, diameter 4 m) on top of an inverted cone (vertical height 3 m, diameter 4 m). There is an outlet at the bottom, B, of the cone which 1 m from the ground.

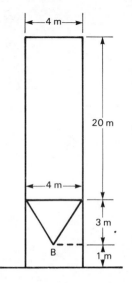

Fig. 19.34

(a) Write down the radius of the cylinder.

(b) Find the volume of the cylinder.

(c) Find the volume of the cone.

(d) Hence find the total volume of the storage tank.

(e) Write down the height of the top of the tank.

Grain is taken from the tank and sold in plastic cylindrical containers. These measure 1 m high and have a diameter of 1 m.

(f) Find the volume of each of the plastic cylindrical containers.

(g) How many plastic cylindrical containers can be filled from the full tank of grain? (EAEB)

8. $ABCD$ is the cross-section of a bar of metal with $AB = 6$ cm, $BC = 13$ cm, $AD = 12$ cm, and $D\widehat{A}B = A\widehat{D}E = D\widehat{E}B = 90°$ (Fig. 19.35).

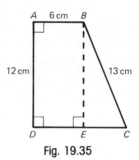

Fig. 19.35

If the bar is 1 m long calculate

(a) the length of $EC$ and hence $DC$,

(b) the area of the cross-section,

(c) the volume of the bar of metal,

(d) the weight of the bar of metal, in kilograms, given that 1 cm³ of metal weighs 2.3 grams. (WJEC)

9.

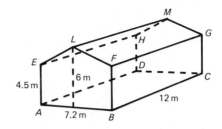

Fig. 19.36

The diagram (Fig. 19.36) shows a large greenhouse which has the following dimensions: length 12 m, width 7.2 m, height of sides 4.5 m and height to roof-ridge (which is parallel to, and half-way between, the long sides) 6 m.

Calculate

(a) the area of the end *ABFLE*,

(b) the volume of air contained in the greenhouse,

(c) the length of the slanting edge *EL*,

(d) the total area of glass, consisting of the four walls and the roof. (O & C)

10.

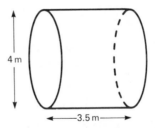

Fig. 19.37

A cylindrical oil tank, with its axis horizontal, is exactly half full of oil. The tank has a diameter of 4 m and a length of 3.5 m (Fig. 19.37).

Calculate

(a) the area of the horizontal oil surface,

(b) the area of the tank in contact with the oil,

(c) the mass of oil in the tank if 1 m³ of oil has a mass of 900 kg. (AEB '81)

11. A cylindrical wooden rod has a diameter of 2 cm and is 1 m long. Calculate

(a) the *total* surface area, in cm², of the rod,

(b) the mass of the rod if 1 cm³ of the wood has a mass of 0.8 g.

Another cylindrical rod, made of the same wood, has a diameter of 1 cm and is 1 m long.

(c) Write down the mass of this rod. (AEB '82)

12.

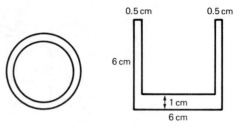

Fig. 19.38

A plan and elevation of a cylindrical glass container are shown in Fig.19.38.

(a)  Calculate the volume of glass in the container.

(b)  Calculate the total surface area of the container.

(c)  A number of identical containers are to be filled with liquid up to 0.5 cm below the brim. How many of these containers may be filled from a litre of liquid?          (Ox)

# 20 MATRICES

A *row* matrix has only one row, e.g. (2  4  7).

A *column* matrix has only one column, e.g. $\begin{pmatrix} 2 \\ 4 \\ 7 \end{pmatrix}$.

A column matrix is sometimes called a *vector* or a *column vector*.

In general, a matrix has $m$ rows and $n$ columns and is described as an $m \times n$ matrix. For example:

(a) a $2 \times 2$ matrix $\begin{pmatrix} 10 & 9 \\ 8 & -7 \end{pmatrix}$    (b) a $3 \times 2$ matrix $\begin{pmatrix} 2 & 1 \\ 3 & 4 \\ 0 & 5 \end{pmatrix}$.

*Note*:

(*i*) A matrix does not take a single value: it is a table of numbers.

(*ii*) Two matrices are equal only if they have the same number of rows and columns and the numbers in corresponding positions are equal.

Thus $\begin{pmatrix} 3 & 8 \\ 8 & 1 \end{pmatrix}$ equals $\begin{pmatrix} 3 & 8 \\ 8 & 1 \end{pmatrix}$ but *not* $\begin{pmatrix} 3 & 8 \\ 8 & 2 \end{pmatrix}$ nor $\begin{pmatrix} 8 & 3 \\ 1 & 8 \end{pmatrix}$.

And (5  4  3) is quite different from $\begin{pmatrix} 5 \\ 4 \\ 3 \end{pmatrix}$ since the arrangement of columns and rows is different.

## ADDITION AND SUBTRACTION

If two matrices are to be added or subtracted, they must have the same number of rows and columns. Then it is simply a matter of adding (or subtracting) the numbers in equivalent positions.

**Examples** (*i*) $\begin{pmatrix} 10 & 9 \\ 8 & -7 \end{pmatrix} + \begin{pmatrix} 2 & 9 \\ 7 & 8 \end{pmatrix} = \begin{pmatrix} 10+2 & 9+9 \\ 8+7 & -7+8 \end{pmatrix} = \begin{pmatrix} 12 & 18 \\ 15 & 1 \end{pmatrix}$

(*ii*) $\begin{pmatrix} 3 & 7 \\ 6 & 3 \end{pmatrix} - \begin{pmatrix} 2 & 4 \\ 4 & 2 \end{pmatrix} = \begin{pmatrix} 3-2 & 7-4 \\ 6-4 & 3-2 \end{pmatrix} = \begin{pmatrix} 1 & 3 \\ 2 & 1 \end{pmatrix}$

# MULTIPLICATION

## Multiplication by numbers

Matrices may be multiplied by ordinary numbers by simply multiplying each number inside the matrix. For example

$$2 \times \begin{pmatrix} 3 & 7 \\ 6 & 3 \end{pmatrix} = \begin{pmatrix} 6 & 14 \\ 12 & 6 \end{pmatrix}$$

## Multiplication by other matrices

Multiplication of two matrices is quite different from ordinary multiplication. It is only possible to multiply matrices $A$ and $B$ if the number of *columns* in $A$ is the same as the number of *rows* in $B$.

**Example**

$$\begin{pmatrix} 2 & 8 \\ 5 & 7 \end{pmatrix} \times \begin{pmatrix} 1 & 3 \\ 4 & 0 \end{pmatrix}$$

$$\quad A \qquad\qquad B$$

Take the first row in $A$, i.e. $\begin{pmatrix} 2 & 8 \end{pmatrix}$ with the first column in $B$,

i.e. $\begin{pmatrix} 1 \\ 4 \end{pmatrix}$.

$$\begin{pmatrix} 2 & 8 \\ 5 & 7 \end{pmatrix} \begin{pmatrix} 1 & 3 \\ 4 & 0 \end{pmatrix}$$

Multiply the first numbers in each, i.e. $2 \times 1$. Then multiply the second numbers in each, i.e. $8 \times 4$. Finally, add the two results:

$$2 \times 1 + 8 \times 4 = 2 + 32 = 34$$

Put 34 in the first row, first column of the answer matrix.

$$\begin{pmatrix} 34 & - \\ - & - \end{pmatrix}$$

Repeat the process with the second column in $B$:

$$\begin{pmatrix} 2 & 8 \\ 5 & 7 \end{pmatrix}\begin{pmatrix} 1 & 3 \\ 4 & 0 \end{pmatrix} = \begin{pmatrix} 34 & 2 \times 3 + 8 \times 0 \\ - & - \end{pmatrix} = \begin{pmatrix} 34 & 6 + 0 \\ - & - \end{pmatrix}$$

$$= \begin{pmatrix} 34 & 6 \\ - & - \end{pmatrix}$$

Then, taking the *second* row of *A* with each column in *B*, repeat the process twice more:

$$\begin{pmatrix} 2 & 8 \\ 5 & 7 \end{pmatrix} \begin{pmatrix} 1 & 3 \\ 4 & 0 \end{pmatrix} = \begin{pmatrix} 34 & 6 \\ 5\times1+7\times4 & 5\times3+7\times0 \end{pmatrix}$$

$$= \begin{pmatrix} 34 & 6 \\ 33 & 15 \end{pmatrix}$$

Similarly

$$\begin{pmatrix} 2 & 3 & 4 \\ 1 & 0 & 2 \end{pmatrix} \begin{pmatrix} 1 \\ 2 \\ 3 \end{pmatrix} = \begin{pmatrix} 2\times1+3\times2+4\times3 \\ 1\times1+0\times2+2\times3 \end{pmatrix}$$

$$= \begin{pmatrix} 2+6+12 \\ 1+0+6 \end{pmatrix} = \begin{pmatrix} 20 \\ 7 \end{pmatrix}$$

Matrix multiplication is not commutative, that is $AB \neq BA$. For example, when *A* *pre*-multiplies *B*, it is placed *before* *B* and gives (as above):

$$\underset{A}{\begin{pmatrix} 2 & 8 \\ 5 & 7 \end{pmatrix}} \underset{B}{\begin{pmatrix} 1 & 3 \\ 4 & 0 \end{pmatrix}} = \underset{AB}{\begin{pmatrix} 34 & 6 \\ 33 & 15 \end{pmatrix}}$$

But if *A* *post*-multiplies *B*, it is placed *after* *B* and the result is different:

$$\underset{B}{\begin{pmatrix} 1 & 3 \\ 4 & 0 \end{pmatrix}} \underset{A}{\begin{pmatrix} 2 & 8 \\ 5 & 7 \end{pmatrix}} = \begin{pmatrix} 1\times2+3\times5 & 1\times8+3\times7 \\ 4\times2+0\times5 & 4\times8+0\times7 \end{pmatrix}$$

$$= \begin{pmatrix} 2+15 & 8+21 \\ 8+0 & 32+0 \end{pmatrix} = \underset{BA}{\begin{pmatrix} 17 & 29 \\ 8 & 32 \end{pmatrix}}$$

**EXERCISE 20a**   1. How many rows and columns are there in these matrices?

(a) $(1 \quad 3 \quad 2)$   (b) $\begin{pmatrix} 2 & 1 \\ 3 & 4 \end{pmatrix}$   (c) $(1 \quad 2)$

(d) $\begin{pmatrix} 1 \\ 2 \end{pmatrix}$   (e) $\begin{pmatrix} 2 & 1 \\ 3 & 4 \\ 5 & 6 \end{pmatrix}$   (f) $\begin{pmatrix} 1 \\ 2 \\ 3 \end{pmatrix}$.

2. Find

(a) $\begin{pmatrix} 2 & 3 \\ 1 & 2 \end{pmatrix} + \begin{pmatrix} 4 & 1 \\ 2 & 8 \end{pmatrix}$

(b) $\begin{pmatrix} 2 & 3 \\ 1 & 2 \end{pmatrix} - \begin{pmatrix} 4 & 1 \\ 2 & 8 \end{pmatrix}$

(c) $\begin{pmatrix} 2 & 3 \\ 1 & 2 \end{pmatrix} \times \begin{pmatrix} 4 & 1 \\ 2 & 8 \end{pmatrix}$

(d) $\begin{pmatrix} 4 & 1 \\ 2 & 8 \end{pmatrix} \times \begin{pmatrix} 2 & 3 \\ 1 & 2 \end{pmatrix}$.

3. Find *if possible*

(a) $\begin{pmatrix} 3 & 2 & 1 \\ 0 & 3 & 2 \end{pmatrix} + \begin{pmatrix} 1 \\ 2 \\ 3 \end{pmatrix}$

(b) $\begin{pmatrix} 3 & 2 & 1 \\ 0 & 3 & 2 \end{pmatrix} \times \begin{pmatrix} 1 \\ 2 \\ 3 \end{pmatrix}$

(c) $(1 \quad 4) \times \begin{pmatrix} 3 & 4 & 5 \\ 2 & 0 & -1 \end{pmatrix}$

(d) $\begin{pmatrix} 1 & 2 \\ 3 & 4 \end{pmatrix} \times \begin{pmatrix} 1 & 2 \\ 3 & 4 \end{pmatrix}$.

4. $A = \begin{pmatrix} 4 & 1 \\ 2 & 1 \end{pmatrix}$ and $B = \begin{pmatrix} 1 & 0 \\ 2 & 1 \end{pmatrix}$. Find

(a) $A + B$   (b) $A - B$   (c) $2A$   (d) $2A - B$

(e) $4A + 2B$   (f) $10A + 3B$   (g) $\frac{1}{2}A$   (h) $-2A$

(i) $\frac{1}{4}B$   (j) $\frac{3}{4}B$   (k) $\frac{1}{2}A + \frac{1}{4}B$   (l) $\frac{3}{4}B - 2A$

(m) $AB$   (n) $BA$   (o) $A^2$   (p) $B^2$

(q) $BAB$   (r) $ABA$   (s) $(BA)^2$   (t) $(AB)^2$.

5. $A = \begin{pmatrix} 2 & 1 & 2 \\ 3 & 2 & 1 \end{pmatrix}$, $B = \begin{pmatrix} 1 & 0 \\ 2 & 1 \\ 1 & 2 \end{pmatrix}$, $C = \begin{pmatrix} 2 & 0 \\ 1 & 2 \end{pmatrix}$, $D = \begin{pmatrix} 3 \\ 4 \\ 5 \end{pmatrix}$,

$E = (1 \quad -2)$, $F = \begin{pmatrix} 1 \\ -2 \end{pmatrix}$. Find *where possible*

(a) $3B$   (b) $2A$   (c) $A - B$   (d) $AB$

(e) $BA$   (f) $\frac{1}{2}C$   (g) $C^2$   (h) $AD$

(i) $BC$   (j) $2(AB)$   (k) $(2A)B$   (l) $BD$

(m) $EC$   (n) $EF$   (o) $FE$   (p) $BF$

(q) $EA$   (r) $CF$   (s) $(3C)(2F)$   (t) $6CF$

(u) $BC$   (v) $CA$   (w) $ECF$   (x) $CFE$.

6. $2\begin{pmatrix} a \\ b \end{pmatrix} + \begin{pmatrix} 3 \\ 1 \end{pmatrix} = \begin{pmatrix} 9 \\ 5 \end{pmatrix}$. Find $a$ and $b$.

7. $2\begin{pmatrix} 3 & x \\ 4 & 2 \end{pmatrix} + 3\begin{pmatrix} 4 & -1 \\ 2 & y \end{pmatrix} = \begin{pmatrix} 18 & 3 \\ 14 & 1 \end{pmatrix}$. Find $x$ and $y$.

8. $3\begin{pmatrix} 5 & a \\ b & 7 \end{pmatrix} + 2\begin{pmatrix} c & 1 \\ 2 & d \end{pmatrix} = \begin{pmatrix} 19 & 5 \\ 1 & 5 \end{pmatrix}$. Find $a$, $b$, $c$ and $d$.

**9.** $\begin{pmatrix} a & 3 \\ b & 2 \end{pmatrix} \begin{pmatrix} -1 \\ 1 \end{pmatrix} = \begin{pmatrix} 2 \\ 4 \end{pmatrix}$. Find $a$ and $b$.

**10.** $\begin{pmatrix} x & (x+1) \\ y & 2y \end{pmatrix} \begin{pmatrix} 1 \\ 2 \end{pmatrix} = \begin{pmatrix} 8 \\ 20 \end{pmatrix}$. Find $x$ and $y$.

**11.** $\begin{pmatrix} x & (x+3) \\ 2y & (y-3) \end{pmatrix} \begin{pmatrix} 2 \\ 3 \end{pmatrix} = \begin{pmatrix} 14 \\ 12 \end{pmatrix}$. Find $x$ and $y$.

**12.** $\begin{pmatrix} 3x & (x-2) \\ y & (2y+3) \end{pmatrix} \begin{pmatrix} 2 \\ 1 \end{pmatrix} = \begin{pmatrix} 19 \\ 3 \end{pmatrix}$. Find $x$ and $y$.

# THE IDENTITY MATRIX, *I*

The *identity* matrix or *unit* matrix multiplies another matrix to leave this other matrix unchanged.

$$I \times A = A \times I = A$$

For a $2 \times 2$ matrix $I = \begin{pmatrix} 1 & 0 \\ 0 & 1 \end{pmatrix}$.

# DETERMINANTS

If $A = \begin{pmatrix} a & b \\ c & d \end{pmatrix}$ then its determinant, written $\det A$ or $|A|$ or

$\begin{vmatrix} a & b \\ c & d \end{vmatrix}$, is a numerical value given by

$$\begin{vmatrix} a & b \\ c & d \end{vmatrix} = ad - bc$$

**Example** $\begin{vmatrix} 6 & 4 \\ 3 & 1 \end{vmatrix} = 6 \times 1 - 4 \times 3 = 6 - 12 = -6.$

# INVERSES

The inverse of a matrix $A$ is written as $A^{-1}$. The original matrix and its inverse multiply together to give the identity matrix, $I$. That is

$$A \times A^{-1} = A^{-1} \times A = I$$

309

## Finding the inverse of a 2 × 2 matrix

(*i*) Swap the element on the top left with that on the bottom right.

(*ii*) Change the signs of the other two elements.

(*iii*) Divide by the value of the determinant.

**Example** Find the inverse of $\begin{pmatrix} 6 & 4 \\ 3 & 1 \end{pmatrix}$.

First, swap the 6 with the 1. Second, change the signs of the 4 and the 3. Then find the determinant (which is $-6$, see previous page) and divide by it. Thus

$$\begin{pmatrix} 6 & 4 \\ 3 & 1 \end{pmatrix}^{-1} = \begin{pmatrix} 1 & -4 \\ -3 & 6 \end{pmatrix} \div -6 = \begin{pmatrix} -\frac{1}{6} & \frac{2}{3} \\ \frac{1}{2} & -1 \end{pmatrix}$$

*Check* $\begin{pmatrix} -\frac{1}{6} & \frac{2}{3} \\ \frac{1}{2} & -1 \end{pmatrix}\begin{pmatrix} 6 & 4 \\ 3 & 1 \end{pmatrix} = \begin{pmatrix} 1 & 0 \\ 0 & 1 \end{pmatrix}.$ ✓

## SINGULAR MATRICES

Some matrices do not have an inverse; they are called *singular* matrices. The determinant of a singular matrix is zero.

**Example** $\begin{pmatrix} 8 & 4 \\ 2 & 1 \end{pmatrix}$ is a singular matrix, as its determinant is zero:

$$\begin{vmatrix} 8 & 4 \\ 2 & 1 \end{vmatrix} = 8 \times 1 - 4 \times 2 = 0$$

So the inverse of $\begin{pmatrix} 8 & 4 \\ 2 & 1 \end{pmatrix}$ does not exist.

**EXERCISE 20b**

1. Multiply $\begin{pmatrix} 1 & 4 \\ 2 & 7 \end{pmatrix}\begin{pmatrix} -7 & 4 \\ 2 & -1 \end{pmatrix}$. What is the inverse of $\begin{pmatrix} 1 & 4 \\ 2 & 7 \end{pmatrix}$?

2. Multiply $\begin{pmatrix} 3 & 1 \\ 2 & 2 \end{pmatrix}\begin{pmatrix} \frac{1}{2} & -\frac{1}{4} \\ -\frac{1}{2} & \frac{3}{4} \end{pmatrix}$. What is the inverse of $\begin{pmatrix} 3 & 1 \\ 2 & 2 \end{pmatrix}$?

3. Find (i) the determinant, (ii) the inverse of the following. In each case, check that the inverse multiplies the original matrix to give $\begin{pmatrix} 1 & 0 \\ 0 & 1 \end{pmatrix}$.

(a) $\begin{pmatrix} 1 & 2 \\ 3 & 7 \end{pmatrix}$   (b) $\begin{pmatrix} 4 & 1 \\ 11 & 3 \end{pmatrix}$   (c) $\begin{pmatrix} 3 & 2 \\ 5 & 3 \end{pmatrix}$   (d) $\begin{pmatrix} 6 & 5 \\ 3 & 3 \end{pmatrix}$

(e) $\begin{pmatrix} 4 & 2 \\ 3 & 2 \end{pmatrix}$    (f) $\begin{pmatrix} 4 & 2 \\ 9 & 5 \end{pmatrix}$    (g) $\begin{pmatrix} 9 & 0 \\ 1 & 1 \end{pmatrix}$    (h) $\begin{pmatrix} 5 & 6 \\ 3 & 4 \end{pmatrix}$

(i) $\begin{pmatrix} 4 & 2 \\ 1 & 2 \end{pmatrix}$    (j) $\begin{pmatrix} 4 & 6 \\ 3 & 4 \end{pmatrix}$    (k) $\begin{pmatrix} 6 & 4 \\ 4 & 3 \end{pmatrix}$    (l) $\begin{pmatrix} 4 & 3 \\ 6 & 4 \end{pmatrix}$.

4. $P = \begin{pmatrix} 1 & 3 \\ 2 & 5 \end{pmatrix}$, $Q = \begin{pmatrix} 2 & 8 \\ -1 & 5 \end{pmatrix}$. Find

     (a) $|P|$      (b) $\det Q$      (c) $P^{-1}$      (d) $Q^{-1}$.

5. Find

     (a) $\begin{vmatrix} 3 & 4 \\ 2 & 1 \end{vmatrix}$      (b) $\begin{pmatrix} 5 & 6 \\ 2 & 3 \end{pmatrix}^{-1}$      (c) $\begin{vmatrix} 2 & 1 \\ 4 & 5 \end{vmatrix}$

     (d) $\det \begin{pmatrix} 3 & 1 \\ 2 & 2 \end{pmatrix}$      (e) $\begin{pmatrix} 3 & 1 \\ 2 & 2 \end{pmatrix}^{-1}$      (f) $\begin{pmatrix} 3 & 4 \\ 2 & 1 \end{pmatrix}^{-1}$.

6. If $X = \begin{pmatrix} 3 & 2 \\ 1 & 1 \end{pmatrix}$, $Y = \begin{pmatrix} 2 & 2 \\ 1 & 3 \end{pmatrix}$, find

     (a) $X^{-1}$      (b) $Y^{-1}$      (c) $XY$      (d) $(XY)^{-1}$

     (e) $YX$      (f) $(YX)^{-1}$      (g) $X^{-1}Y^{-1}$      (h) $Y^{-1}X^{-1}$.

     Hence show that $(XY)^{-1} = Y^{-1}X^{-1}$ and $(YX)^{-1} = X^{-1}Y^{-1}$.

7. What is the value of the determinant of a singular matrix, i.e. one that has no inverse? Which of these are singular matrices?

     (a) $\begin{pmatrix} 2 & 3 \\ 4 & 6 \end{pmatrix}$      (b) $\begin{pmatrix} 4 & -5 \\ 2 & -2\frac{1}{2} \end{pmatrix}$      (c) $\begin{pmatrix} 6 & 9 \\ 2 & 3 \end{pmatrix}$

     (d) $\begin{pmatrix} 2 & 3 \\ -8 & -12 \end{pmatrix}$      (e) $\begin{pmatrix} -1\frac{1}{2} & 2\frac{1}{2} \\ 3 & -5 \end{pmatrix}$.

## USING MATRICES TO SOLVE SIMULTANEOUS EQUATIONS

**Example** Solve $2x - 3y = 2$

             $x + 2y = 8$.

Rewrite the equation in matrix form:

$$\begin{pmatrix} 2 & -3 \\ 1 & 2 \end{pmatrix} \begin{pmatrix} x \\ y \end{pmatrix} = \begin{pmatrix} 2 \\ 8 \end{pmatrix}$$

Note that this multiplies out to give $\begin{pmatrix} 2x - 3y \\ x + 2y \end{pmatrix} = \begin{pmatrix} 2 \\ 8 \end{pmatrix}$.

Find the inverse of $\begin{pmatrix} 2 & -3 \\ 1 & 2 \end{pmatrix}$:

$$\begin{pmatrix} 2 & -3 \\ 1 & 2 \end{pmatrix}^{-1} = \begin{pmatrix} 2 & 3 \\ -1 & 2 \end{pmatrix} \div 7 = \begin{pmatrix} \frac{2}{7} & \frac{3}{7} \\ -\frac{1}{7} & \frac{2}{7} \end{pmatrix}$$

Pre-multiply both sides of the matrix equation by this inverse:

$$\begin{pmatrix} \frac{2}{7} & \frac{3}{7} \\ -\frac{1}{7} & \frac{2}{7} \end{pmatrix}\begin{pmatrix} 2 & -3 \\ 1 & 2 \end{pmatrix}\begin{pmatrix} x \\ y \end{pmatrix} = \begin{pmatrix} \frac{2}{7} & \frac{3}{7} \\ -\frac{1}{7} & \frac{2}{7} \end{pmatrix}\begin{pmatrix} 2 \\ 8 \end{pmatrix}$$

Remembering that any matrix multiplied by its own inverse gives the identity matrix, we get:

$$\begin{pmatrix} 1 & 0 \\ 0 & 1 \end{pmatrix}\begin{pmatrix} x \\ y \end{pmatrix} = \begin{pmatrix} 4 \\ 2 \end{pmatrix}$$

Hence

$$\begin{pmatrix} x \\ y \end{pmatrix} = \begin{pmatrix} 4 \\ 2 \end{pmatrix}$$

which means that $x = 4$ and $y = 2$.

*Check*
$$2 \times (4) - 3 \times (2) = 2$$
$$4 + 2 \times (2) = 8 \quad \checkmark$$

**EXERCISE 20c**   1. (a) Multiply out the matrices $\begin{pmatrix} 3 & 7 \\ 2 & 5 \end{pmatrix}\begin{pmatrix} x \\ y \end{pmatrix}$. Hence show that the matrix equation

$$\begin{pmatrix} 3 & 7 \\ 2 & 5 \end{pmatrix}\begin{pmatrix} x \\ y \end{pmatrix} = \begin{pmatrix} 11 \\ 7 \end{pmatrix}$$

is equivalent to the two simultaneous equations

$$3x + 7y = 11$$
$$2x + 5y = 7$$

(b) Show that the inverse of $\begin{pmatrix} 3 & 7 \\ 2 & 5 \end{pmatrix}$ is $\begin{pmatrix} 5 & -7 \\ -2 & 3 \end{pmatrix}$.

(c) Now simplify the two sides of the equation.

$$\begin{pmatrix} 5 & -7 \\ -2 & 3 \end{pmatrix}\begin{pmatrix} 3 & 7 \\ 2 & 5 \end{pmatrix}\begin{pmatrix} x \\ y \end{pmatrix} = \begin{pmatrix} 5 & -7 \\ -2 & 3 \end{pmatrix}\begin{pmatrix} 11 \\ 7 \end{pmatrix}$$

and so solve the simultaneous equations.

Check your results by substituting them into the original equations.

2. A pair of simultaneous equations

$$3x + 5y = 22$$
$$x + 2y = 8$$

are to be solved by a matrix method. Complete the matrices below, which show the equations in matrix form.

$$\begin{pmatrix} 3 & \cdot \\ \cdot & \cdot \end{pmatrix} \begin{pmatrix} x \\ y \end{pmatrix} = \begin{pmatrix} \cdot \\ \cdot \end{pmatrix}$$

Show that the inverse of $\begin{pmatrix} 3 & 5 \\ 1 & 2 \end{pmatrix}$ is $\begin{pmatrix} 2 & -5 \\ -1 & 3 \end{pmatrix}$.

Pre-multiply each side of this matrix equation by $\begin{pmatrix} 2 & -5 \\ -1 & 3 \end{pmatrix}$ and so solve the equations.

Check your results by substituting them into the original equations.

3. The simultaneous equations

$$2x + 3y = 7$$
$$x + y = 3$$

are to be solved using matrices. Write down a $2 \times 2$ matrix, $M$, such that $M \begin{pmatrix} x \\ y \end{pmatrix} = \begin{pmatrix} 7 \\ 3 \end{pmatrix}$.

Find the inverse of $M$. Hence solve the equations.

Check your results.

4. Find the inverse of $\begin{pmatrix} 5 & 3 \\ 3 & 2 \end{pmatrix}$. Use it to solve the matrix equations

(a) $\begin{pmatrix} 5 & 3 \\ 3 & 2 \end{pmatrix} \begin{pmatrix} x \\ y \end{pmatrix} = \begin{pmatrix} 9 \\ 5 \end{pmatrix}$   (b) $\begin{pmatrix} 5 & 3 \\ 3 & 2 \end{pmatrix} \begin{pmatrix} a & 2 \\ 1 & b \end{pmatrix} = \begin{pmatrix} -2 & 19 \\ -1 & 12 \end{pmatrix}$

Check your results.

Use matrices to solve the following simultaneous equations; in each case check your results in the given equations.

5. $2x + 3y = 4$
   $4x + 7y = 10$

6. $3x + 2y = 16$
   $5x + 4y = 22$

7. $8x + 2y = 15$
   $x + y = 3$

8. $x - 2y = -7$
   $3x + 4y = 29$

9. $2a + 4b = 3$
   $2a + 3b = 5$

10. $4p - 2q = 13$
    $3p + q = 15$

313

11. $3x - 2y = 5$
    $2y + 3x = 7$

12. $5x - 3y = 4$
    $7y + x = 16$

13. $3y = -7$
    $2x + y = 11$

14. $5y + 2x = 8$
    $2x - 3y = 4$

15. $2x - 3y = 12$
    $3x - 2y = 6$

16. $10x - 2y = 3$
    $5x - 2y = -4$

17. $3x + 2y = -11$
    $6x - y = 8$

18. $3x - 5y = -1$
    $x + y = 1$

## MATRIX ARITHMETIC

Matrices are just tables of numbers. Cumbersome problems of arithmetic can often be set out in matrix form. This must be done with some care, so that when the various matrices are combined by the rules of matrix addition, subtraction and multiplication they give meaningful results. The amount of work involved is not reduced by setting out the problem in this way — but the systematic presentation is a considerable advantage.

**Example** Laurie and Diana buy flowers for Mother's Day. Laurie buys 2 bunches of daffodils, costing 25 p per bunch, a bunch of violets at 20 p and two tulip blooms at 22 p each. Diana buys 3 bunches of violets, no daffodils but 4 tulip blooms.

We might begin a problem of this sort by setting out the information given as a table, showing the purchases of each child. Obviously we must be careful to get the right numbers under each heading.

| Daffodils | Violets | Tulips | |
|-----------|---------|--------|--------|
| 2 | 1 | 2 | Laurie |
| 0 | 3 | 4 | Diana |

In effect, we have written the information as a $2 \times 3$ matrix. We shall call this matrix $F$:

$$F = \begin{pmatrix} 2 & 1 & 2 \\ 0 & 3 & 4 \end{pmatrix} \begin{matrix} \text{L} \\ \text{D} \end{matrix}$$

with column headings d, v, t above.

In the same way we could write the cost of the flowers as a $3 \times 1$ matrix, $C$

$$C = \begin{matrix} \text{Cost (pence)} \\ \begin{pmatrix} 25 \\ 20 \\ 22 \end{pmatrix} \begin{matrix} \text{d} \\ \text{v} \\ \text{t} \end{matrix} \end{matrix}$$

Multiplying $F$ and $C$ together will create a further matrix, $FC$.

$$FC = \begin{pmatrix} 2 & 1 & 2 \\ 0 & 3 & 4 \end{pmatrix} \begin{pmatrix} 25 \\ 20 \\ 22 \end{pmatrix} = \begin{pmatrix} 2 \times 25 + 1 \times 20 + 2 \times 22 \\ 0 \times 25 + 3 \times 20 + 4 \times 22 \end{pmatrix} = \begin{pmatrix} 114 \\ 148 \end{pmatrix}$$

Now consider Laurie's spending. He spends $2 \times 25$ p on daffodils, $1 \times 20$ p on violets and $2 \times 22$ p on tulips, making a total of $2 \times 25 + 1 \times 20 + 2 \times 22 = 114$ p. But this is *exactly* the calculation made when the matrices were multiplied together: the top row of *FC* therefore shows how much Laurie has spent. Similarly, the bottom row of *FC* shows how much Diana spent.

We could find the total spent by both children by pre-multiplying *FC* by (1  1):

$$(1 \quad 1) \begin{pmatrix} 114 \\ 148 \end{pmatrix} = 1 \times 114 + 1 \times 148 = (262)$$

That is, the children spent a total of 262 p or £2.62.

When laying out a problem in this way remember that the order in which matrices are multiplied and the arrangement of rows and columns are *crucial* if the final values are to have sensible meaning.

## ROUTE MATRICES

Matrices can store many kinds of information. For example, the network shown in Fig. 20.1 shows possible routes for travelling from either A or B to destinations P, Q and R.

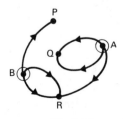

Fig. 20.1

The same information could be shown on a *route matrix*:

$$\begin{array}{c} & \text{To} \\ \text{From} & \begin{array}{c} A \\ B \end{array} \begin{array}{ccc} P & Q & R \\ \begin{pmatrix} 0 & 2 & 1 \\ 1 & 0 & 2 \end{pmatrix} \end{array} \end{array}$$

The first 0 indicates it is not possible to travel from A to P. The 2 indicates that there are two routes from A to Q and so on.

If we have a second route matrix showing, say, the number of possible routes from P, Q and R to final destinations X and Y:

$$\begin{array}{c} & \text{To} \\ \text{From} & \begin{array}{c} P \\ Q \\ R \end{array} \begin{array}{cc} X & Y \\ \begin{pmatrix} 2 & 1 \\ 1 & 0 \\ 2 & 0 \end{pmatrix} \end{array} \end{array}$$

then multiplying the first and second matrices will give the number of possible routes from the starting points A and B to the final destinations X and Y:

$$\text{From} \begin{array}{c} A \\ B \end{array} \begin{pmatrix} 0 & 2 & 1 \\ 1 & 0 & 2 \end{pmatrix} \begin{pmatrix} 2 & 1 \\ 1 & 0 \\ 2 & 0 \end{pmatrix} \quad \begin{pmatrix} 4 & 0 \\ 6 & 1 \end{pmatrix} \begin{array}{c} A \\ B \end{array} \text{From}$$

Thus there are 4 possible routes for a journey from A to X (travelling via P, Q or R), none from A to Y and so on.

**EXERCISE 20d**  1. Three local football teams, City, Rovers and United, should have each played 10 games in the league but United are still to play their tenth match. City have won 6, drawn 2 and lost 2; Rovers have won 4, drawn 4 and lost 2; United have won only 3 matches, drawn 1 and lost 5. This information can be written as a matrix, $R$, part of which is shown:

$$\begin{array}{c} & \text{Won} \quad \text{Drawn} \quad \text{Lost} \\ \begin{array}{c} \text{City} \\ \text{Rovers} \\ \text{United} \end{array} \begin{pmatrix} 6 & 2 & 2 \\ - & - & - \\ - & - & - \end{pmatrix} = R \end{array}$$

(a) Copy and complete the matrix.

(b) The matrix $G$ is $\begin{pmatrix} 1 \\ 1 \\ 1 \end{pmatrix}$. Find $RG$. What do the numbers in $RG$ mean?

(c) If a win earns 2 points, a draw 1 point and a loss 0 points, write a $3 \times 1$ matrix, $P$, so that $RP$ gives the points won by each team. Find $RP$.

2. Bill and Ben go shopping. Their purchases are shown in the table.

|  | New flowerpots | Packets of fertiliser | Packets of weed killer |
|---|---|---|---|
| Bill | 2 | 1 | 2 |
| Ben | 3 | 2 | 1 |

(a) Write this information as a $2 \times 3$ matrix, $P$.

(b) Flowerpots cost 30p each, fertiliser costs 70p a packet and weed killer costs 80p. Write this information as a $3 \times 1$ matrix, $C$, so that $PC$ shows the total spent by Bill and Ben. Work out $PC$.

(c) Use (1  1) to pre-multiply $PC$. What does this tell you?

3. The local telephone manager at Barchester Exchange monitors for a day the telephone calls through the exchange. Calls are either local or trunk and may be made at peak, standard or cheap rates according to the time of day. The results are shown in the table:

|  | Peak | Standard | Cheap |
|---|---|---|---|
| Local | 800 | 900 | 500 |
| Trunk | 1000 | 1200 | 200 |

(a) Show this information as a $2 \times 3$ matrix, $T$.

(b) Trunk calls use five 'call-units' and local calls use only one. Work out the matrix $U = (1 \quad 5)T$ and explain its meaning.

(c) If peak-time call-units cost 50p, standard units cost 30p and cheap-period units cost only 10p, write down a $3 \times 1$ matrix, $C$, so that $UC$ gives the total cost *in pounds* of the calls made through the Barchester Exchange on that day.

(d) Find $UC$.

4. In one week a newsagent sells 3000 newspapers, 420 comics, 1320 magazines and 150 paperbacks. In the following week he sells 3100 newspapers, 425 comics, 1320 magazines and 140 paperbacks. The price of a newspaper is 24p, of a comic 40p, of a magazine £1 and of a paperback £2.

Set out this information as two matrices and use them to work out the receipts of the newsagent for each week. Find another matrix that will multiply your previous answer to give the receipts over the fortnight.

5. Copy and complete the following matrix which shows the number of routes from A and B to P, Q and R illustrated in the network shown in Fig. 20.2.

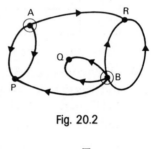

Fig. 20.2

$$\text{From} \quad \begin{array}{c} A \\ B \end{array} \begin{array}{c} \text{To} \\ \begin{array}{ccc} P & Q & R \end{array} \\ \begin{pmatrix} 2 & 0 & - \\ - & - & - \end{pmatrix} \end{array}$$

Given the following route matrix showing the number of ways of travelling from P, Q and R to final destinations X, Y and Z calculate the number of possible routes from A and B to X, Y and Z.

$$\text{From} \quad \begin{array}{c} P \\ Q \\ R \end{array} \begin{array}{c} \text{To} \\ \begin{array}{ccc} X & Y & Z \end{array} \\ \begin{pmatrix} 2 & 1 & 0 \\ 1 & 2 & 1 \\ 0 & 3 & 1 \end{pmatrix} \end{array}$$

6. Fig. 20.3 shows the number of roads leading from towns at A and B to the ports N, P and Q, as well as the number of possible sea-crossings to the mainland ports at X, Y and Z.

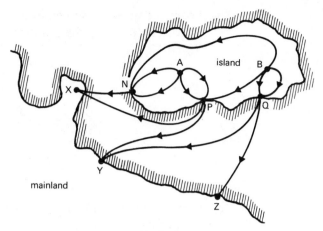

**Fig. 20.3**

(a) Copy and complete the matrix $R$ showing the number of roads leading from A and B to N, P and Q.

$$
\text{From}\quad
\begin{array}{c}
\\ A \\ B
\end{array}
\overset{\displaystyle \overset{\text{To}}{\begin{array}{ccc} N & P & Q \end{array}}}{
\begin{pmatrix}
2 & - & - \\
- & - & -
\end{pmatrix}} = R
$$

(b) Copy and complete the matrix $S$ showing the number of possible sea-crossings from N, P and Q to the mainland ports.

$$
\text{From}\quad
\begin{array}{c}
\\ N \\ P \\ Q
\end{array}
\overset{\displaystyle \overset{\text{To}}{\begin{array}{ccc} X & Y & Z \end{array}}}{
\begin{pmatrix}
1 & - & - \\
- & - & - \\
- & - & -
\end{pmatrix}} = S
$$

(c) Calculate the matrix product $RS$ and state clearly what information each element in matrix $RS$ represents.

7. The matrix $M$ shows the number of possible routes from A, B and C to destinations P and Q.

$$
\text{From}\quad
\begin{array}{c}
\\ A \\ B \\ C
\end{array}
\overset{\displaystyle \overset{\text{To}}{\begin{array}{cc} P & Q \end{array}}}{
\begin{pmatrix}
1 & 2 \\
1 & 0 \\
2 & 1
\end{pmatrix}} = M
$$

(a) How many routes are there from (i) B to P, (ii) C to Q?

(b) From the network shown in Fig. 20.4 construct a second matrix, $N$, to show the number of routes from P and Q to X and Y.

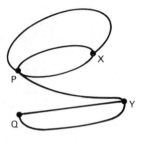

Fig. 20.4

(c) Find the matrix $MN$ and state clearly what information each of its four elements represent.

## MISCELLANEOUS EXERCISE 20

1. Find $a$ and $b$ in the matrix $\begin{pmatrix} a & 1 \\ b & 0 \end{pmatrix}$ if $\begin{pmatrix} a & 1 \\ b & 0 \end{pmatrix}\begin{pmatrix} 2 \\ 5 \end{pmatrix} = \begin{pmatrix} 7 \\ 8 \end{pmatrix}$.

2. $A = \begin{pmatrix} 2 & 1 \\ 3 & 2 \end{pmatrix}$ and $B = \begin{pmatrix} -1 & 2 \\ -2 & 0 \end{pmatrix}$.

   (a) Determine $AB$, $BA$, $A^2$, $A^{-1}$.

   (b) Calculate $m$ and $n$, where $m$ and $n$ are real numbers such that $A^2 = mA + nI$ and $I$ is the unit matrix.

   (c) Find the matrix $C$ if $BC = A$.                                    (SUJB)

3. (a) If $A = \begin{pmatrix} a & b \\ 6 & -3 \end{pmatrix}$ and $A^2 = A$, determine the elements $a$ and $b$.

   (b) If $B = \begin{pmatrix} 2 & 3 \\ 2 & 4 \end{pmatrix}$ and $BC = \begin{pmatrix} 1 & 0 \\ 3 & 2 \end{pmatrix}$ find $B^{-1}$ and hence, or otherwise, find $C$ (where $C$ is a $2 \times 2$ matrix).

   (c) If $D = \begin{pmatrix} 2 \\ 5 \end{pmatrix}$ and $E = (-3 \quad 1)$ determine $DE$ and $ED$.
                                                                            (SUJB)

4. (a) Find the inverse of $\begin{pmatrix} 5 & 6 \\ 4 & 5 \end{pmatrix}$.

   (b) Use it to solve the equation $\begin{pmatrix} 5 & 6 \\ 4 & 5 \end{pmatrix}\begin{pmatrix} x \\ y \end{pmatrix} = \begin{pmatrix} 17 \\ 13 \end{pmatrix}$.

   (c) Use it again to find $a$, $b$, $c$ and $d$ if

$$\begin{pmatrix} 5 & 6 \\ 4 & 5 \end{pmatrix}\begin{pmatrix} a & b \\ c & d \end{pmatrix} = \begin{pmatrix} -5 & 2 \\ -4 & 2 \end{pmatrix}$$

5. Matrices $P$ and $Q$ are defined: $P = \begin{pmatrix} 0 & 1 \\ -1 & 2 \end{pmatrix}$, $Q = \begin{pmatrix} 0 & 2 \\ -1 & 2 \end{pmatrix}$.

   (a) Write down the inverses, $P^{-1}$ and $Q^{-1}$, of $P$ and $Q$, and hence evaluate the product $P^{-1}Q^{-1}$.

   (b) Evaluate the products $PQ$ and $QP$.

   (c) Write down the inverses, $(PQ)^{-1}$ and $(QP)^{-1}$, of $PQ$ and $QP$. (Ox)

6. During September an apple costs 3 p, an orange 5 p and a pear 4 p. This information can be written as a $3 \times 1$ cost matrix.

$$M = \begin{pmatrix} 3 \\ 5 \\ 4 \end{pmatrix}$$

   (a) In the first week a boy buys 2 apples, 4 oranges and 1 pear, and in the next week 3 apples, 1 orange and 2 pears. Write this information as a matrix F in such a way that FM can be evaluated.

   (b) Evaluate FM and say what information is contained in this product.

   (c) When the product FM is pre-multiplied by a certain matrix K, KFM gives the total in pence that the boy spent on fruit during the fortnight. Write down the matrix K. (O & C)

7. The matrix below records how many 1 p, 2 p, 5 p, 10 p and 50 p coins each of three children Alan, Bob and Carol have:

$$
\begin{array}{c c}
 & \begin{array}{ccccc} 1\text{p} & 2\text{p} & 5\text{p} & 10\text{p} & 50\text{p} \end{array} \\
\begin{array}{c} \text{Alan} \\ \text{Bob} \\ \text{Carol} \end{array} &
\begin{pmatrix} 3 & 0 & 0 & 1 & 1 \\ 1 & 0 & 1 & 2 & 0 \\ 0 & 1 & 1 & 0 & 1 \end{pmatrix}.
\end{array}
$$

   (a) Denoting the above matrix by $Q$, calculate $Q \begin{pmatrix} 1 \\ 2 \\ 5 \\ 10 \\ 50 \end{pmatrix}$.

   What do the numbers in your answer tell you?

   (b) The answer to the matrix multiplication QX is the number of coins which each child has. Write down the matrix X.

   (c) Evaluate $(1 \quad 1 \quad 1)Q$. What do the numbers in your answer represent?

   (d) Write down, but do not work out, a product of three matrices which would give the total sum of money which these children have altogether. (O & C)

321

8. (a) After they had each played 14 matches, the results of the games played by six of the clubs in a hockey league can be summarised by the matrix

|          | Won | Drawn | Lost |
|----------|-----|-------|------|
| Penton   | 11  | 2     | 1    |
| Radley   | 10  | 3     | 1    |
| Henham   | 8   | 6     | 0    |
| Denby    | 10  | 0     | 4    |
| Lanwick  | 8   | 3     | 3    |
| Calder   | 6   | 5     | 3    |

The points given for a match which is won, drawn or lost are shown in the matrix

|       |   |
|-------|---|
| Won   | 2 |
| Drawn | 1 |
| Lost  | 0 |

By matrix multiplication, find a matrix which shows, after 14 matches, the number of points obtained by each of these six clubs.

(b) In their fifteenth match, each of the above six clubs played one of the other five. The results of these matches were

Penton lost to Denby,
Radley won against Lanwick,
Henham and Calder drew.

Express in matrix form
(i) the number of matches won, drawn and lost by each of these six clubs after they had each played 15 matches,
(ii) the number of points each club had obtained after 15 matches.

(c) The matrix $\begin{pmatrix} 26 \\ 25 \\ 24 \\ 23 \\ 21 \\ 18 \end{pmatrix}$ represents the number of points

that each of the above six clubs had obtained after 16 matches.

List which of these clubs won, drew and lost their sixteenth match. (LEAG)

9. Fig. 20.25 below shows the sea routes from the mainland ports R, S and T to the ports X, Y and Z on the island of *Iblos*.

(a) Copy and complete the matrix below which represents this network of 1-stage routes.

$$
\begin{array}{c}
 & & \text{To} \\
 & & \begin{array}{ccc} \text{X} & \text{Y} & \text{Z} \end{array} \\
\text{From} & \begin{array}{c} \text{R} \\ \text{S} \\ \text{T} \end{array} & \left( \begin{array}{ccc} - & - & - \\ - & - & - \\ - & - & - \end{array} \right)
\end{array}
$$

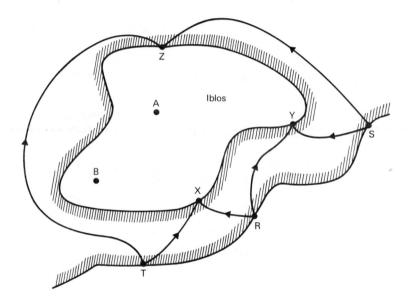

Fig. 20.5

(b) The matrix below represents the network of 1-stage routes from the ports X, Y and Z to the airports A and B on the island. On a copy of Fig. 20.5, draw in the network of routes represented by this matrix.

$$
\begin{array}{c}
 & & \text{To} \\
 & & \begin{array}{cc} \text{A} & \text{B} \end{array} \\
\text{From} & \begin{array}{c} \text{X} \\ \text{Y} \\ \text{Z} \end{array} & \left( \begin{array}{cc} 1 & 2 \\ 2 & 0 \\ 1 & 1 \end{array} \right)
\end{array}
$$

(c) Find the single matrix which represents the network of 2-stage routes from ports R, S and T to the airports A and B.　　　　(LREB)

10.

Fig. 20.6

The possible routes on this network are as shown on this matrix:

To

|  | | P | Q | R | S |
|---|---|---|---|---|---|
| | P | 0 | 0 | 1 | 1 |
| From | Q | 1 | 0 | 1 | 0 |
| | R | 1 | 1 | 0 | 0 |
| | S | 1 | 0 | 1 | 0 |

(a) Explain why the elements on the leading diagonal (from top left to bottom right) of this matrix are all zero.

(b) Copy the network and use arrows to indicate which are one- and which are two-way streets.

11. $\begin{pmatrix} 1 & 2 \\ 1 & 1 \end{pmatrix} \begin{pmatrix} 2 \\ 1 \end{pmatrix} = \begin{pmatrix} 4 \\ 3 \end{pmatrix}$    and  $4/3 = 1.3333$

$\begin{pmatrix} 1 & 2 \\ 1 & 1 \end{pmatrix} \begin{pmatrix} 4 \\ 3 \end{pmatrix} = \begin{pmatrix} 10 \\ 7 \end{pmatrix}$    and  $10/7 = 1.4286$

$\begin{pmatrix} 1 & 2 \\ 1 & 1 \end{pmatrix} \begin{pmatrix} 10 \\ 7 \end{pmatrix} = \begin{pmatrix} 24 \\ 17 \end{pmatrix}$    and  $24/17 = 1.4118$

$\begin{pmatrix} 1 & 2 \\ 1 & 1 \end{pmatrix} \begin{pmatrix} 24 \\ 17 \end{pmatrix} = ?$

Notice how the fractions are better and better approximations to $\sqrt{2}$ (= 1.4142). Continue with the matrix multiplications, what happens?

What if we started with a number other than 2? Investigate.

# 21 TRANSFORMATIONS

A point on a graph, $P(x,y)$, can be mapped to another point, the *image*, $P'(x',y')$, by various *transformations* — such as translation, rotation, reflection, enlargement, and stretch.

## TRANSLATION

Suppose, for example, three points, A, B, C, are mapped to their images, A′, B′, C′, by adding two units to their $x$-coordinates and subtracting one unit from their $y$-coordinates:

$$A(2,2) \longrightarrow (4,1)A'$$
$$B(3,4) \longrightarrow (5,3)B'$$
$$C(1,3) \longrightarrow (3,2)C'$$

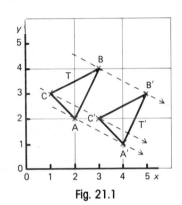

Fig. 21.1

If the three points are plotted on a graph (Fig. 21.1) and joined to make a triangle, T, then the three image points are the corners of another triangle, T′, which looks exactly like T except that it has moved a short distance in a rightward and downward direction. This type of transformation is called a *translation*.

In general terms, the point $P(x,y)$ maps on to the point $P'(x+2, y-1)$. If the point $(x,y)$ is written as the column matrix, or *vector*, $\begin{pmatrix} x \\ y \end{pmatrix}$ then

$$\begin{pmatrix} x \\ y \end{pmatrix} \longrightarrow \begin{pmatrix} x+2 \\ y-1 \end{pmatrix}$$

This is equivalent to addition of a vector $\begin{pmatrix} 2 \\ -1 \end{pmatrix}$:

$$\begin{pmatrix} x \\ y \end{pmatrix} + \begin{pmatrix} 2 \\ -1 \end{pmatrix} = \begin{pmatrix} x+2 \\ y-1 \end{pmatrix}$$

## INVERSE TRANSFORMATIONS

The reverse of any transformation is called its *inverse*. The inverse transformation will map the image back on to the original. In this example, the reverse of the translation $\begin{pmatrix} 2 \\ -1 \end{pmatrix}$ is another translation: $\begin{pmatrix} -2 \\ 1 \end{pmatrix}$.

$$\begin{pmatrix} x+2 \\ y-1 \end{pmatrix} + \begin{pmatrix} -2 \\ 1 \end{pmatrix} = \begin{pmatrix} x \\ y \end{pmatrix}$$

In general, any translation may be represented by the addition of the vector $\begin{pmatrix} a \\ b \end{pmatrix}$ and be reversed by the translation $\begin{pmatrix} -a \\ -b \end{pmatrix}$.

**EXERCISE 21a**

1. Find the images of A(2, 2), B(3, 4) and C(1, 3) under the translation $\begin{pmatrix} 3 \\ 2 \end{pmatrix}$.

   Draw the triangle ABC and its image A'B'C' on a graph.
   What transformation is the inverse of this translation?

2. What translation would map the following points to their given images?

   (a) (4, 6) to (7, 3)          (b) (6, 5) to (9, 5)
   (c) (4, 3) to (3, 4)          (d) (5, 6) to (2, 6)
   (e) (7, 9) to (2, 3)          (f) (5, 9) to (19, −8).

3. What single translation is equivalent to a translation $\begin{pmatrix} 2 \\ 3 \end{pmatrix}$ followed by another translation $\begin{pmatrix} 1 \\ 2 \end{pmatrix}$?

4. A translation transforms the point (3, 7) to (7, 3). Write down the column matrix equivalent of this translation. Where would the point (2, 3) be moved to under this translation?

5. What are the inverses of the following translations (give your answers as column matrices)?

   (a) $\begin{pmatrix} 2 \\ 1 \end{pmatrix}$     (b) $\begin{pmatrix} -1 \\ 2 \end{pmatrix}$     (c) $\begin{pmatrix} 3 \\ -1 \end{pmatrix}$     (d) $\begin{pmatrix} 5 \\ 3 \end{pmatrix}$     (e) $\begin{pmatrix} 4 \\ -2 \end{pmatrix}$.

**6.**

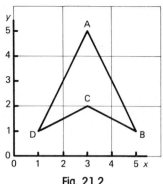

Fig. 21.2

The arrow-head shape ABCD shown in Fig. 21.2 is moved to A'B'C'D' by the translation $\begin{pmatrix} -2 \\ 2 \end{pmatrix}$.

Show ABCD and its image on a diagram of your own.

Show also A"B"C"D", the image of A'B'C'D' under this same translation. What single translation would map A"B"C"D" on to the original ABCD?

**7.** Plot the points P(1, 7), Q(4, 3), R(4, 5) and S(1, 1) on a grid marked from −3 to +11 on both axes. Join them up to make the shape PQRS. Show on the same graph the images of PQRS after translation by

(a) $\begin{pmatrix} 4 \\ 0 \end{pmatrix}$    (b) $\begin{pmatrix} 0 \\ 4 \end{pmatrix}$    (c) $\begin{pmatrix} 4 \\ 4 \end{pmatrix}$    (d) $\begin{pmatrix} -4 \\ -4 \end{pmatrix}$.

**8.** In Fig. 21.3, what translations will map

(a) figure A on to B,
(b) figure A on to C,
(c) figure B on to C,
(d) figure C on to B,

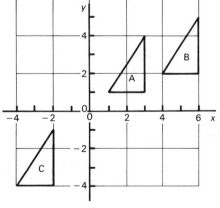

Fig. 21.3

What is the relationship between the translations in (c) and (d)?

# REFLECTION

## Reflection in the y-Axis, $M_y$

Consider the point $(2, 1)$. Its distance from the $y$-axis is given by its $x$-coordinate. It is two units in front, and so, under reflection in the $y$-axis, will be reflected to a point two units behind, i.e. to $(-2, 1)$ (Fig. 21.4).

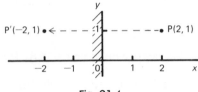

Fig. 21.4

In general, the point $(x, y)$ maps to $(-x, y)$ when reflected in the $y$-axis.

If three points, A, B, C, are the corners of a triangle, T, then their images, A′, B′, C′, are the three corners of another triangle, T′ (see Fig. 21.5).

$$A(2, 2) \longrightarrow (-2, 2)\ A'$$
$$B(3, 4) \longrightarrow (-3, 4)\ B'$$
$$C(1, 3) \longrightarrow (-1, 3)\ C'$$

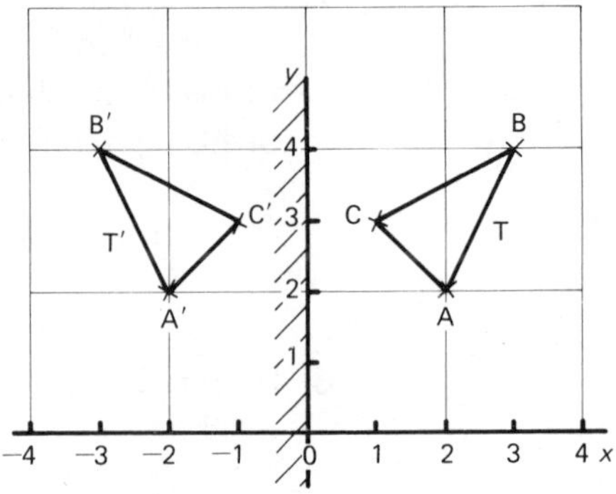

Fig. 21.5

Notice that reflecting A′B′C′ in the $y$-axis maps it back to the original triangle ABC. That is, reflection in the $y$-axis is its own inverse.

## Matrix equivalent

Note that the transformation of triangle T in Fig. 21.5 corresponds to the matrix multiplication

$$
\begin{array}{ccc} A & B & C \end{array} \qquad \begin{array}{ccc} A' & B' & C' \end{array}
$$
$$
\begin{pmatrix} -1 & 0 \\ 0 & 1 \end{pmatrix} \begin{pmatrix} 2 & 3 & 1 \\ 2 & 4 & 3 \end{pmatrix} = \begin{pmatrix} -2 & -3 & -1 \\ 2 & 4 & 3 \end{pmatrix}
$$

Under reflection in the $y$-axis, $P(x, y) \longrightarrow P'(-x, y)$. Writing the points as column vectors:

$$\begin{pmatrix} x \\ y \end{pmatrix} \longrightarrow \begin{pmatrix} -x \\ y \end{pmatrix}$$

Now,
$$\begin{pmatrix} -1 & 0 \\ 0 & 1 \end{pmatrix}\begin{pmatrix} x \\ y \end{pmatrix} = \begin{pmatrix} -x \\ y \end{pmatrix}$$

Thus pre-multiplication by the matrix $\begin{pmatrix} -1 & 0 \\ 0 & 1 \end{pmatrix}$ is equivalent to reflection in the $y$-axis.

Note that
$$\begin{pmatrix} -1 & 0 \\ 0 & 1 \end{pmatrix}^{-1} = \begin{pmatrix} -1 & 0 \\ 0 & 1 \end{pmatrix}$$

i.e. the matrix is its own inverse, just as reflection in the $y$-axis is its own inverse.

## Reflection in the $x$-Axis, $M_x$

Reflections in other lines follow the same principles as reflection in the $y$-axis. If a point is reflected in the $x$-axis, for example, then it is moved to a point as far below the axis as the original point is above (see Fig. 21.6).

In general
$$(x, y) \longrightarrow (x, -y)$$

which is equivalent to the matrix $\begin{pmatrix} 1 & 0 \\ 0 & -1 \end{pmatrix}$ pre-multiplying $\begin{pmatrix} x \\ y \end{pmatrix}$.

$P(2, 1) \longrightarrow (2, -1) \; P'$

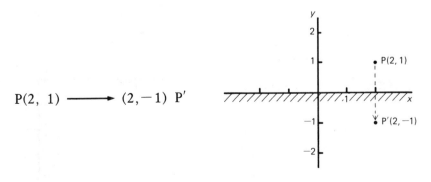

Fig. 21.6

## Reflection in the line $y = x$, $M_{y=x}$

In general, a reflection in the line $y = x$ maps $(x, y) \longrightarrow (y, x)$ (see Fig. 21.7), which is equivalent to the matrix $\begin{pmatrix} 0 & 1 \\ 1 & 0 \end{pmatrix}$ pre-multiplying $\begin{pmatrix} x \\ y \end{pmatrix}$.

$$P(3, 1) \longrightarrow (1, 3)\, P'$$
$$Q(3, 5) \longrightarrow (5, 3)\, Q'$$

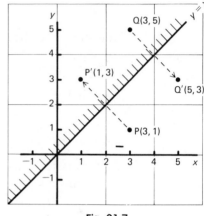

Fig. 21.7

## Reflection in the line $y = -x$, $M_{y=-x}$

In general, a reflection in $y = -x$ maps $(x, y) \longrightarrow (-y, -x)$ (Fig. 21.8), which is equivalent to the matrix $\begin{pmatrix} 0 & -1 \\ -1 & 0 \end{pmatrix}$ pre-multiplying $\begin{pmatrix} x \\ y \end{pmatrix}$.

$$P(3, 2) \longrightarrow (-2, -3)\, P'$$
$$Q(-4, 2) \longrightarrow (-2, 4)\, Q'$$

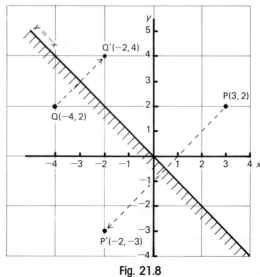

Fig. 21.8

# Properties of reflection

 (*i*) The mirror line is the same distance from a point and its image, and is an *axis of symmetry*.

 (*ii*) Points actually on the mirror line do not move. (The mirror line is said to be *invariant*.)

 (*iii*) The shape of a reflected figure is unaltered.

 (*iv*) Reflection is its own inverse.

 (*v*) Reflections in the $x$ and $y$ axes and in the lines $y = x$ and $y = -x$ have simple matrix equivalents.

# Finding the line of reflection

To find an unknown line of reflection given a point P and its image P′, join P to P′ and construct the mirror line as the perpendicular bisector of PP′.

**EXERCISE 21b** 1. Show the letters J, S and F reflected in:

  (a) the $x$-axis       (b) the $y$-axis

  (c) $y = x$        (d) $y = -x$.

  2.

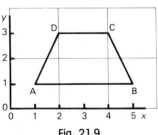

Fig. 21.9

The trapezium ABCD with vertices at A(1, 1), B(5, 1), C(4, 3) and D(2, 3), as shown in Fig. 21.9, is reflected in

331

the $x$-axis. Draw ABCD and its image $A'B'C'D'$ on a graph of your own. List the coordinates of $A'$, $B'$, $C'$ and $D'$ and show that they could have been found using the matrix multiplication:

$$\begin{pmatrix} 1 & 0 \\ 0 & -1 \end{pmatrix} \begin{pmatrix} 1 & 5 & 4 & 2 \\ 1 & 1 & 3 & 3 \end{pmatrix} = \begin{pmatrix} - & - & - & - \\ - & - & - & - \end{pmatrix}$$

$$\quad\quad\quad\quad\; A \;\; B \;\; C \;\; D \quad\quad A' \;\; B' \;\; C' \;\; D'$$

3. The trapezium in Question 2 undergoes another transformation to a different image $A''(-1,-1)$, $B''(-1,-5)$, $C''(-3,-4)$ and $D''(-3,-2)$. Show $A''B''C''D''$ on your graph. What is this second transformation? What matrix multiplication is equivalent to this?

4. The trapezium in Question 2 is reflected again so that $A \to B$, $B \to A$, $C \to D$ and $D \to C$. What is the equation of the mirror-line?

5.

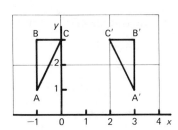

Fig. 21.10

The triangle ABC, shown in Fig. 21.10, is reflected in a line (not the $x$- or $y$-axis) to $A'B'C'$, as indicated. What is the equation of the mirror line?

6. For each of the reflections illustrated in Fig. 21.11, copy the diagram and mark in the line of reflection.

(a)
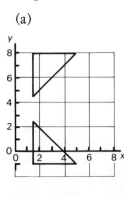

(b)
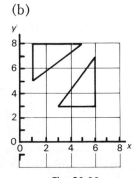

(c)
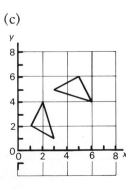

Fig. 21.11

332

7. The point $(3, 7)$ is mapped on to the point $(7, 3)$ by a reflection. Write down the equation of the mirror line. Where would the point $(2, 3)$ be moved under this reflection?

8. The triangle ABC with vertices at $A(1, 1)$, $B(5, 1)$ and $C(5, 5)$ is first reflected in the $y$-axis and then translated by the vector $\begin{pmatrix} 0 \\ -2 \end{pmatrix}$. (Such a combined reflection and translation is called a *glide*.) Show ABC and its final image on a graph.

9. Points $A(3, 5)$, $B(5, 1)$, $C(3, 2)$ and $D(1, 1)$ are joined to form an arrow-head shape ABCD (see Fig. 21.2, page 327). Draw graphs showing ABCD and its images after reflection in the following lines:
   (a) the $y$-axis   (b) $x = -1$   (c) $y = -x$   (d) $y = x$.

10. Illustrate on a grid, the shape PQRS with vertices $P(1, 7)$, $Q(4, 3)$, $R(4, 5)$ and $S(1, 1)$. Show also its images $P'Q'R'S'$ and $P''Q''R''S''$ under transformations represented by
   $$A = \begin{pmatrix} 0 & 1 \\ 1 & 0 \end{pmatrix} \text{ and } B = \begin{pmatrix} 0 & -1 \\ -1 & 0 \end{pmatrix}$$ respectively. Describe the transformations $A$ and $B$.

   Find $A^{-1}$ and $B^{-1}$, the inverses of $A$ and $B$. What do these matrix inverses tell you about the inverses of the transformations they represent?

# ROTATION, R

A point that has been moved through an arc of a circle is said to have been *rotated*. The *centre* of this rotation O is the centre of the circular path (Fig. 21.12). The centre is often (but *not* always) the origin.

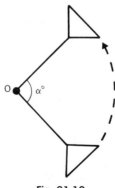

Fig. 21.12

## Properties of rotation

(*i*) Anticlockwise rotation is considered positive; clockwise is negative.

(*ii*) Only the centre of the rotation, O, does not move (remains *invariant*).

(*iii*) Every point (except O) moves through the same angle; thus rotation does not alter the shape or size of the rotated object.

## Locating the centre of rotation

**Example** Figure 21.13 shows a triangle ABC and its image A'B'C' after rotation about an unknown centre.

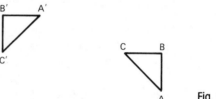

Fig. 21.13(a)

Join two corresponding corners of the triangles, say C and its image C'. Construct the perpendicular bisector of this line.

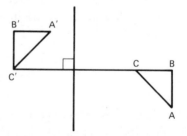

Fig. 21.13(b)

Repeat the process for another pair of corresponding points, say B and B'.

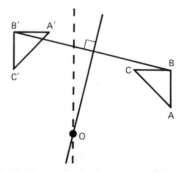

Fig. 21.13(c)

The centre of rotation, O, is the point where the second perpendicular bisector meets the first.

# ROTATION ABOUT THE ORIGIN

Only rotations centred on the origin have $2 \times 2$ matrix equivalents.

## 90° Rotation, $R_{90°}$

$$(x, y) \longrightarrow (-y, x)$$

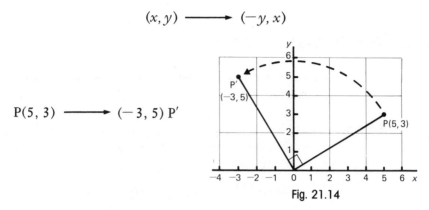

$$P(5, 3) \longrightarrow (-3, 5) \, P'$$

Fig. 21.14

which is equivalent to the matrix $\begin{pmatrix} 0 & -1 \\ 1 & 0 \end{pmatrix}$ pre-multiplying $\begin{pmatrix} x \\ y \end{pmatrix}$.

## 180° Rotation, $R_{180°}$

$$(x, y) \longrightarrow (-x, -y)$$

$$P(4, 2) \longrightarrow (-4, -2) \, P'$$

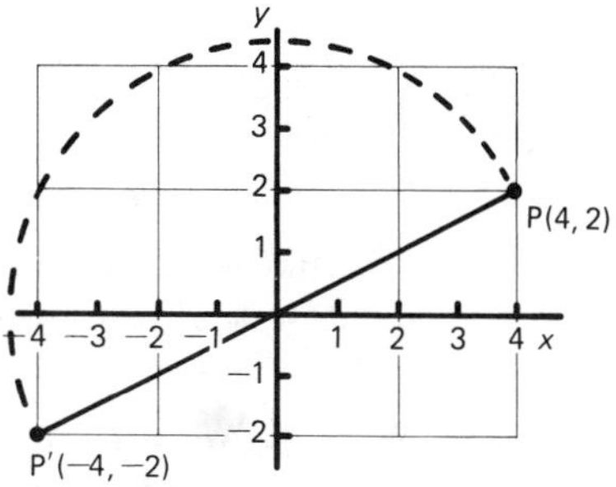

Fig. 21.15

equivalent to the matrix $\begin{pmatrix} -1 & 0 \\ 0 & -1 \end{pmatrix}$ pre-multiplying $\begin{pmatrix} x \\ y \end{pmatrix}$.

## 270° Rotation, $R_{270°}$

Similarly we can show that $R_{270°}$ is equivalent to the matrix

$\begin{pmatrix} 0 & 1 \\ -1 & 0 \end{pmatrix}$ pre-multiplying $\begin{pmatrix} x \\ y \end{pmatrix}$. Notice this is equivalent to a

rotation of $-90°$.

## 360° Rotation, $R_{360°}$

A full turn restores the point to its original position, and the co-ordinates of P and P' are the same. So a rotation of 360° is represented by the identity matrix.

## SUCCESSIVE TRANSFORMATIONS

Two or more transformations performed successively, one after another, may be combined into a single transformation.

**Example** A rectangle is reflected in the $x$-axis and then reflected in the $y$-axis. Find the single transformation equivalent to the combined transformation.

Using $M_x$ and $M_y$ to denote the two transformations, the reflections act as follows:

$$M_y[M_x(\triangle)]$$

Notice the order, the *second* transformation (reflection in the $y$-axis) is placed to the *left* of the first. This compares exactly with the rules for composite functions (see Chapter 8).

Then, using matrices, we find

$$M_y \quad \cdot \quad M_x \quad = \quad R_{180°}$$

$$\begin{pmatrix} -1 & 0 \\ 0 & 1 \end{pmatrix} \begin{pmatrix} 1 & 0 \\ 0 & -1 \end{pmatrix} = \begin{pmatrix} -1 & 0 \\ 0 & -1 \end{pmatrix}$$

that is, the equivalent of the two reflections is rotation by 180°. Check this graphically for yourself.

**Example** A figure is twice rotated by 180°. What is the single transformation equivalent to this?

We use powers to denote several applications of the same transformation.

Thus two rotations of 180° would be denoted $R_{180°}^2$.

$$R^2 = \begin{pmatrix} -1 & 0 \\ 0 & -1 \end{pmatrix}^2 = \begin{pmatrix} -1 & 0 \\ 0 & -1 \end{pmatrix} \begin{pmatrix} -1 & 0 \\ 0 & -1 \end{pmatrix} = \begin{pmatrix} 1 & 0 \\ 0 & 1 \end{pmatrix}$$

Thus two rotations of 180° are equivalent to the identity transformation, $I$, represented by the identity matrix, $\begin{pmatrix} 1 & 0 \\ 0 & 1 \end{pmatrix}$, which is the equivalent to a rotation of 360°.

**EXERCISE 21c**

1. Copy Fig. 21.16 on to squared paper and show on your graph the images after
   (a) rotation by $90°$ about A,
   (b) rotation by $180°$ about B,
   (c) rotation by $270°$ about C,
   (d) rotation by $-90°$ about D.

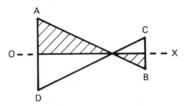

Fig. 21.16

2. The trapezium ABCD with vertices at A(1, 1), B(5, 1), C(4, 3) and D(2, 3) is rotated through $90°$ anticlockwise about the origin. Draw ABCD and its image $A'B'C'D'$ on a graph. List the coordinates of $A', B', C'$ and $D'$, and show that they could have been found using the equivalent matrix multiplication:

$$\begin{pmatrix} 0 & -1 \\ 1 & 0 \end{pmatrix}\begin{pmatrix} 1 & 5 & 4 & 2 \\ 1 & 1 & 3 & 3 \end{pmatrix} = \begin{pmatrix} - & - & - & - \\ - & - & - & - \end{pmatrix}$$
$$\phantom{xxxxxxx} A \ \ B \ \ C \ \ D \phantom{xxxx} A' \ \ B' \ \ C' \ \ D'$$

3. The trapezium in Question 2 is subjected to another transformation, giving images $A''(-1, -1)$, $B''(-5, -1)$, $C''(-4, -3)$ and $D''(-2, -3)$. Draw $A''B''C''D''$ on your graph. What is this second transformation? What matrix multiplication is equivalent to this?

4. The trapezium in Question 2 is rotated again, but *not* about the origin. If $A \to (6, 6)$, $B \to (6, 2)$, $C \to (8, 3)$ and $D \to (8, 5)$, show the effect of this transformation on a graph and write down the centre and angle of rotation.

5. Find the centre of the $90°$ rotations illustrated in Fig. 21.17.

(a)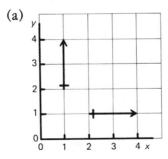

(b)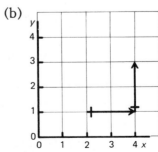

Fig. 21.17

337

6. The point $(3, 7)$ is mapped on to the point $(7, 3)$ by a rotation centred on $(7, 7)$. What is the angle of turn?

7. The point $(3, 7)$ is mapped on to the point $(7, 3)$ by a rotation of $180°$. Where is the centre of this rotation?

8. The triangle ABC with vertices at $A(1, 1)$, $B(5, 1)$ and $C(5, 5)$ is first reflected in the $y$-axis and then reflected in the $x$-axis. Show ABC and the final image on a graph. What single transformation is equivalent to these two reflections?

9. Points $A(3, 5)$, $B(5, 1)$, $C(3, 2)$ and $D(1, 1)$ are joined to form an arrow-head shape ABCD (see Fig. 21.2, page 327). Draw graphs showing ABCD and its images after rotations of:
   (a) $90°$ centred on the origin,
   (b) $180°$ centred on $(3, 2)$,
   (c) $90°$ centred on the origin followed by another of $180°$ centred on $(3, 2)$,
   (d) $180°$ centred on $(3, 2)$ followed by another of $90°$ centred on the origin.

10. Illustrate, on a grid, the shape PQRS with vertices at $P(1, 7)$, $Q(4, 3)$, $R(4, 5)$ and $S(1, 1)$. Show also its images $P'Q'R'S'$ and $P''Q''R''S''$ under transformations represented by
$$A = \begin{pmatrix} 0 & -1 \\ 1 & 0 \end{pmatrix} \text{ and } B = \begin{pmatrix} 0 & 1 \\ -1 & 0 \end{pmatrix} \text{ respectively.}$$

    Work out the matrices
    (a) $AB$      (b) $B^{-1}$      (c) $A^2$.
    What is the effect of the transformations they represent?

11. Plot the points $O(0, 0)$, $A(3, 0)$ and $B(3, 5)$ on a grid. Place the origin near the centre of the page and allow room on both axes for values from $-6$ to $+6$. Join OAB to form a triangle.
    (a) Find by construction the images of ABC after rotation about the origin by
       (i) $90°$      (ii) $180°$      (iii) $270°$.
    (b) Use matrices to show that
       (i) $R^2_{90°} = R_{180°}$    (ii) $R^3_{90°} = R_{270°}$    (iii) $R^4_{90°} = I$.
    (c) Show that your answers to (a) and (b) are consistent.

12. Use matrices to find the single transformation equivalent to
    (a) reflection in the $x$-axis followed by reflection in the line $y = x$
    (b) reflection in the $y$-axis followed by reflection in the line $y = x$

(c) reflection in the line $y = -x$ followed by reflection in the line $y = x$.

Illustrate your results geometrically, using the triangle OAB formed by joining the points O(0, 0), A(3, 0) and B(3, 5).

13. Show that $M_x M_y M_x = M_y$.

14. (a) A combined transformation is denoted $M_x R_{90°}$. Which acts first, the reflection or the rotation?

(b) Is the effect of $M_x R_{90°}$ identical to $R_{90°} M_x$? Investigate.

## ENLARGEMENT, *E*

Enlargement is rather like projecting a slide on to a screen. The *centre of enlargement* is often (but not always) the origin. If the point P moves to P′ under an enlargement, then the distance of P′ from O is $k$ times the distance of P from O, i.e. OP′ = $k$OP (Fig. 21.18). $k$ is called the *linear scale factor* of the enlargement.

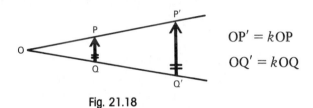

$$OP' = kOP$$
$$OQ' = kOQ$$

Fig. 21.18

Consider, for example, an enlargement with $(0, 0)$ as centre and a scale factor of 3, acting on the three corners of the triangle T in Fig. 21.19. A (2, 2), B (3, 4) and C (1, 3).

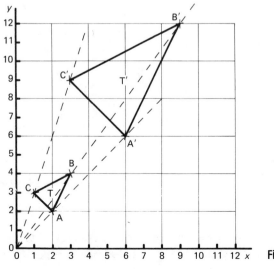

Fig. 21.19

From the definition of enlargement:

$$OA' = 3OA$$
$$OB' = 3OB$$
$$OC' = 3OC$$

Also, from the diagram:

$$A\,(2,2) \longrightarrow (6,6)\ A'$$
$$B\,(3,4) \longrightarrow (9,12)\ B'$$
$$C\,(1,3) \longrightarrow (3,9)\ C'$$

*If the centre of the enlargement is the origin*, then we may generalise and say

$$(x,y) \longrightarrow (kx, ky)$$

which is equivalent to the matrix $\begin{pmatrix} k & 0 \\ 0 & k \end{pmatrix}$ pre-multiplying $\begin{pmatrix} x \\ y \end{pmatrix}$.

*If the centre of the enlargement is* not *the origin* then no simple matrix equivalent exists, and questions will depend upon a drawing technique.

**Example** A triangle ABC has corners $(1,4)$, $(2,3)$ and $(3,5)$ respectively. It is enlarged under a transformation E, to A'B'C' at $(1,8)$, $(4,5)$, and $(7,11)$ respectively. Find the centre and the scale factor of this enlargement.

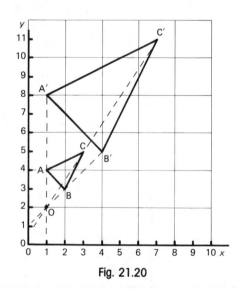

Fig. 21.20

By drawing the lines A'A, B'B, C'C and extending them until they meet (Fig. 21.20), we can see that the point where they

340

intersect $(1, 2)$ is the centre of the enlargement, O. Moreover, by measuring, we find

$$OA' = 3OA$$
$$OB' = 3OB$$
$$OC' = 3OC$$

so the scale factor is 3.

## Properties of enlargement

(*i*)    The shape of the original figure is unaltered but its size is changed.

(*ii*)    Side lengths in the enlarged figure are $k$ times the corresponding length in the original figure.

(*iii*)    The area of the enlarged figure is $k^2$ times the area of the original, i.e.

$$\frac{\text{area of image}}{\text{area of original}} = k^2$$

(*iv*)    If the scale factor is negative, then the image lies on the opposite side of the enlargement centre and is turned upside down (Fig. 21.21). None the less, $OP' = kOP$ and $OQ' = kOQ$ as before.

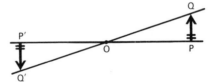

Fig. 21.21

(*v*)    If the scale factor is less than 1, then the image will be smaller than the original figure and closer to O (though the transformation is still called an enlargement!).

## ONE-WAY STRETCH

A figure is stretched if it is 'enlarged' in one direction only. Clearly this will distort the shape.

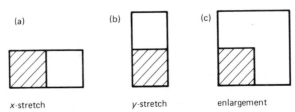

(a)    *x*-stretch      (b)    *y*-stretch      (c)    enlargement      Fig. 21.22

## x-stretch

Only the x-coordinates are altered: $(x, y) \rightarrow (kx, y)$.

This is equivalent to the matrix $\begin{pmatrix} k & 0 \\ 0 & 1 \end{pmatrix}$ pre-multiplying $\begin{pmatrix} x \\ y \end{pmatrix}$.

## y-stretch

Only the y-coordinates are altered: $(x, y) \rightarrow (x, ky)$.

This is equivalent to the matrix $\begin{pmatrix} 1 & 0 \\ 0 & k \end{pmatrix}$ pre-multiplying $\begin{pmatrix} x \\ y \end{pmatrix}$.

In both cases,

$$\frac{\text{area of the image}}{\text{area of original}} = k$$

**Example** The stretch $\begin{pmatrix} 3 & 0 \\ 0 & 1 \end{pmatrix}$ acts on triangle ABC as follows:

$$\begin{matrix} & \text{A} & \text{B} & \text{C} \\ \begin{pmatrix} 3 & 0 \\ 0 & 1 \end{pmatrix} & \begin{pmatrix} 2 & 3 & 1 \\ 2 & 4 & 3 \end{pmatrix} \end{matrix} \longrightarrow \begin{matrix} \text{A}' & \text{B}' & \text{C}' \\ \begin{pmatrix} 6 & 9 & 3 \\ 2 & 4 & 3 \end{pmatrix} \end{matrix}$$

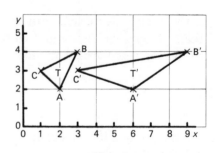

Fig. 21.23

Clearly, this transformation changes the shape of the figure (see Fig. 21.23). Corresponding angles are not equal, and the sides of the triangles are not in proportion.

The area of the image A'B'C' is three times the area of ABC.

**EXERCISE 21d**

1. (a) Figure 21.24 shows the first steps of an enlargement centred on the point $(2, 1)$ but is incomplete. Copy the diagram and use it to show how you would enlarge $\triangle ABC$ by scale factors of

(i) 2  (ii) $\frac{1}{2}$.

(b) How should the diagram be modified for *negative* enlargements?

Show, on a second copy of the figure and using the same centre $(2, 1)$, how you would enlarge $\triangle ABC$ by

(i) $-2$  (ii) $-\frac{1}{2}$.

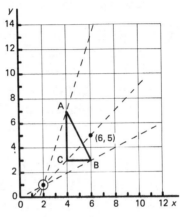

Fig. 21.24

2. Copy the figure in Fig. 21.25 and enlarge it by scale factor of 2 centred on the points

(a) $P(2, 9)$  (b) $Q(5, 6)$  (c) $R(-1, 4)$.

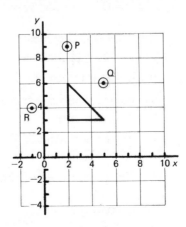

Fig. 21.25

343

3. A square ABCD has vertices at A(1, 1), B(1, 3), C(3, 3) and D(3, 1). This can be summarised by matrix $M$ where

$$
\begin{array}{cccc}
\text{A} & \text{B} & \text{C} & \text{D}
\end{array}
$$
$$
M = \begin{pmatrix} 1 & 1 & 3 & 3 \\ 1 & 3 & 3 & 1 \end{pmatrix}
$$

Use this matrix to find the images of ABCD after the following enlargements:

(a) $\begin{pmatrix} 2 & 0 \\ 0 & 2 \end{pmatrix}$    (b) $\begin{pmatrix} 3 & 0 \\ 0 & 3 \end{pmatrix}$    (c) $\begin{pmatrix} -2 & 0 \\ 0 & -2 \end{pmatrix}$    (d) $\begin{pmatrix} \frac{1}{2} & 0 \\ 0 & \frac{1}{2} \end{pmatrix}$

Show ABCD and its four images on a graph.

4. A trapezium ABCD, with vertices at A(1, 1), B(5, 1), C(4, 3) and D(2, 3), is subjected to an enlargement, centred on the origin, of scale factor 2.

(a) Draw ABCD and its image A′B′C′D′ on a graph. List the coordinates of A′B′C′D′ and show that they could have been found using the equivalent matrix multiplication:

$$
\begin{pmatrix} 2 & 0 \\ 0 & 2 \end{pmatrix}\begin{pmatrix} 1 & 5 & 4 & 2 \\ 1 & 1 & 3 & 3 \end{pmatrix} = \begin{pmatrix} - & - & - & - \\ - & - & - & - \end{pmatrix}
$$
$$
\begin{array}{cccc}
\text{A} & \text{B} & \text{C} & \text{D}
\end{array}\qquad
\begin{array}{cccc}
\text{A}' & \text{B}' & \text{C}' & \text{D}'
\end{array}
$$

(b) The area of ABCD is 6 square units. What is the area of A′B′C′D′?

5. The same trapezium in Question 4 is subjected to another transformation represented by $\begin{pmatrix} \frac{1}{2} & 0 \\ 0 & \frac{1}{2} \end{pmatrix}$. Show the image A″B″C″D″ on your graph and state its area.

6. The trapezium in Question 4 is enlarged so that A → $(-1\frac{1}{2}, -1\frac{1}{2})$, B → $(-7\frac{1}{2}, -1\frac{1}{2})$, C → $(-6, -4\frac{1}{2})$ and D → $(-3, -4\frac{1}{2})$. Show this image on your graph.

(a) What is the scale factor and where is the centre of this enlargement?

(b) What matrix multiplication is equivalent to this transformation?

(c) What is the area of the enlarged trapezium?

(d) What is the ratio $\dfrac{\text{area of enlarged trapezium}}{\text{area of original trapezium}}$?
How is this related to the scale factor?

7. (a) Draw a grid with the $x$-axis ranging from 0 to $+10$ and the $y$-axis ranging from $-5$ to $+10$. On it show the triangle ABC with vertices at A(1, 1), B(3, 1) and C(3, 3).

   (b) Show the triangle A′B′C′, the image of ABC after enlargement by $\begin{pmatrix} 3 & 0 \\ 0 & 3 \end{pmatrix}$.

   (c) Write down the ratio $\dfrac{\text{area A′B′C′}}{\text{area ABC}}$.

   (d) A′B′C′ is subjected to the translation $T$ where $T = \begin{pmatrix} -2 \\ -8 \end{pmatrix}$. Show this second image A″B″C″ on your diagram.

   (e) A further enlargement, *not* centred on the origin, will transform A″B″C″ back on to the original triangle ABC. Find the scale factor and the centre of this enlargement.

8. (a) Draw a grid ranging from $-2$ to $+3$ on the $x$-axis and from 0 to $+6$ on the $y$-axis. On it show the arrow shape ABCD with vertices at A(2, 1), B(3, 3), C(2, 2) and D(1, 3).

   (b) Show the image of ABCD after an enlargement of scale factor 2, centred on (4, 0). Label this image A′B′C′D′.

   (c) Write down the ratio $\dfrac{\text{area A′B′C′D′}}{\text{area ABCD}}$.

   (d) Show the image of A′B′C′D′ after translation by $\begin{pmatrix} 2 \\ 0 \end{pmatrix}$. Label this A″B″C″D″.

   (e) Find the centre and scale factor of the enlargement that will map A″B″C″D″ back on to the original shape ABCD.

9. (a) On a grid ranging from $-3$ to $+5$ on both axes, draw the arrow-head shape ABCD with vertices at A(3, 5), B(5, 1), C(3, 2) and D(1, 1).

   (b) Show on the same diagram A′B′C′D′, the image of ABCD after enlargement by scale factor $-\frac{1}{2}$ about the centre (1, 3).

   (c) Show also A″B″C″D″, the image of A′B′C′D′ after translation by $\begin{pmatrix} 3 \\ -4\frac{1}{2} \end{pmatrix}$.

   (d) Find the centre and scale factor of the enlargement that will map A″B″C″D″ on to ABCD.

345

10. An enlargement is represented by the matrix $E = \begin{pmatrix} 2 & 0 \\ 0 & 2 \end{pmatrix}$.

Find the matrices

(a) $E^{-1}$    (b) $E^2$    (c) $E^3$

and describe the geometric meaning of your results.

What single transformation is equivalent to E followed by a rotation of $180°$ about the origin? Give reasons for your answer.

11. The unit square OABC with vertices at $O(0,0)$, $A(1,0)$, $B(1,1)$ and $C(0,1)$ is subjected to a series of different stretches. On separate graphs, show OABC and its images under

(a) $\begin{pmatrix} 1 & 0 \\ 0 & 2 \end{pmatrix}$    (b) $\begin{pmatrix} 1 & 0 \\ 0 & 3 \end{pmatrix}$    (c) $\begin{pmatrix} 2 & 0 \\ 0 & 1 \end{pmatrix}$    (d) $\begin{pmatrix} 3 & 0 \\ 0 & 1 \end{pmatrix}$

(e) $\begin{pmatrix} \frac{1}{2} & 0 \\ 0 & 1 \end{pmatrix}$.

In each case write down the ratio $\dfrac{\text{area of image}}{\text{area of OABC}}$.

12. The trapezium ABCD has vertices at $A(1,1)$, $B(5,1)$, $C(4,3)$ and $D(2,3)$. Plot ABCD on a grid, allowing for both $x$ and $y$ to vary from 0 to 10.

(a) ABCD is mapped on to $A'B'C'D'$ by a stretch represented by $X = \begin{pmatrix} 2 & 0 \\ 0 & 1 \end{pmatrix}$. Find the coordinates of $A', B', C'$ and $D'$ and plot them on your graph.

(b) Find the inverse matrix $X^{-1}$. Plot on your diagram the image of ABCD after transformation by $X^{-1}$. Describe the transformation represented by $X^{-1}$.

(c) What is the image of $A'B'C'D'$ under the transformation $X^{-1}$?

13. The trapezium in Question 12 is to be stretched again. Draw a second diagram, again allowing for $x$ and $y$ to vary from 0 to 10, and plot ABCD.

(a) Plot $A'B'C'D'$, the image of ABCD under $X = \begin{pmatrix} 2 & 0 \\ 0 & 1 \end{pmatrix}$.

(b) Plot A″B″C″D″, the image of ABCD under $Y = \begin{pmatrix} 1 & 0 \\ 0 & 2 \end{pmatrix}$.

Describe the transformation $Y$.

(c) Plot A‴B‴C‴D‴, the image of A′B′C′D′ under $Y$. Describe the effect of the combined transformation $YX$ and write down its matrix equivalent.

14. What are the inverses of the following three matrices?

(a) $\begin{pmatrix} k & 0 \\ 0 & k \end{pmatrix}$      (b) $\begin{pmatrix} k & 0 \\ 0 & 1 \end{pmatrix}$      (c) $\begin{pmatrix} 1 & 0 \\ 0 & k \end{pmatrix}$

What does this tell you about the transformations that will reverse the effect of an enlargement or of a one-way stretch?

## MISCELLANEOUS EXERCISE 21

1. The diagram (Fig. 21.26) shows a square board in which there is a circular hole centre O. Six points A, B, C, D, E and F are marked on the board, equally spaced, and a piece of plastic in the shape of a regular hexagon is placed in the hole as shown.

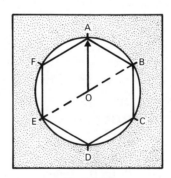

Fig. 21.26

(a) (i) Explain why angle AOF = 60°.
(ii) Explain why angle AOE = 120°.

(b) If **L** means 'reflect the hexagon in the line BE' and **M** means 'rotate the hexagon through 120° anticlockwise about O', write down the position of the arrowed corner after each of the following (starting with the arrowed corner at A every time):
(i) **L**   (ii) **M**   (iii) **L²**   (iv) **M²**   (v) **ML**     (EMREB)

2. (a) Draw and label the rectangle $ABCD$, the vertices of which are
$$A(1,0), \quad B(1,1), \quad C(3,1) \quad \text{and} \quad D(3,0)$$

(b) Rotate $ABCD$ through $90°$ clockwise about the origin and label it $EFGH$.
$$A \to E, \quad B \to F, \quad C \to G, \quad D \to H.$$

(c) Translate $EFGH$ using the vector $\begin{pmatrix} 4 \\ 4 \end{pmatrix}$ and label it $JKLM$.
$$E \to J, \quad F \to K, \quad G \to L, \quad H \to M.$$

(d) State fully the single transformation that will transform $JKLM$ back to $ABCD$.

(e) $W$ is the transformation matrix $\begin{pmatrix} \frac{1}{2} & 0 \\ 0 & \frac{1}{2} \end{pmatrix}$.

   (i) Find the coordinates of the images of the points $A$, $B$, $C$ and $D$ under the mapping whose matrix is $W$.
   (ii) Plot and join these points on the grid and label them $PQRS$.
$$A \to P, \quad B \to Q, \quad C \to R, \quad D \to S.$$
   (iii) From parts (i) and (ii) state fully the geometrical transformation that $W$ represents. (SEREB)


3. (a) On graph paper, using a scale of 1 cm to 1 unit on each axis, construct a pair of axes for values of $x$ from $-5$ to $+10$ and for values of $y$ from $-10$ to $+15$. Label the origin $O$.

(b) On your axes, plot
   (i) triangle $ABC$ so that $A$ is $(1,3)$; $B$ is $(1,6)$; $C$ is $(3,6)$,
   (ii) the line $y = x$.

(c) On your axes.
   (i) draw the image of $ABC$ after reflection in the $y$-axis and label this $P$,
   (ii) draw the image of $ABC$ after rotation of $180°$ about $O$ as centre and label this $Q$,
   (iii) draw the image of $ABC$ after reflection in the line $y = x$ and label this $R$.

(d) The matrix $M\begin{pmatrix} 0 & 1 \\ -1 & 0 \end{pmatrix}$ is a matrix of transformation.
   (i) Plot the image of triangle $ABC$ under transformation $M$ and label this $S$.
   (ii) Describe the transformation in words. (EAEB)

348

4. $A = \begin{pmatrix} 1 & 0 \\ 0 & -1 \end{pmatrix}$, $B = \begin{pmatrix} -1 & 0 \\ 0 & 1 \end{pmatrix}$ and $C = \begin{pmatrix} -1 & 0 \\ 0 & -1 \end{pmatrix}$ are transformation matrices.

(a) On the squared paper plot the triangle $PQR$ where $P$ is $(1, 1)$, $Q$ is $(2, 2)$ and $R$ is $(1, 3)$.

(b) Plot the image of $PQR$ when it is reflected in the $x$-axis. Label the image $P_1 Q_1 R_1$.

(c) Describe the transformation which occurs when $PQR$ is operated on by $B$. Plot the new image of $PQR$, and label it $P_2 Q_2 R_2$.

(d) (i) Plot the position of $PQR$ when transformed by $C$, and label the image $P_3 Q_3 R_3$.
   (ii) Describe this transformation.

(e) (i) Ring the position of $P$ when operated upon first by $A$ and then by $B$.
   (ii) What conclusion can you make about the relationship between the transformation matrices $A$, $B$ and $C$?

(NWREB)

5. On squared paper, draw the usual rectangular axes, placing the origin near the centre of the page. On your diagram, plot and draw the triangle $T$ whose vertices are $(1, 1), (1, 3), (2, 3)$.

(a) $P$ is the image of $T$ under an anticlockwise rotation of $90°$ about the point $(1, 1)$. Draw and label $P$ on your diagram.

(b) $Q$ is the image of $P$ under an anticlockwise rotation of $90°$ about the point $(-2, 0)$. Draw and label $Q$ on your diagram.

(c) State the angle and centre of the rotation which maps $T$ to $Q$.

(d) $A$ is the image of $T$ under reflection in the line $y = x$. Draw and label $A$ on your diagram.

(e) $B$ is the image of $A$ under the translation $\begin{pmatrix} 2 \\ -2 \end{pmatrix}$. Draw and label $B$ on your diagram.

(f) Draw and label clearly on your diagram the line $m$ which is the axis of the reflection which maps $T$ to $B$. (O & C)

6. Lines *l*, *m* and *n*, intersecting at O, are fixed in the plane, and ABCDEF is a regular hexagon, centre O, whose original position is as shown (Fig. 21.27). The following transformations of the hexagon are defined.

$R$  is an anticlockwise rotation of 60° about O;

$L$  is a reflection in line *l*;

$M$  is a reflection in line *m*;

$N$  is a reflection in line *n*.

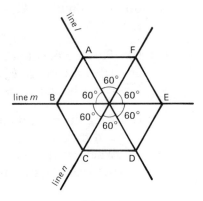

Fig. 21.27

(a)  What single rotations are equivalent to  $R^2, R^6, R^{-1}$?

(b)  Show that *LM* and *ML* are equivalent to rotations, and express each of them in the form  $R^p$ where $p$ is a positive whole number.

(c)  Express *LMN* and *LML* as single reflections.            (Ox)

7. The following transformations in a plane are defined:

$P$  is an enlargement, centre $(0,0)$, scale factor 2;

$Q$  is a reflection in the line  $x = -1$;

$R$  is an enlargement, centre $(-4,0)$, scale factor $\frac{1}{2}$.

The square $S$ has vertices,  $O(0,0)$, $A(1,0)$, $B(1,1)$ and $C(0,1)$. Show on a single sheet of graph paper, labelling each image carefully,

(a)  $S$,          (b) $P(S)$,        (c) $QP(S)$,        (d) $RQP(S)$.

State fully what single transformation produces the same effect as $RQP$.                                (Ox)

8.

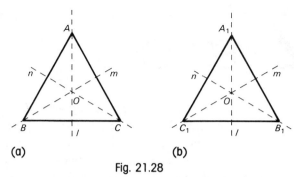

(a)                              (b)

Fig. 21.28

Triangle $ABC$ is equilateral, and is symmetrical about the lines
$l$, $m$ and $n$, which are fixed and intersect at $O$ (Fig. 21.28(a)).
The triangle is reflected in $l$ so that $A \rightarrow A_1$, $B \rightarrow B_1$ and
$C \rightarrow C_1$, as shown in the second diagram (Fig. 21.28(b)).

(a) Under reflection in $m$, $A_1 \rightarrow A_2$, $B_1 \rightarrow B_2$ and $C_1 \rightarrow C_2$.
   (i) Draw a diagram to show $l, m, n$ and the positions of
       $A_2, B_2, C_2$.
   (ii) Describe the single transformation which is equivalent
        to reflection in $l$ followed by reflection in $m$.

(b) The triangle $A_2B_2C_2$ is now reflected in $n$ so that $A_2 \rightarrow A_3$,
    $B_2 \rightarrow B_3$ and $C_2 \rightarrow C_3$.
   (i) On another diagram, show $l, m, n$ and the positions
       of $A_3, B_3, C_3$.
   (ii) What transformation would map $A_3 \rightarrow A$, $B_3 \rightarrow B$,
        $C_3 \rightarrow C$?                                    (O & C)

9. Placing the origin near the centre of the graph paper, draw
   $\triangle ABC$, where $A$ is $(3,3)$, $B$ is $(5,3)$ and $C$ is $(3,4)$. Draw
   also $\triangle PQR$ where $P$ is $(-1,5)$, $Q$ is $(-1,7)$ and $R$ is $(-2,5)$.

   By construction, find the centre $M$ of the rotation which can
   be used to rotate $\triangle ABC$ on to $\triangle PQR$.

   Mark on your diagram an angle of rotation. Measure it and
   write down its value.

   The triangle $PQR$ is to be enlarged by a scale factor of 2 with
   centre $(1,4)$. Construct the image triangle, and write down
   the coordinates of its vertices.                            (LU)

# 22 VECTORS

Time, energy, heat and mass are all *scalar* quantities; that is they are fully described by their size or *magnitude*. *Vector* quantities need a direction as well as a magnitude if they are to be fully described. For example, a force of 100 newtons acting vertically has an effect (squashing) different from another force of 100 newtons acting horizontally (which would push along). So describing a force simply as '100 newtons' is incomplete. Other vector quantities that similarly require a direction to be specified are position, velocity and acceleration.

## REPRESENTING VECTORS

Vectors may be represented by accurately scaled lines, since these show both magnitude and direction.

If a line AB represents a vector, then the vector is written $\overrightarrow{AB}$ (notice the top arrow) or $AB$ (i.e. in heavy type).

Frequently, vectors are given as '$x$ units along and $y$ units up', as if they were lines drawn on a grid. Vectors given in this component form are written as *column* matrices, e.g.

$$v_1 = \begin{pmatrix} 2 \\ 3 \end{pmatrix} \quad \text{and} \quad v_2 = \begin{pmatrix} 3 \\ -1 \end{pmatrix}$$

(see Fig. 22.1). [This convention distinguishes vectors from points, which are always written as row matrices, e.g. $(2, 3)$ or $(3, -1)$.]

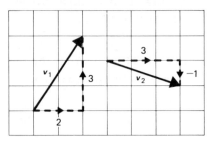

Fig. 22.1

When vectors are written in this way, their link with translation (the first transformation discussed in the previous chapter) should be clear.

Alternatively, but on exactly the same basis, we may write:

$$v_1 = 2i + 3j \quad \text{and} \quad v_2 = 3i - j$$

where $i$ and $j$ are *unit vectors* (i.e. vectors of magnitude one unit) parallel to the $x$- and $y$-axis respectively.

## MAGNITUDE AND DIRECTION

If a vector is given as $\begin{pmatrix} x \\ y \end{pmatrix}$ or in the form $xi + yj$ we may find its magnitude and direction from Pythagoras' theorem and elementary trigonometry (Fig. 22.2).

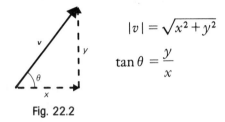

$$|v| = \sqrt{x^2 + y^2}$$

$$\tan \theta = \frac{y}{x}$$

Fig. 22.2

The magnitude of a vector $v$ is sometimes called its *modulus*, and is written $|v|$. Its direction is usually denoted by the Greek letter theta, $\theta$.

**Example** $v_1 = 2i + 3j$.

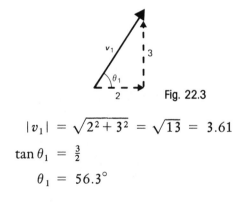

Fig. 22.3

$$|v_1| = \sqrt{2^2 + 3^2} = \sqrt{13} = 3.61$$

$$\tan \theta_1 = \tfrac{3}{2}$$

$$\theta_1 = 56.3°$$

**Example** $v_2 = \begin{pmatrix} 3 \\ -1 \end{pmatrix}$

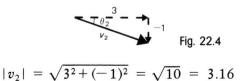

Fig. 22.4

$$|v_2| = \sqrt{3^2 + (-1)^2} = \sqrt{10} = 3.16$$

353

$$\tan \theta_2 = \frac{-1}{+3} = -\frac{1}{3}$$

$$\theta_2 = -18.4°$$

Note that the negative angle −18.4° is measured clockwise, below the x-axis. As always, positive angles are measured anticlockwise. This angle of −18.4° could equally well have been given as 360° − 18.4° = +341.6°. Be sure to sketch a vector when finding θ, for you may mistake the direction for its precise reverse, especially if you use a calculator.

**Example** $v_3 = \begin{pmatrix} -3 \\ 1 \end{pmatrix}$.

$$|v_3| = \sqrt{(-3)^2 + 1^2} = \sqrt{10} = 3.16$$

$$\tan \theta_3 = \frac{+1}{-3} = -\frac{1}{3}$$

Now, using the inverse tan key, most calculators will give $\theta = -18.4°$, suggesting that $v_3$ has the same direction as $v_2$. This is incorrect, for $v_3$ acts in precisely the reverse direction. A quick sketch of the vector representing three steps back and one step up makes this obvious

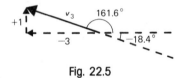

Fig. 22.5

In fact,

$$\theta_3 = 180° + (-18.4°) = 161.6°$$

Notice that the *magnitudes* of $v_2$ and $v_3$ are the same. $v_3$ is the reverse of $v_2$, i.e. $v_3 = -v_2$ (Fig. 22.6).

Fig. 22.6

In general, any vector $-v$, is of equal magnitude to $+v$ but acts in the opposite direction. If $v = \overrightarrow{AB}$ then $-v = \overrightarrow{BA}$.

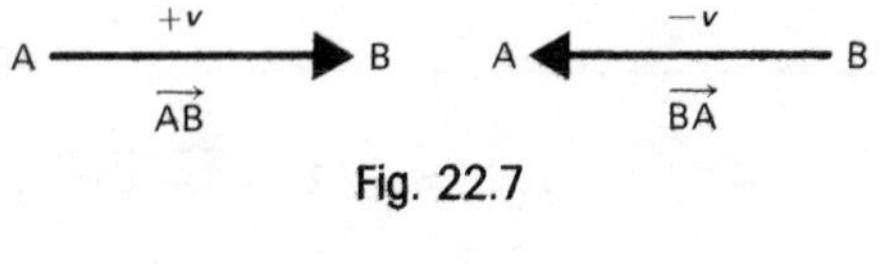

Fig. 22.7

**EXERCISE 22a**

1. Represent these vectors by scaled lines:
   (a) 4 newtons acting vertically upwards
   (b) 5 km due east
   (c) $3 \text{ m s}^1$ at an angle of $70°$ with the horizontal
   (d) $10 \text{ m s}^{-2}$ at an angle of $-90°$
   (e) 7.2 newtons at $135°$.

2. The lines shown in Fig. 22.8 represent vectors. Write each one in the equivalent component form $\begin{pmatrix} x \\ y \end{pmatrix}$.

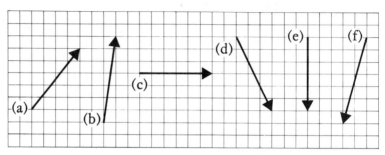

Fig. 22.8

3. Show the following vectors as lines drawn on graph paper:
   (a) $\begin{pmatrix} 2 \\ 2 \end{pmatrix}$     (b) $4i + 3j$     (c) $4i - 3j$     (d) $\begin{pmatrix} 5 \\ -3 \end{pmatrix}$
   (e) $\begin{pmatrix} -7 \\ 1 \end{pmatrix}$     (f) $-3i - 5j$.

4. Find (i) by measurement (ii) by calculation the magnitude and the direction of the vectors in Question 3.

5. Find the magnitude and direction of the following:
   (a) $\begin{pmatrix} 5 \\ 12 \end{pmatrix}$     (b) $\begin{pmatrix} -5 \\ 12 \end{pmatrix}$     (c) $\begin{pmatrix} -5 \\ -12 \end{pmatrix}$     (d) $\begin{pmatrix} 5 \\ -12 \end{pmatrix}$
   (e) $\begin{pmatrix} 12 \\ 5 \end{pmatrix}$     (f) $\begin{pmatrix} -12 \\ -5 \end{pmatrix}$.

6. If $\overrightarrow{PQ} = \begin{pmatrix} 3 \\ 2 \end{pmatrix}$, find
   (a) $\overrightarrow{QP}$     (b) $|\overrightarrow{PQ}|$     (c) $|\overrightarrow{QP}|$.

7. Find the magnitude and direction of
   (a) $\begin{pmatrix} -4 \\ 5 \end{pmatrix}$     (b) $\begin{pmatrix} -8 \\ 10 \end{pmatrix}$     (c) $\begin{pmatrix} -10 \\ 12\frac{1}{2} \end{pmatrix}$.
   What can you say about these vectors?

**8.** Which of these vectors are parallel?

$$a = \begin{pmatrix} 2 \\ 5 \end{pmatrix} \quad b = \begin{pmatrix} 5 \\ 2 \end{pmatrix} \quad c = \begin{pmatrix} 3 \\ 1 \end{pmatrix} \quad d = \begin{pmatrix} 2 \\ 0 \end{pmatrix}$$

$$e = \begin{pmatrix} 6 \\ 2 \end{pmatrix} \quad f = \begin{pmatrix} -5 \\ 2 \end{pmatrix}.$$

## ADDING VECTORS

Adding (or subtracting) vectors written in component form is simply a matter of adding (or subtracting) the horizontal components and then, separately, adding (or subtracting) the vertical components.

**Example**
$$\begin{pmatrix} 2 \\ 3 \end{pmatrix} + \begin{pmatrix} 3 \\ -1 \end{pmatrix} = \begin{pmatrix} 2+3 \\ 3+(-1) \end{pmatrix} = \begin{pmatrix} 5 \\ 2 \end{pmatrix}.$$

The same vectors written in $i, j$ form are treated in exactly the same way:

$$(2i + 3j) + (3i - j) = (2+3)i + (3-1)j$$
$$= 5i + 2j$$

Vectors can be added graphically by arranging them 'nose to tail'. The vector $v_1 + v_2$ completes the triangle and is called the *resultant* (Fig. 22.9).

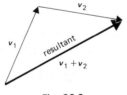

Fig. 22.9

This *triangle law* is equivalent to adding together the separate components of vectors represented algebraically (Fig. 22.10).

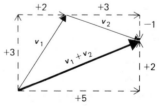

Fig. 22.10

$$\begin{pmatrix} 2 \\ 3 \end{pmatrix} + \begin{pmatrix} 3 \\ -1 \end{pmatrix} = \begin{pmatrix} 5 \\ 2 \end{pmatrix}$$

Any number of vectors can be added in this way. The resultant vector joins the 'tail' of the first vector to the 'nose' of the last (Fig. 22.11):

$$\overrightarrow{OA} + \overrightarrow{AB} + \overrightarrow{BC} + \overrightarrow{CD} = \overrightarrow{OD}$$

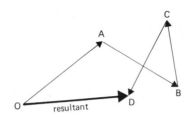

Fig. 22.11

## SUBTRACTION

As $-\overrightarrow{CD} = +\overrightarrow{DC}$ we can treat $\overrightarrow{AB} - \overrightarrow{CD}$ as $\overrightarrow{AB} + \overrightarrow{DC}$.

**Example** $a = \begin{pmatrix} 2 \\ 3 \end{pmatrix}$ and $b = \begin{pmatrix} 3 \\ -1 \end{pmatrix}$ (Fig. 22.12).

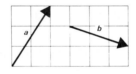

Fig. 22.12

Using column matrices:

$$a - b = \begin{pmatrix} 2 \\ 3 \end{pmatrix} - \begin{pmatrix} 3 \\ -1 \end{pmatrix} = \begin{pmatrix} -1 \\ 4 \end{pmatrix}$$

By first reversing the direction of $b$ (to get $-b$) and repositioning $-b$ so that it follows on 'nose to tail' with $a$, we can show the same result on a graph (Fig. 22.13).

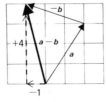

Fig. 22.13

357

## MULTIPLICATION

Vectors may be multiplied by ordinary numbers. For example if $v = \begin{pmatrix} 3 \\ 2 \end{pmatrix}$ then $2v = \begin{pmatrix} 6 \\ 4 \end{pmatrix}$, $3v = \begin{pmatrix} 9 \\ 6 \end{pmatrix}$, and so on. The vector $2v$ has twice the magnitude of $v$ but acts in the same direction; likewise $3v$ has three times and $\frac{1}{2}v$ has half the magnitude of $v$ and both are parallel to it (Fig. 22.14).

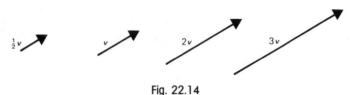

Fig. 22.14

**EXERCISE 22b**

1. Draw the vector $\begin{pmatrix} 4 \\ 5 \end{pmatrix}$ on graph paper. Draw a second vector $\begin{pmatrix} 3 \\ 2 \end{pmatrix}$ 'nose to tail' with the first. Hence show that

$$\begin{pmatrix} 4 \\ 5 \end{pmatrix} + \begin{pmatrix} 3 \\ 2 \end{pmatrix} = \begin{pmatrix} 7 \\ 7 \end{pmatrix}$$

2. Draw the vector $\begin{pmatrix} 4 \\ 5 \end{pmatrix}$, again, and the vector $-\begin{pmatrix} 3 \\ 2 \end{pmatrix}$ 'nose to tail' with it. Hence show that $\begin{pmatrix} 4 \\ 5 \end{pmatrix} - \begin{pmatrix} 3 \\ 2 \end{pmatrix} = \begin{pmatrix} 1 \\ 3 \end{pmatrix}$.

3. Draw the vectors $\begin{pmatrix} 8 \\ 10 \end{pmatrix}$, $\begin{pmatrix} 12 \\ 15 \end{pmatrix}$, $\begin{pmatrix} 2 \\ 2\frac{1}{2} \end{pmatrix}$ and $\begin{pmatrix} 10 \\ 12\frac{1}{2} \end{pmatrix}$ on graph paper. Hence show that these vectors are all parallel to $\begin{pmatrix} 4 \\ 5 \end{pmatrix}$, but of different magnitudes. Find the magnitude of each vector by measuring it.

In Questions 4 to 15 $a = \begin{pmatrix} 1 \\ 4 \end{pmatrix}$, $b = \begin{pmatrix} 3 \\ -1 \end{pmatrix}$, $c = \begin{pmatrix} -2 \\ -1 \end{pmatrix}$.

Find (without drawing)

4. $a + b$       5. $a - b$       6. $2a$

7. $2a - c$       8. $2a + 3c$       9. $a + 2b + c$

10. $b + \frac{1}{2}(a + c)$       11. $c - a - 2b$       12. $3b - 2a + 7c$

13. $a + 2b + 1\frac{1}{2}c$       14. $5b - 3c$       15. $2a - 3b + c$.

Find $k$ in the following equations:

16. $2\begin{pmatrix}3\\1\end{pmatrix} + k\begin{pmatrix}3\\0\end{pmatrix} = \begin{pmatrix}9\\2\end{pmatrix}$

17. $3\begin{pmatrix}2\\1\end{pmatrix} + 2k\begin{pmatrix}2\\1\end{pmatrix} = k\begin{pmatrix}6\\3\end{pmatrix}$

18. $-k\begin{pmatrix}3\\2\end{pmatrix} + 2k\begin{pmatrix}1\frac{1}{2}\\k\end{pmatrix} = \begin{pmatrix}0\\12\end{pmatrix}$

19. $k\begin{pmatrix}3\\-1\end{pmatrix} + \begin{pmatrix}-2\\-1\end{pmatrix} = \begin{pmatrix}k^2\\1-k^2\end{pmatrix}$.

20. Find $m$ and $n$ in the equation $2\begin{pmatrix}3\\m\end{pmatrix} + n\begin{pmatrix}1\\2\end{pmatrix} = \begin{pmatrix}8\\4\end{pmatrix}$.

21. Find $p$ and $q$ in the equation $3\begin{pmatrix}p\\2\end{pmatrix} + q\begin{pmatrix}5\\1\end{pmatrix} = \begin{pmatrix}4\\8\end{pmatrix}$.

22. Find $a$ and $b$ in the equation $a\begin{pmatrix}3\\-1\end{pmatrix} + \begin{pmatrix}2\\b\end{pmatrix} = \begin{pmatrix}8\\0\end{pmatrix}$.

23. Find $x$ and $y$ in the equation $x\begin{pmatrix}3\\4\end{pmatrix} - \begin{pmatrix}y\\2\end{pmatrix} = \begin{pmatrix}2\\10\end{pmatrix}$.

24. Find $m$ and $n$ in the equation $m\begin{pmatrix}2\\3\end{pmatrix} + n\begin{pmatrix}1\\2\end{pmatrix} = \begin{pmatrix}10\\17\end{pmatrix}$.

25. Find $p$ and $q$ in the equation $p\begin{pmatrix}1\\3\end{pmatrix} + q\begin{pmatrix}2\\-2\end{pmatrix} = \begin{pmatrix}2\\4\end{pmatrix}$.

26. Find $r$ and $s$ in the equation $2\begin{pmatrix}r\\s\end{pmatrix} + \begin{pmatrix}2s\\-r\end{pmatrix} = \begin{pmatrix}4\\4\end{pmatrix}$.

27. Find $c$ in the equation $c\begin{pmatrix}c\\1\end{pmatrix} + 2c\begin{pmatrix}3\\c\end{pmatrix} + 2\begin{pmatrix}4\\-3\end{pmatrix} = \begin{pmatrix}0\\0\end{pmatrix}$.

28. Find $x$ in the equation $x\begin{pmatrix}x-2\\x\end{pmatrix} - 2\begin{pmatrix}x\\x+1\end{pmatrix} = \begin{pmatrix}5\\13\end{pmatrix}$.

# VECTOR GEOMETRY

Many geometrical results can be established using vectors. Remember the following points:

(i) The reverse of a vector is negative:

$\overrightarrow{AB}$      $-\overrightarrow{AB}$ or $\overrightarrow{BA}$

(*ii*) Vectors represented by parallel lines are multiples of each other:

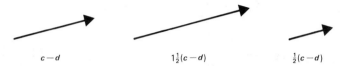

Conversely, lines representing multiples of the same vector are parallel.

(*iii*) Vectors arranged nose to tail have a single equivalent: $\overrightarrow{OA} + \overrightarrow{AB} + \overrightarrow{BC} = \overrightarrow{OC}$. This works in reverse, too. So a single vector can be broken up into a series of consecutive steps: $\overrightarrow{OC} = \overrightarrow{OA} + \overrightarrow{AB} + \overrightarrow{BC}$. You might like to think of this as a journey from O to C made in a very roundabout way: 'O to A, A to B, then B to C'.

**Example** ABCDEF is a regular hexagon (Fig. 22.15). If $\overrightarrow{AB} = a$ and $\overrightarrow{BC} = b$, write in terms of $a$ and $b$ the vectors

(a) $\overrightarrow{ED}$     (b) $\overrightarrow{EF}$     (c) $\overrightarrow{AD}$     (d) $\overrightarrow{CD}$     (e) $\overrightarrow{EA}$.

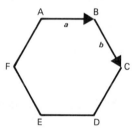

Fig. 22.15

(a) The opposite sides of a regular hexagon are equal in length and parallel, i.e. ED = AB and ED ∥ AB. So the vectors $\overrightarrow{ED}$ and $\overrightarrow{AB}$ are equal:
$$\overrightarrow{ED} = \overrightarrow{AB} = a$$

(b) Similarly, the sides EF and BC are equal and parallel: EF = BC and EF ∥ BC. However, the vector $\overrightarrow{EF}$ acts upwards and to the left; vector $\overrightarrow{BC}$ acts downwards and to the right. So
$$\overrightarrow{EF} = -\overrightarrow{BC} = -b$$

(c) The diagonal, AD, of the regular hexagon is parallel to the side BC but twice its length: AD = 2BC and AD ∥ BC. So
$$\overrightarrow{AD} = 2\overrightarrow{BC} = 2b$$

(d) To find $\overrightarrow{CD}$ we must choose an indirect route from C to D using vectors that we already know. We can go from C to B, B to A and then A to D. That is

$$\overrightarrow{CD} = \overrightarrow{CB} + \overrightarrow{BA} + \overrightarrow{AD}$$
$$= -\overrightarrow{BC} + (-\overrightarrow{AB}) + \overrightarrow{AD}$$
$$= -b - a + 2b$$
$$= b - a$$

(e) To find $\overrightarrow{EA}$ we again choose a route using known vectors:

$$\overrightarrow{EA} = \overrightarrow{ED} + \overrightarrow{DC} + \overrightarrow{CB} + \overrightarrow{BA}$$
$$= \overrightarrow{ED} - \overrightarrow{CD} - \overrightarrow{BC} - \overrightarrow{AB}$$
$$= a - (b - a) - b - a$$
$$= a - 2b$$

(As an alternative method we could have established that $\overrightarrow{FA} = \overrightarrow{DC}$ and then used $\overrightarrow{EA} = \overrightarrow{EF} + \overrightarrow{FA}$: the result would have been the same.)

**Example** ABCD is a parallelogram. K, L, M and N are the mid-points of the sides (Fig. 22.16). If $\overrightarrow{AB} = a$ and $\overrightarrow{BC} = b$, find in terms of $a$ and $b$

(a) $\overrightarrow{KB}$  (b) $\overrightarrow{KL}$  (c) $\overrightarrow{ND}$  (d) $\overrightarrow{NM}$.

Use your results to prove that KLMN is also a parallelogram.

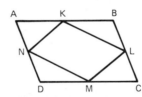

Fig. 22.16

(a) $KB = \frac{1}{2}AB$ and has the same direction as AB since it is part of the same line. So

$$\overrightarrow{KB} = \tfrac{1}{2}\overrightarrow{AB} = \tfrac{1}{2}a$$

(b) Similarly, $\overrightarrow{BL} = \frac{1}{2}\overrightarrow{BC} = \frac{1}{2}b$. So

$$\overrightarrow{KL} = \overrightarrow{KB} + \overrightarrow{BL} = \tfrac{1}{2}a + \tfrac{1}{2}b$$

(c) $AD \parallel BC$ and $AD = BC$ (opposite sides of parallelogram ABCD). Thus

$$\overrightarrow{AD} = \overrightarrow{BC} = b$$

Hence $\qquad \overrightarrow{ND} = \tfrac{1}{2}\overrightarrow{AD} = \tfrac{1}{2}b$

(d) Similarly, $\qquad \overrightarrow{DC} = \overrightarrow{AB} = a$

and $\qquad \overrightarrow{DM} = \tfrac{1}{2}\overrightarrow{DC} = \tfrac{1}{2}a$

Therefore $\qquad \overrightarrow{NM} = \overrightarrow{ND} + \overrightarrow{DM}$

$$= \tfrac{1}{2}b + \tfrac{1}{2}a$$

As both $\overrightarrow{KL}$ and $\overrightarrow{NM}$ are represented by $\tfrac{1}{2}a + \tfrac{1}{2}b$ they are the same vector: equal in magnitude and direction. That is KL = MN and KL ‖ NM. So the quadrilateral KLMN is a parallelogram as opposite sides are equal and parallel.

**EXERCISE 22c**　1. In Fig. 22.17, $\overrightarrow{OA} = a$, $\overrightarrow{OB} = b$ and $\overrightarrow{BC} = 2a$. Find

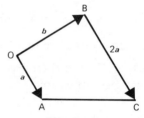

Fig. 22.17

(a) $\overrightarrow{AO}$　　(b) $\overrightarrow{AB}$　　(c) $\overrightarrow{BA}$　　(d) $\overrightarrow{OC}$.

2.

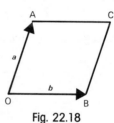

Fig. 22.18

OACB is a parallelogram; $\overrightarrow{OA} = a$ and $\overrightarrow{OB} = b$ (see Fig. 22.18). Find, in terms of $a$ and $b$, the vectors

(a) $\overrightarrow{AC}$　　　(b) $\overrightarrow{BC}$　　　　(c) $\overrightarrow{OC}$　　　　(d) $\overrightarrow{AB}$

(e) $\overrightarrow{CA}$　　　(f) $\overrightarrow{CB}$　　　　(g) $\overrightarrow{CO}$　　　　(h) $\overrightarrow{BA}$.

3.

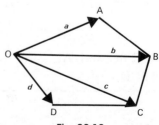

Fig. 22.19

Given the pentagon OABCD, in which $\overrightarrow{OA} = a$, $\overrightarrow{OB} = b$, $\overrightarrow{OC} = c$ and $\overrightarrow{OD} = d$ (Fig. 22.19), find in terms of $a, b, c$ and $d$ the vectors

(a) $\overrightarrow{AB}$    (b) $\overrightarrow{BD}$    (c) $\overrightarrow{BC}$    (d) $\overrightarrow{AD}$    (e) $\overrightarrow{DA}$

(f) $\overrightarrow{DB}$    (g) $\overrightarrow{DC}$    (h) $\overrightarrow{DO}$.

4.

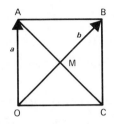

Fig. 22.20

OABC is a square; the diagonals OB and AC intersect at M (Fig. 22.20). If $\overrightarrow{OA} = a$ and $\overrightarrow{OB} = b$ find in terms of $a$ and $b$ the vectors

(a) $\overrightarrow{AB}$    (b) $\overrightarrow{OC}$    (c) $\overrightarrow{BC}$    (d) $\overrightarrow{OM}$    (e) $\overrightarrow{BM}$

(f) $\overrightarrow{MC}$    (g) $\overrightarrow{MA}$.

5.

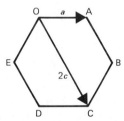

Fig. 22.21

OABCDE is a regular hexagon. Given that $\overrightarrow{OA} = a$ and $\overrightarrow{OC} = 2c$ (Fig. 22.21) find in terms of $a$ and $c$ the vectors

(a) $\overrightarrow{AB}$    (b) $\overrightarrow{OB}$    (c) $\overrightarrow{BC}$    (d) $\overrightarrow{CD}$    (e) $\overrightarrow{DE}$

(f) $\overrightarrow{EO}$    (g) $\overrightarrow{DA}$    (h) $\overrightarrow{DB}$    (i) $\overrightarrow{DO}$    (j) $\overrightarrow{EC}$.

6.

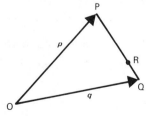

Fig. 22.22

In the triangle OPQ, $\overrightarrow{OP} = p$ and $\overrightarrow{OQ} = q$ (Fig. 22.22). If R is a point on PQ such that $PR = \frac{3}{4}PQ$ find, in terms of $p$ and $q$, the vectors

(a) $\overrightarrow{PQ}$    (b) $\overrightarrow{PR}$    (c) $\overrightarrow{OR}$.

7.

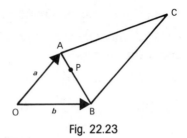

Fig. 22.23

In the trapezium OACB, OA ‖ BC and $\overrightarrow{OA} = \frac{1}{2}\overrightarrow{BC}$ (Fig. 22.23). If $\overrightarrow{OA} = a$ and $\overrightarrow{OB} = b$, find in terms of $a$ and $b$ the vectors

(a) $\overrightarrow{BC}$    (b) $\overrightarrow{OC}$    (c) $\overrightarrow{AB}$    (d) $\overrightarrow{AC}$.

If the point P lies on the diagonal AB such that $AP = \frac{1}{2}PB$ show that $\overrightarrow{AP} = \frac{1}{3}(b-a)$. Find the vector $\overrightarrow{OP}$ and hence show that P also lies on the diagonal OC. Write down the ratio OP : PC.

8.

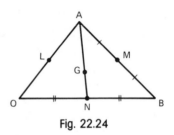

Fig. 22.24

In the triangle OAB, M and N are the mid-points of the sides AB and OB respectively. G is a point on AN such that $AG = \frac{2}{3}AN$ (Fig. 22.24). $\overrightarrow{OA} = 2a$ and $\overrightarrow{OB} = 2b$. Find in terms of $a$ and $b$ the vectors

(a) $\overrightarrow{ON}$    (b) $\overrightarrow{AN}$    (c) $\overrightarrow{AG}$    (d) $\overrightarrow{OG}$    (e) $\overrightarrow{AB}$

(f) $\overrightarrow{AM}$    (g) $\overrightarrow{OM}$.

Use your answers to prove that G also lies on the line OM. Write down the ratio OG : GM.

If L is the mid-point of OA, find the vectors $\overrightarrow{OL}, \overrightarrow{BL}, \overrightarrow{BA}$ and $\overrightarrow{BG}$. Show that G also lies on BL.

9.

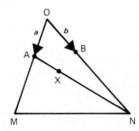

Fig. 22.25

In the triangle OMN shown in Fig. 22.25, $\overrightarrow{OA} = a$, $\overrightarrow{OM} = 3a$, $\overrightarrow{OB} = b$ and $\overrightarrow{ON} = 3b$. Find vectors $\overrightarrow{AB}$ and $\overrightarrow{MN}$ in terms of $a$ and $b$. Hence prove that AB ∥ MN. X is a point on AN such that AN = 4AX. Find the vectors $\overrightarrow{AX}$, $\overrightarrow{BX}$ and $\overrightarrow{BM}$ in terms of $a$ and $b$, and hence prove that X also lies on BM.

10. OVWXYZ is a regular hexagon. If $\overrightarrow{OV} = v$ and $\overrightarrow{OZ} = z$, write down in terms of $v$ and $z$ the vectors

(a) $\overrightarrow{ZW}$    (b) $\overrightarrow{OW}$   (c) $\overrightarrow{VZ}$.

If $P$ is a point on VZ such that VP = $\frac{1}{3}$VZ, find the vectors

(d) $\overrightarrow{VP}$     (e) $\overrightarrow{OP}$.

Hence show that P lies on OW and that OP = $\frac{1}{3}$OW.

11. If OACB is a rhombus and $\overrightarrow{OA} = a$ and $\overrightarrow{OB} = b$, show that

(a) $|a| = |b|$    (b) $a - b$ is perpendicular to $a + b$.

12. (a)  P, Q, R, are three points such that $\overrightarrow{OP} = a + 3b$, $\overrightarrow{OQ} = 2a + 5b$ and $\overrightarrow{OR} = 7a + 15b$. Find the vectors $\overrightarrow{PQ}$ and $\overrightarrow{PR}$, and hence show that P, Q and R lie on the same line.

(b)  X, Y and Z are three other points such that $\overrightarrow{OX} = a - b$, $\overrightarrow{OY} = 4a + 5b$ and $\overrightarrow{OZ} = -3b$. Show that X, Y and Z also lie on one line.

(c)  Write down two facts relating the lines PR and XZ.

# MISCELLANEOUS EXERCISE 22

1. If $a = \begin{pmatrix} 3 \\ 4 \end{pmatrix}$, $b = \begin{pmatrix} -4 \\ 3 \end{pmatrix}$, $c = \begin{pmatrix} 2 \\ 1 \end{pmatrix}$. Find

(a) $|a|$           (b) $|b|$          (c) $|a - b|$.

Does $|a - b| = |a| - |b|$?

Find also

(d) $|\frac{1}{2}(a - b)|$     (e) $|3c - 2a|$      (f) $|a + 2b - 3c|$.

2. (a)  The vectors a and b are given by $a = \begin{pmatrix} 2 \\ -3 \end{pmatrix}$ and $b = \begin{pmatrix} -4 \\ 2 \end{pmatrix}$.

(i)  Find the vector y such that $y = 2a - 3b$.

(ii) Find the vector x such that $2x + 3a = b$.

(iii) Find numbers $h$ and $k$ such that $ha + kb = \begin{pmatrix} 6 \\ -17 \end{pmatrix}$.

(b) The origin is $O$ and $\overrightarrow{OP} = p$, $\overrightarrow{OQ} = q$. The mid-point of $PQ$ is $M$. Express $\overrightarrow{PQ}$ and $\overrightarrow{OM}$ in terms of p and q. (C)

3. In the diagram $\overrightarrow{PQ} = \underline{a}$, $\overrightarrow{SR} = 2\underline{a}$, and $\overrightarrow{SP} = \underline{b}$, $ST = 2TQ$.

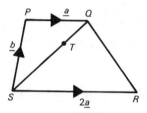

Fig. 22.26

(a) (i) How does the length of the straight line $PQ$ compare with that of the straight line $SR$?

(ii) If $SQ$ was 9 cm long what would be the length of $ST$?

(b) Find in terms of $\underline{a}$ and $\underline{b}$

(i) $\overrightarrow{SQ}$ (ii) $\overrightarrow{TQ}$ (iii) $\overrightarrow{RQ}$ (iv) $\overrightarrow{PT}$ (v) $\overrightarrow{TR}$.

(c) By examination of your answers to (b) parts (iv) and (v), state

(i) how the length of $PT$ is related to the length of $TR$,

(ii) what other conclusion you can make about the straight lines $PT$ and $TR$. (NWREB)

4.

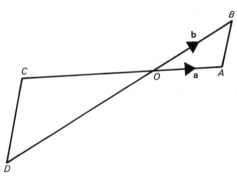

Fig. 22.27

In Fig. 22.27 $\overrightarrow{OA} = a$ and $\overrightarrow{OB} = b$.

(a) Write down an expression for $\overrightarrow{AB}$ in terms of a and b.

(b) $COA$ and $DOB$ are straight lines such that $CA = 3OA$ and $DB = 3OB$.

(i) Write down an expression for $\overrightarrow{CO}$ in terms of a.

366

(ii) Write down an expression for $\overrightarrow{DO}$ in terms of b.

(iii) Write down an expression for $\overrightarrow{DC}$ in terms of a and b.

(iv) State the value of the ratio $DC : AB$.          (EAEB)

5. In Fig. 22.28 vectors $\overrightarrow{OA} = \underline{a}$ and $\overrightarrow{OB} = \underline{b}$.

$C$ is the mid-point of $OA$ and the lines $OB$ and $AB$ are divided equally into thirds by the points $E$, $F$ and $G$, $H$ respectively.

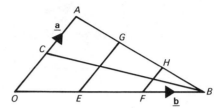

Fig. 22.28

(a) Express each of the following vectors in terms of $\underline{a}$ and $\underline{b}$.
(i) $\overrightarrow{AB}$   (ii) $\overrightarrow{OC}$   (iii) $\overrightarrow{CB}$   (iv) $\overrightarrow{OE}$.

(b) Show that $\overrightarrow{AG} = \frac{1}{3}(\underline{b} - \underline{a})$.

(c) Express $\overrightarrow{OG}$ in terms of $\underline{a}$ and $\underline{b}$.

(d) Using a similar method express $\overrightarrow{AH}$ and $\overrightarrow{OH}$ in terms of a and b.

(e) Observe that
$$\overrightarrow{EG} = -\overrightarrow{OE} + \overrightarrow{OA} + \overrightarrow{AG}$$
$$= -\tfrac{1}{3}\underline{b} + \underline{a} + \tfrac{1}{3}(\underline{b} - \underline{a})$$
$$= \tfrac{2}{3}\underline{a}$$

Use a similar method to find $\overrightarrow{FH}$ in terms of $\underline{a}$ and $\underline{b}$.

(f) Show that $\overrightarrow{OA}$, $\overrightarrow{EG}$ and $\overrightarrow{FH}$ are related and explain clearly the relationship.          (EAEB)

6.

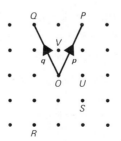

Fig. 22.29

(a) On the grid of squares shown (Fig. 22.29), **OP** = p and **OQ** = q. Express in terms of either p or q or both:
(i) **OR**;   (ii) **RQ**;   (iii) **QP**.
Hence express both **OU** and **OV** in terms of p and q.

(b) Denoting **OU** by u and **OV** by v, express **OS** in terms of u and v, and hence in terms of p and q. Simplify your answer.

(c) Use the diagram to express p and q in terms of u and v. Hence express the vector **OA** in terms of u and v, where $OA = \frac{5}{4}p - \frac{3}{4}q$. Draw a sketch of the grid, and mark the points $O$ and $A$ on it. (O & C)

7.

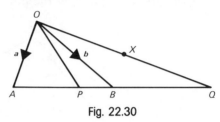

Fig. 22.30

In the diagram (Fig. 22.30), the point $P$ is such that $\mathbf{AP} = 3\mathbf{PB}$ and the point $Q$ is such that $\mathbf{AB} = \mathbf{BQ}$.

(a) Given that $\mathbf{OA} = a$ and $\mathbf{OB} = b$, express as simply as possible, in terms of a and b, the vectors
(i) **AB**, (ii) **AP**, (iii) **OP**, (iv) **AQ**.

The point $X$ is on $QO$ and is such that $\mathbf{QX} = \frac{1}{2}a - b$. Use vectors to prove that **BX** is parallel to **AO**.

(b) Given also that $A\widehat{O}Q = 90°$, $O\widehat{Q}A = 20°$ and $|a| = 5$, calculate
(i) $A\widehat{B}O$, (ii) $|\mathbf{BX}|$. (C)

8.

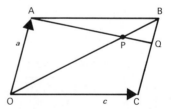

Fig. 22.31

In the parallelogram OABC, $\mathbf{OP} = \frac{3}{4}\mathbf{OB}$ and APQ is a straight line. $\mathbf{OA} = a$ and $\mathbf{OC} = c$ (Fig. 22.31).

(a) Find **OB**, **OP** and **AP** in terms of a and c.

(b) By writing **OQ** as $\mathbf{OA} + x\mathbf{AP}$ express **OQ** in terms of a, c and $x$.

(c) By writing **OQ** as $\mathbf{OC} + y\mathbf{CB}$ express **OQ** in terms of a, c and $y$.

(d) Find the value of $x$ which makes the terms in c equal in the two expressions for **OQ**. Hence find the value of $y$.

(e) Use the value of $y$ to find $\dfrac{CQ}{QB}$. (O & C)

9.

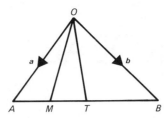

Fig. 22.32

(a) In the diagram (Fig. 22.32), $T$ is the mid-point of $AB$ and $M$ is the mid-point of $AT$. Given that $\mathbf{OA} = a$ and $\mathbf{OB} = b$, express as simply as possible in terms of a and b,
(i) **AB**, (ii) **AM**, (iii) **OM**.

(b) Two points $P$ and $Q$ have position vectors p and q respectively, relative to the origin $O$. Given that $p = \begin{pmatrix} 5 \\ 3 \end{pmatrix}$ and $PQ = \begin{pmatrix} -2 \\ 1 \end{pmatrix}$, find

(i) q, (ii) $|PQ|$,
(iii) the coordinates of the point $R$, which is such that **OR = QP**.
Given also that $s = \begin{pmatrix} 1 \\ 1 \end{pmatrix}$, $t = \begin{pmatrix} 8 \\ 2 \end{pmatrix}$ and $l\mathbf{p} + m\mathbf{s} = \mathbf{t}$, write down two simultaneous equations in $l$ and $m$, and solve them. (C)

10.

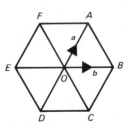

Fig. 22.33

The figure (Fig. 22.33) shows a regular hexagon $ABCDEF$ whose diagonals $AD$, $BE$, $CF$ meet at $O$.

$$\overrightarrow{OA} = a \quad \text{and} \quad \overrightarrow{OB} = b.$$

In terms of a and b write down

(a) $\overrightarrow{EF}$, (b) $\overrightarrow{OF}$, (c) $\overrightarrow{CA}$.

Explain why the position vector, relative to $O$, of any point on the line $CA$ may be expressed as

$$a + p(2a - b)$$

where $p$ is a number. Write down an expression for the position vector of any point on the line $EF$. Hence, or otherwise, find the position vector, in terms of a and b, of the point where the line $CA$ meets the line $EF$. (Ox)

369

# 23 PROBABILITY

## DEFINITION

If all possible outcomes are equally likely, then the chance or *probability* that an event X occurs is given by

$$p(X) = \frac{\text{number of ways that X can happen}}{\text{number of all possible outcomes}}$$

Thus if an ordinary coin is spun, the probability of it showing 'heads' is

$$p(H) = \frac{\text{number of ways that coin can show heads}}{\text{number of all possible ways the coin can land}}$$

$$= \frac{1}{2}$$

If a card is drawn from a well-shuffled pack, then the probability that it is, say, an ace is

$$p(\text{ace}) = \frac{\text{number of ways of drawing an ace}}{\text{number of all possible ways of drawing a card}}$$

$$= \frac{4}{52} = \frac{1}{13}$$

A *certain* outcome will happen every time and an *impossible* outcome will never happen, so

$$p(\text{certainty}) = 1; \qquad p(\text{impossibility}) = 0$$

It follows that all other probabilities must lie between 0 and 1. It also follows that

$$p(\text{event happens}) + p(\text{event does } not \text{ happen}) = 1$$

(since the number of ways an event can happen and the number of ways it does not happen make up the total of all possible outcomes).

**EXERCISE 23a**

1. If I throw a die, what is the chance I score

   (a) 6      (b) 2      (c) an even number?

2. In general, I am late for work one morning a week in a five day working week. What is the chance that I shall be late tomorrow?

3. If I take a card from a pack at random, what is the chance that it is

   (a) the ace of spades        (b) any queen

   (c) any diamond?

4. In a raffle, 2455 tickets are sold. I bought 5 of them. What is my chance of winning the first prize?

5. Asked the chance of a coin showing tails after he has spun it, a boy answers '$\frac{1}{2}$'. Is he right? Asked the chance of spinning three heads in a row, the boy answers '3 times $\frac{1}{2}$ or $1\frac{1}{2}$'. Why *must* he be wrong?

6. What is the probability that it will get dark tonight?

7. What is the probability that the Sun will still be shining at midnight tonight?

8. Three chestnuts in a bag of 20 are bad. What is my chance of picking a good one?

9. The chance of my being late for work is 0.1. What is the chance I am on time?

10. A boy has 0.8 chance of success in a maths test. What is the chance he fails.

11. A rifleman has 0.95 chance of hitting a target. What is his chance of missing it?

12. In a raffle, I have 1/100 chance of winning the first prize. What is my chance of not winning?

# EITHER ONE OR ANOTHER

Provided the two events A and B cannot both happen together, the probability that *either A or B happens* is given by:

$$p(A \; or \; B) \; = \; p(A) + p(B)$$

**Example** A card is drawn from a well-shuffled pack. What is the chance of it being either a diamond or a heart?

$$p(\text{a diamond or a heart}) \; = \; p(\text{a diamond}) + p(\text{a heart})$$

$$= \; \frac{13}{52} + \frac{13}{52} = \frac{26}{52} = \frac{1}{2}$$

(This would seem a reasonable answer, as half the pack is red.)

**Example** What is the chance of scoring 1 or 6 on a normal die?

$$p(1 \text{ or } 6) = p(1) + p(6) = \frac{1}{6} + \frac{1}{6} = \frac{2}{6} = \frac{1}{3}$$

**EXERCISE 23b**

1. If I draw a card from an ordinary pack what is the chance it is
   (a) either a heart or a club      (b) either a 4 or a 5?

2. If I throw an ordinary die, what is the chance I score
   (a) either 1 or 2            (b) 1, 2 or 3?

3. A bag contains 12 marbles, of which 5 are green, 3 are yellow, 2 are blue and 2 are red. What is the chance that the marble I pick is
   (a) either green or red      (b) either green or blue?
   (c) either yellow, green or blue.

4. The Boss always visits my district office once each week. To keep us 'on our toes' he never says which day he will come. What is the chance of him coming on either Thursday or Friday of next week?

5. In my collection of 100 records, 11 are scratched and 5 are warped. If I select a record at random, what is the chance it will be either scratched or warped?

6. In a bag of 100 Scrabble tiles, there are 12 tiles marked E, 8 marked O and 9 marked I. If I take a tile at random, what is the chance it is
   (a) either an E or an O      (b) an E, an O or an I?

7. When I turn on my television set the probability that it is tuned to any one of four stations is $\frac{1}{4}$. What is the chance that it is tuned to BBC1 or BBC2 when I turn it on tonight?

8. The chance that I pick a banana at random from a basket of mixed fruit is $\frac{1}{3}$; the chance that I pick an apple is $\frac{1}{4}$. What is the chance I pick an apple or a banana?

9. The chance that I pick a red jelly-baby out of a packet is $\frac{1}{7}$; the chance that I pick a black one is $\frac{1}{5}$. What is the chance I pick either a red or a black jelly-baby out of the packet? What is the chance that the one I pick is *neither* red *nor* black?

10. Late for a date, I grab a rose from a large vase to present to my girlfriend by way of apology. In my haste I fail to notice the colour (she likes red or pink). If the chance of picking a red rose is $\frac{1}{8}$ and the chance of a pink one is $\frac{1}{6}$, what is the chance that the rose I have is neither of these colours?

## EVENTS FOLLOWING ON

The probability that two events, A and B, *both happen* and happen *in that order*, i.e. A followed by B, is

$$p(A \text{ then } B) = p(A) \times p(B)$$

where $p(B)$ has been worked out assuming that A has already happened.

Similarly, the probability of three events A, B and C happening *in that order* is

$$p(A \text{ then } B \text{ then } C) = p(A) \times p(B) \times p(C)$$

and so on.

Order *must* be taken into account, even when the events happen simultaneously or when order is not specified. Thus

$$p(A \text{ and } B \text{ in any order}) = p(A \text{ then } B) + p(B \text{ then } A)$$

**Example** Two cards are drawn, one by one and without replacing them, from a pack of 52. What is the chance that they are an ace and a king (a) in that order, (b) in any order?

(a) Since there are 52 cards in the pack, of which 4 are aces

$$p(\text{ace on first draw}) = \frac{4}{52}$$

Once an ace has been removed, there are only 51 cards in the pack, of which 4 are kings. Hence

$$p(\text{king on second draw}) = \frac{4}{51}$$

The sequence ace then king will happen with chance

$$p(\text{ace then king}) = \frac{4}{52} \times \frac{4}{51} = \frac{16}{2652} = \frac{4}{663}$$

(b) We can show also that

$$p(\text{king then ace}) = \frac{4}{52} \times \frac{4}{51} = \frac{4}{663}$$

So

$$p(\text{ace and king in any order}) = p(\text{ace then king})$$
$$+ p(\text{king then ace})$$

$$= \frac{4}{663} + \frac{4}{663} = \frac{8}{663}$$

**Example** Two dice are thrown together. What is the chance of the combined score on the dice being (a) 12, (b) 11?

(a) To score a total of 12 requires a 6 on both dice:

$$p(\text{6 then 6}) = p(\text{6 on first die}) \times p(\text{6 on second die})$$

$$= \frac{1}{6} \times \frac{1}{6} = \frac{1}{36}$$

(b) To score 11 requires a 6 on one die and a 5 on the other, *in either order*:

$$p(11) = p(\text{6 then 5}) + p(\text{5 then 6})$$

$$= \frac{1}{36} + \frac{1}{36} = \frac{1}{18}$$

**EXERCISE 23c**

1. I throw two dice, one red, one blue. What is the chance
   (a) the red die shows a 3 and the blue die a 4
   (b) the dice show a 3 and a 4?

2. I take two cards out of a pack of 52. What is the chance that I draw
   (a) a queen and then a king
   (b) a queen and a king in any order?

3. I spin a coin three times. What is the probability that it will show
   (a) heads, then tails, then heads
   (b) two heads and a tail in any order?

4. The chance that an egg produced on a particular farm is brown is $\frac{1}{3}$. If I select six eggs at random what is the chance I select three white eggs and then three brown eggs (in that order)?

5. The probability that a darts player hits the target area he is aiming at with any one dart is $\frac{1}{4}$. What is the chance that, with three darts, he

(a) hits the target, misses it and then hits it again

(b) hits the target twice and misses once, in any order?

6. I throw two dice, one red, one blue. What is the chance that

(a) the red shows 5 and the blue shows 6

(b) the blue shows 5 and the red shows 6

(c) my total score is 11?

There are four possible ways of my score totalling 9. What are they? What is the chance that my total score is 9?

7. I throw a die three times. What is the chance of scoring

(a) three 6s                  (b) two 6s and then a 5

(c) two 6s and then something else

(d) two 6s and a 5 (in any order)

(e) two 6s and something else (in any order)?

8.

Fig. 23.1

A bag contains 15 white beads and 12 black ones. If I take two beads out of the bag at random, one at a time and without replacing the first, find the probability that

(a) that both are white

(b) that both are black

(c) that both are the same colour.

9. How is your answer to Question 8 altered if the first bead *is* replaced before the second is taken out?

10. A bag contains 10 marbles: 5 are red, 3 are orange and 2 are yellow. If I take two marbles out of the bag, one after the other without replacing the first, what is the chance that

(a) both are red

(b) the first is red then the second orange

(c) one is red and the other orange?

11. How are your answers to Question 10 altered if the first marble *is* replaced before the second is taken out?

12. A large bag of 100 draw tickets contains 40 red tickets, 30 blue and 30 white. What is the chance, if three tickets are taken out, of drawing
    (a) a red, a blue and then a white ticket
    (b) a red, a blue and a white ticket in any order?

## AT LEAST ONCE

The chance that, in a long chain of events, something happens *at least once* should be worked out using:

$p$(event happens at least once) $= 1 - p$(event does not happen at all)

**Example** I take three markers out of a box containing 10 white and 10 black markers. What is the chance of at least one white marker among the three?

$$p(\text{at least one white}) = 1 - p(\text{all black})$$

Now

$$p(\text{1st black}) = \frac{10}{20}$$

$$p(\text{2nd black}) = \frac{9}{19} \quad \text{(as one black marker has been removed)}$$

$$p(\text{3rd black}) = \frac{8}{18} \quad \text{(as two black markers have been removed)}$$

Hence

$$p(\text{three black markers}) = \left(\frac{10}{20}\right) \times \left(\frac{9}{19}\right) \times \left(\frac{8}{18}\right) = \frac{2}{19}$$

$$p(\text{at least one white}) = 1 - \frac{2}{19} = \frac{17}{19}$$

**EXERCISE 23d**   1. I throw a die twice. What is the chance that I throw
    (a) two 6s                    (b) one 6 exactly
    (c) no 6 at all               (d) at least one 6?

376

2. I throw two dice together. What is the chance that I throw
   (a) no odd numbers
   (b) one odd number and one even number
   (c) at least one odd number?

3. If I spin three coins, what is the chance that they land showing
   (a) no heads                    (b) at least one head?

4. I cut a pack of cards twice. Prove that the chance of showing an ace at least once is $\frac{25}{169}$. What is the chance of finding at least one club?

5. The chance that I am late for work is 0.2. What is the chance of my not being late for a whole week (5 days). What is the chance that I am late at least once?  [$(0.8)^5 = 0.328$.]

6. A rather naughty boy is in trouble in one-third of his lessons. If he has six lessons in one day, what is the chance that he stays out of trouble all day? What is the chance of him being in trouble at least once in the day?

7. A girl falls off her horse, on average, once every ten rides. What is the chance she will fall off *at least once* in her next ten rides?

8. A bag contains ten beads: three are yellow, two are red and the rest are green. If I take a bead out at random, what is the chance that it is green? If I take out two beads together, what is the chance that exactly one of them is green? What is the chance of at least one being green?

9. In a box of 32 chess pieces, half are white and the rest are black. If I take out three pieces at random, what is the chance that at least one is white?
   There are 8 white pawns and 8 black pawns in the box. If I take out three pieces, what is the chance that I have
   (a) at least one pawn             (b) at least one white pawn?

10. I withdraw three cards from a normal pack, one after the other without replacing them. Find the probability that the cards include
   (a) at least one picture card    (b) at least one red card
   (c) at least one diamond.

## PROBABILITY TREES

Complicated sequences can be 'mapped out' by means of a *probability tree*. Each *branch* or *path* of the tree illustrates one possible chain of events. The probabilities of each stage are written on the tree; these probabilities are multiplied together to find the chance of the whole sequence.

**Example** A rat in a maze must choose between left and right at the next junction. If he turns left, he is free; if he turns right he will meet another junction at which he must choose between left, right and straight on. Both left and right turns lead to dead ends; only if he goes straight on will he be free. Assuming the rat chooses between paths at random, what is the chance the rat will escape the maze without turning back?

The possibilities can be plotted on a probability tree (Fig. 23.2).

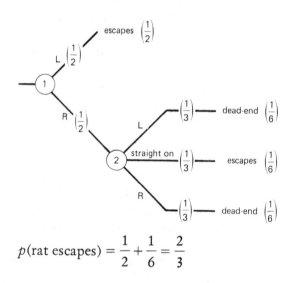

$$p(\text{rat escapes}) = \frac{1}{2} + \frac{1}{6} = \frac{2}{3}$$

**Fig. 23.2**

At junction 1, the rat has two choices — to turn left or to turn right. He makes his choice at random, i.e.

$$p(\text{turns left}) \ = \ p(\text{turns right}) \ = \ \tfrac{1}{2}$$

At junction 2, he has three choices. He is as likely to go straight on as he is to turn left or right, i.e.

$$p(\text{straight on}) \ = \ p(\text{turns left}) \ = \ p(\text{turns right}) \ = \ \tfrac{1}{3}$$

He escapes the maze either by turning left at junction 1 or by carrying on to junction 2 and then going straight on. The probability tree makes this clear. The chance that he escapes is therefore

$p$(left at junction 1) + $p$(right at junction 1, then straight on)

$$= \frac{1}{2} + \left(\frac{1}{2} \times \frac{1}{3}\right) = \frac{1}{2} + \frac{1}{6} = \frac{2}{3}$$

**EXERCISE 23e**  1. The chance that the 8.30 a.m. train from Worplesdon to Waterloo is late is $\frac{1}{10}$. If that one is late, the chance that the next train at 9.00 a.m. is also late is $\frac{5}{8}$.

However, if the 8.30 a.m. train is on time, the chance that the 9.00 a.m. train is late is only $\frac{1}{18}$.

Copy and complete the following tree diagram:

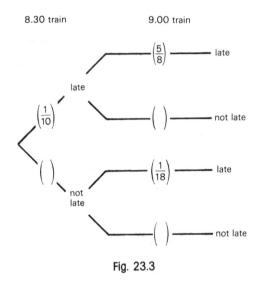

8.30 train        9.00 train

Fig. 23.3

Use your diagram to find the probability that
(a) both trains are late,
(b) both trains are on time,
(c) one or the other train is late (but not both).

2. A bag contains five marbles: two are red, two blue, and one green. I take out two marbles. Complete the probability tree (Fig. 23.4), and use it to find the chance that

(a) one marble is blue and one is red,

(b) the two marbles are of different colour.

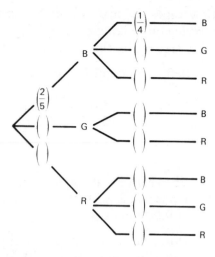

Fig. 23.4

3. In a fairground draw, I win a prize for 'finding the lady', i.e. drawing the one queen in a pack of 12 cards. If I draw one of the four kings, the card is replaced and I can have another go. Otherwise I lose. If I draw a second king, then I can have a third go, after which the game finishes.

Copy and complete the probability tree in Fig. 23.5 and find my chance of winning.

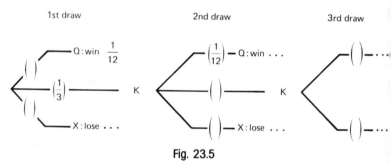

Fig. 23.5

4. A ferret in a rabbit warren turns left or right at junction A at random. Having turned left or right once, he is twice as likely

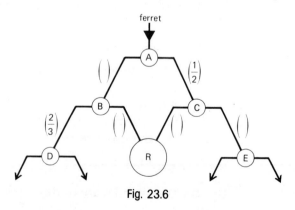

Fig. 23.6

380

to repeat himself at the next junction (B or C) as he is to turn the other way. Copy the probability tree in Fig. 23.6 and mark on the appropriate probabilities. Find the chance that the ferret finds the rabbits hiding at R.

5. A bag contains ten marbles: seven red, two orange and one yellow. I play a game in which I try to find the yellow marble, taking marbles unseen out of the bag. If I draw a red one at any stage, I lose. If I draw an orange one, I keep it out and have another go. How many marbles, at most, could I take out of the bag? Draw a probability tree to show all the possibilities. What is my chance of winning?

6. A young girl picks chocolates out of a box at random. Though she loves chocolate and would not normally stop until she had eaten all six of the sweets that remain, unfortunately she cannot bear the taste of coffee. If she picks one of the two coffee-creams at any point, she is certain to put it back and stop immediately.

Show, with a probability tree, all the possibilities. What is the chance she will stop, leaving

(a) five sweets,

(b) at least four sweets in the box?

## MISCELLANEOUS EXERCISE 23

*You are advised to work in fractions throughout this exercise.*

1. A 'spinner' used in a game has 10 sections, of which 6 are coloured red and the remainder green.

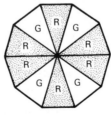

Fig. 23.7

(a) For one turn of the spinner,
   (i) explain why the probability of obtaining a red is $\frac{3}{5}$.
   (ii) find the probability, expressed as a fraction in its lowest terms, of obtaining a green.

(b) How many times would you expect to obtain a red in 90 separate turns of the spinner?

(c) Copy and complete the following tree diagram to show the probabilities for two turns of the spinner.

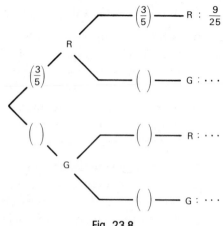

Fig. 23.8

(d) For *two* turns of the spinner, find the probability of obtaining
  (i)   red then green in that order,
  (ii)  at least one green.

(e) For *three* turns of the spinner, find the probability of obtaining three reds.　　　　　(EMREB)

2. (a) Write down, as a fraction, the probability of scoring a 6 with one throw of an ordinary die.

The diagram below shows part of a *Snakes and Ladders* board.

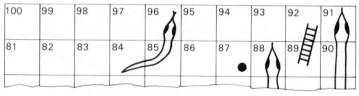

Fig. 23.9

You throw a die and move your counter forward the number of squares indicated by the number on the die. If you land on the bottom of a ladder, you move to the top of the ladder.

Your counter is on square 87.

Starting from this square, write down, as a fraction, the probability in one throw of

(b) landing on the foot of the ladder,

(c) landing on the head of a snake,

(d) finishing on square 92.

During your turn, if you throw a 6, you are allowed another throw. Your turn continues until you throw a number other than 6.

Starting from square 87, calculate, as a fraction, the probability in *one turn* of

(e) landing on square 95,

(f) landing on square 100. (LREB)

3. As part of a competition, three features K, L, M of a car have to be put in order of importance.

   (a) List all the different orders in which K, L, M can be put.

   (b) A competitor writes down the order of the three features at random. There is only one correct order.
   (i) Calculate the probability that the competitor has the correct order.
   (ii) Calculate the probability that the competitor has none of the three features in its correct position in the order. (MEG)

4. Two unbiased spinners are labelled with the numbers 1, 2, 3, 4, 5. An experiment consists of spinning them together and the score is calculated by subtracting the smaller number from the larger number.

   (a) Copy and complete the following table to show all the possible scores.

Number on second spinner

|  |  | 1 | 2 | 3 | 4 | 5 |
|---|---|---|---|---|---|---|
|  | 1 | 0 |  |  |  |  |
| Number on | 2 |  |  |  |  | 3 |
| first | 3 |  |  |  |  |  |
| spinner | 4 |  | 2 |  |  |  |
|  | 5 |  |  |  |  |  |

   (b) Calculate the probability of a score of
   (i) 0,
   (ii) at least 2,
   (iii) 5.

   (c) Calculate the probability of a total score of 0 after two experiments.

   (d) Calculate the probability of a total score of 1 after two experiments. (LREB)

5. Copy and complete the table below which shows the 36 possible results from throwing two ordinary dice and adding the scores obtained.

Red die

|        |   | 1 | 2 | 3 | 4 | 5 | 6 |
|--------|---|---|---|---|---|---|---|
|        | 1 | 2 | 3 | 4 | 5 | 6 | 7 |
|        | 2 | 3 | 4 |   |   |   |   |
| Blue   | 3 | 4 |   |   |   |   |   |
| die    | 4 |   |   |   |   |   |   |
|        | 5 |   |   |   |   |   |   |
|        | 6 |   |   |   |   |   |   |

Use the table to answer the following questions.

(a) How many possible ways are there for scoring 12? What is the chance of scoring 12?

(b) How many possible ways are there of scoring 11? What is the chance of scoring 11?

(c) What is the most likely score?

Now copy and complete this table:

| Score, $x$ | 2 | 3 | 4 | 5 | 6 | 7 | 8 | 9 | 10 | 11 | 12 |
|------------|---|---|---|---|---|---|---|---|----|----|----|
| p($x$)     |   |   |   |   |   |   |   |   |    |    |    |

Describe in your own words the pattern you find.

6. Calculate the probabilities that, when two ordinary dice are thrown,

(a) both dice show 5,

(b) at least one of the two dice shows 5,

(c) the total score of the two dice is 5.

Given that one die is thrown four times, calculate the probability that

(d) the die will show 5 on each of the four throws,

(e) the die will show 5 on at least three of the four throws.

(JMB)

7. I throw two ordinary fair dice, one of which is red and the other is white. Calculate, giving your answer in each case as a fraction in its lowest terms, the probability that

(a) the total shown on the dice is eight;

(b) the score on the red die is exactly three more than the score on the white die;

(c) the score on one die is exactly three more than the score on the other die. (Ox)

8. The probabilities that each of three marksmen, Tom, Dick and Harry, will hit a target at a single attempt are $\frac{1}{3}, \frac{1}{4}, \frac{1}{5}$ respectively.

(a) If they all fire simultaneously at the target, find the probabilities that:
(i)   Harry misses it;
(ii)  all three men hit it;
(iii) all three men miss it;
(iv)  at least one man hits it.

(b) They now each prepare to fire once at the target in the order Tom, Dick and Harry. In this case once the target has been hit no more shots are fired. Copy and complete the tree diagram (Fig. 23.10) by inserting all the outcomes and one-stage probabilities in the correct places on it.

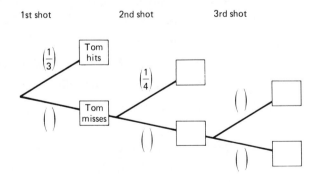

Fig. 23.10

Find the probabilities that
(i)   the target is hit by Dick;
(ii)  the target is hit by either Tom or Dick;
(iii) the target is hit by Harry;
(iv)  the target is hit. (O & C)

9. The probability that there are one or more misprints on any one page of the *Wessex Mercury* is $\frac{1}{3}$. The sports section of this newspaper always contains two pages.

State the probability that a page contains no misprints and calculate the probability that in the sports section

(a) there are no misprints,

(b) at least one of the pages contains one or more misprints.

In the *New Herald*, some of the pages are completely filled with full-page advertisements. On such pages, the probability that there are one or more misprints is $\frac{1}{10}$; on all other pages it is $\frac{1}{3}$.

Given that on any particular day the probability that page three contains a full-page advertisement is $\frac{1}{4}$, calculate the probability that

(c) page three contains a full-page advertisement and one or more misprints,

(d) page three contains one or more misprints.

Last year the *New Herald* appeared 280 times. Estimate the number of times that page three had no misprints. (AEB '82)

10. A student is supposed to attend a course of six lectures. He is sure to attend the first lecture, and the probability that he will attend the second one is $\frac{3}{4}$. If he ever misses a lecture, he is sure to attend the next one, and the probability that he will attend the one after that is $\frac{3}{4}$. If he has attended two or more lectures in succession, the probability that he will attend the next one is $\frac{1}{2}$. Find the probability that he will attend

(a) the first three lectures,

(b) the first and third, but not the second,

(c) the third lecture, whether or not he attends the second,

(d) all six lectures.

Find

(e) the smallest number of lectures he can attend, and the probability that he will attend this smallest number. (LU)

# 24 AVERAGES

## MEAN

The *mean* is the proper name for the common idea of average (strictly it should be called the 'arithmetic mean').

$$\text{mean} = \frac{\text{total of all the numbers}}{\text{number of numbers}}$$

For example, the set of seven numbers $\{2, 3, 4, 7, 8, 8, 9\}$ has a mean average given by

$$\text{mean} = \frac{2 + 3 + 4 + 7 + 8 + 8 + 9}{7} = \frac{41}{7} = 5.86$$

It follows that the total of a set of numbers can be found from the mean:

$$\text{total} = \text{number of numbers} \times \text{mean}$$

This is important for solving problems.

**Example** A batsman has a mean average of 23 runs over his last five innings. How many must he score in his next innings if he is to increase his average to 25?

The batsman's total number of runs in five innings $= 5 \times 23 = 115$. If the mean is to rise to 25 in six innings, his total must rise:

$$\text{new total for six innings} = 6 \times 25 = 150$$

Therefore he must score $150 - 115 = 35$ runs during his sixth innings.

## MODE

The *mode* is the number that occurs most frequently. For example, the mode of $\{2, 3, 4, 7, 8, 8, 9\}$ is 8, since there are two 8s in the set but only one each of the other numbers.

Sometimes, there is no mode; sometimes there is more than one. For example, the set $\{2, 3, 4, 5, 6, 7\}$ has no mode, as no number is repeated. But the set $\{2, 2, 2, 3, 4, 5, 5, 5, 7, 7\}$ has *two* modes, 2 and 5, since both numbers occur three times. (7 is repeated too, but not as often as 2 or 5.)

# MEDIAN

The *median* value in a set of numbers is the one in the middle *when they are arranged in order*. For example, the median value of $\{2, 3, 4, 7, 8, 8, 9\}$ is 7 since it lies exactly in the middle.

If *two* numbers lie in the centre of the set (which is always the case when the set contains an even number of numbers) the median is the mean of the two numbers. There can *never* be two medians.

**Example** Find the median of the set of six numbers $\{6, 1, 3, 5, 4, 2\}$.

Rearranging the numbers into order gives $\{1, 2, 3, 4, 5, 6\}$.

Now *two* numbers, 3 and 4, lie in the middle, so the median is

$$\frac{3 + 4}{2} = 3\tfrac{1}{2}$$

**EXERCISE 24a** Calculate (i) the mean (ii) the mode(s) (iii) the median for the following. Which do you think best represents the data?

1. $2, 4, 5, 8, 3, 4, 7, 2, 1.$

2. $3, 4, 9, 2, 8, 4, 6, 7, 3, 6, 7, 3, 3.$

3. $11, 3, 9, 3, 9, 8, 12, 9.$

4. $-3, -1, 0, 7, 6, 4, 1.$

5. $56.5, 52.1, 53.2, 53.1, 51.1.$

6. $103, 104, 105, 106, 104, 108.$

7. Charlotte scores 63% in maths, 43% in English, 57% in French and 67% in Science. What is her mean score?

8. The wages paid in a small local factory are (per week) £90, £90, £90, £90, £90, £90 and £440 (for the boss). The workers claim the average wage is £90. The boss says it is £140 per week. Both are right — explain.

9. Five numbers have a mean of 6. If a sixth number is added to the set, the mean rises to 7. What is the extra number?

10. A set of ten numbers have a mean of 6.5. An eleventh number raises the mean to 6.6. What is the number?

11. A set of four odd numbers have a mode of 3, a median of 4 and a mean of $4\tfrac{1}{2}$. What are the numbers?

12. The set $\{2, 7, x, 4, 3\}$ has a mean of 4.4. Find $x$.

13. The set $\{2, 5, 9, 3, 2, 6, 2, x\}$ has a mean of 5. Find $x$.

14. The set $\{-6, -5, -4, 0, 3, 7, 9, x\}$ has a mean of 1. Find $x$.

15. The set $\{2, 3, 4, 2, 3, y\}$ has a mode of 2. Find $y$.

16. In a class of 18 boys and 12 girls, the boys' mean score in a maths test was $7\frac{1}{2}$ out of 10. How many marks did the 18 boys gain altogether?

    The girls scored an average of 8 out of 10. How many marks did the 12 girls gain altogether?

    What was the mean for the whole class of 30?

17. The same class of 18 boys and 12 girls also took a French test. The boys' mean score was 11 out of 20 and the girls' was only 9. Find the mean score for the whole class.

18. Over 20 games of golf, I have a mean score of 60 strokes per round. If my average over the first 12 games was 64 strokes, what has been my mean score in the last 8?

19. In a class of 15 girls and 12 boys, the girls' mean score in a test was 21 marks and the boys' mean score was 18. What was the mean score for the whole class?

20. Jack and Jill bring back, on average, 8.8 litres of water whenever they are asked to fetch it. If they fall down and spill it all on one journey in five, what must be their (mean) average for the *successful* journeys?

21. The mean of five numbers is 39. Two of the numbers are 103 and 35 and each of the other three is equal to $x$. Find the numerical value of

    (a) the total of the five numbers,    (b) $x$.    (C)

22. Wanderers have a mean goal average of 2.25 after eight matches. What was their score in the ninth match if, afterwards, the average fell to exactly 2?

23. The average age of a group of 6 fifth-formers is 16 years and 5 months. Another student joins the group and the average age rises to 16 years 7 months. How old is the newcomer?

24. When is the mean of the means of two sets of numbers the same as the mean of all the numbers taken together? Investigate.

## FREQUENCY DISTRIBUTIONS

A large set of numbers can be summarised by a table, called a *frequency distribution*, showing the number of times (or *frequency*) each number occurs. Such a table reduces the amount of work involved in finding the mean, mode and median.

**Example** The following set of thirty-five numbers

$$\{8, 2, 1, 5, 2, 5, 2, 6, 7, 2, 8, 5, 6, 9, 2, 3, 7, 1, 6, 7, 4, 3, 6, 7, 7, 2, 4,$$
$$7, 9, 3, 4, 6, 7, 9, 7\}$$

have been counted off using a *tally chart* as shown:

| Number $x$ | Tally | Frequency $f$ |
|:---:|:---:|:---:|
| 1 | I I | 2 |
| 2 | LHT I | 6 |
| 3 | I I I | 3 |
| 4 | I I I | 3 |
| 5 | I I I | 3 |
| 6 | LHT | 5 |
| 7 | LHT I I I | 8 |
| 8 | I I | 2 |
| 9 | I I I | 3 |
| | Total | 35 |

Thus in the set of thirty-five numbers, there are two 1s, six 2s, three 3s, three 4s, and so on. You should check the set for yourself to make sure you understand where the numbers in the table have come from.

*The mode* — the one that occurs most often — is easy to find. Look at the frequencies of the numbers: there are eight 7s, but only six 2s, five 6s, and so on. There are more 7s than any other number, and hence the mode is 7.

We can find *the median* — the one in the middle — using the *cumulative frequency*, shown in Column (*iii*) of the following table:

| (i) | (ii) | (iii) | (iv) |
|---|---|---|---|
| Number $x$ | Frequency $f$ | Cumulative frequency c.f. | $f \times x$ |
| 1 | 2 | 2 | $1 \times 2 = 2$ |
| 2 | 6 | $2 + 6 = 8$ | $2 \times 6 = 12$ |
| 3 | 3 | $8 + 3 = 11$ | $3 \times 3 = 9$ |
| 4 | 3 | $11 + 4 = 14$ | $4 \times 3 = 12$ |
| 5 | 3 | $14 + 3 = 17$ | $5 \times 3 = 15$ |
| 6 | 5 | $17 + 5 = 22$ | $6 \times 5 = 30$ |
| 7 | 8 | $22 + 8 = 30$ | $7 \times 8 = 56$ |
| 8 | 2 | $30 + 2 = 32$ | $8 \times 2 = 16$ |
| 9 | 3 | $32 + 3 = 35$ | $9 \times 3 = 27$ |
| | Total 35 | | 179 |

The cumulative frequency builds up stage by stage, as we count through the thirty-five numbers in the set. So, when we have counted the 2s, there are eight numbers marked off (six 2s and two 1s); when we have marked off the three 3s then eleven numbers have been counted, and so on, until all thirty-five have been checked off. As there are thirty-five numbers, the eighteenth lies exactly in the centre and is the median value. The cumulative frequency shows that when all the 5s have been marked off we will have counted *seventeen* numbers, i.e. one short of the eighteenth. So the eighteenth must be a 6: the median value is 6.

Column (*iv*) in the table above shows the calculations necessary to find *the mean*. The two 1s contribute 2 (i.e. $2 \times 1$) to the final total of all the numbers; the six 2s contribute 12 (i.e. $6 \times 2$) to the total; the three 3s contribute 9 (i.e. $3 \times 3$); the three 4s contribute 12 (i.e. $3 \times 4$), and so on. In each case the number is multiplied by its frequency. The results are then added to find the total of all thirty-five numbers. In this example, the total is 179: thus the mean is $179 \div 35 = 5.11$.

# GROUPED DATA

Sometimes it is not convenient to show all the numbers individually in a frequency distribution and instead the data is grouped together in *classes* such as '0–9', '10–19' etc. It is not possible to calculate the *exact* value of the mean in such cases (since we do not have the exact value of the individual numbers); but it is possible to *estimate* it, if we assume that all the numbers in a class are represented by the mid-value of that class. So the class '0–9' is taken to be the value $4\frac{1}{2}$ $=$ $\left(\dfrac{0+9}{2}\right)$; the class '10–19' is taken to be $14\frac{1}{2}$ $=$ $\left(\dfrac{10+19}{2}\right)$, and so on. Otherwise the procedur is the same as above.

**Example** Estimate the mean of the following frequency distribution:

|  | Mid-point, $x$ | Frequency, $f$ | $f \times x$ |
|---|---|---|---|
| 5–9 | 7 | 3 | $7 \times 3 = 21$ |
| 10–14 | 12 | 5 | $12 \times 5 = 60$ |
| 15–19 | 17 | 4 | $17 \times 4 = 68$ |
| 20–24 | 22 | 3 | $22 \times 3 = 66$ |
|  | Total | 15 | 215 |

$$\text{estimated mean} = \frac{\text{total of all the numbers}}{\text{number of numbers}} = \frac{215}{15} = 14\frac{1}{3}$$

**EXERCISE 24b**　1. Use a tally chart similar to that on page 390 to form a frequency distribution for the following 45 numbers ranging from 0 to 9:

> 0, 5, 3, 2, 0, 7, 5, 3, 0, 7, 5, 6, 0, 7, 9,
> 7, 5, 3, 0, 4, 1, 0, 6, 3, 9, 6, 3, 2, 1, 8,
> 2, 8, 4, 9, 3, 0, 4, 6, 8, 5, 9, 3, 9, 5, 7.

Use your distribution to find

(a) the mode,

(b) the median,

(c) the mean of the numbers.

2. Repeat Question 1 for these numbers. There are 75 numbers this time.

> 3, 7, 4, 6, 8, 9, 5, 3, 8, 5, 3, 9, 5, 3, 5,
> 1, 2, 8, 5, 9, 5, 2, 1, 0, 6, 4, 2, 9, 5, 2,
> 5, 7, 3, 9, 6, 4, 6, 2, 9, 5, 2, 9, 0, 4, 2,
> 5, 2, 0, 1, 8, 6, 4, 3, 2, 0, 8, 6, 5, 4, 3,
> 5, 4, 3, 6, 5, 3, 7, 6, 4, 6, 8, 5, 4, 7, 8.

In Questions 3, 4 and 5 find (a) the mean (b) the mode and (c) the median of the following distributions.

3.

| Number | 1 | 2 | 3 | 4 | 5 | 6 |
|---|---|---|---|---|---|---|
| Frequency | 2 | 3 | 6 | 3 | 4 | 2 |

4.

| Number | 2 | 3 | 4 | 5 | 6 | 7 |
|---|---|---|---|---|---|---|
| Frequency | 1 | 3 | 5 | 10 | 8 | 3 |

5.

| Number | 0 | 1 | 2 | 3 | 4 |
|---|---|---|---|---|---|
| Frequency | 10 | 8 | 6 | 4 | 2 |

6. A survey of 50 families showed the number of children per family distributed as follows:

| Number of children | 1 | 2 | 3 | 4 | 5 |
|---|---|---|---|---|---|
| Frequency | 19 | 18 | 9 | 3 | 1 |

(a) Write down the modal number of children per family.

(b) Find the median number of children per family.

(c) Calculate the mean number of children per family.

(AEB '81)

7. The hours of sunshine per day were recorded at a seaside resort over a period of 50 days. The results were as follows:

| Hours of sunshine per day | 5 | 6 | 7 | 8 | 9 | 10 | 11 |
|---|---|---|---|---|---|---|---|
| Frequency of days | 6 | 11 | 9 | 8 | 7 | 5 | 4 |

(a) Write down the modal hours of sunshine per day.

(b) Find the median number of hours of sunshine per day.

(c) Calculate the mean hours of sunshine per day. (AEB '82)

8. In a football season a team played 54 matches, the number of goals they scored in each match was recorded and the following results obtained:

3, 2, 2, 0, 0, 1, 0, 5, 1, 3, 2, 2, 1, 3, 4, 0, 0, 2,
4, 1, 2, 3, 3, 0, 1, 0, 0, 0, 5, 2, 2, 0, 1, 2, 3, 1,
3, 2, 1, 1, 0, 1, 0, 2, 2, 4, 3, 3, 1, 1, 0, 0, 1, 2.

Construct a frequency distribution table for the number of goals scored and state the mode. (JMB)

9. A die was thrown 40 times and the frequency of each score was as follows:

| Score | 1 | 2 | 3 | 4 | 5 | 6 |
|-------|---|---|---|---|---|---|
| Frequency | 5 | 4 | 9 | 8 | 8 | 6 |

(a) Write down the modal score.

(b) Find the median score.

(c) Calculate the mean of these scores.

The die was then thrown another 20 times. The mean of these 20 throws was 3.4.

(d) Calculate the overall mean for all 60 throws.   (AEB '81)

10. A shopkeeper examines 100 records and lists the number of faults on each record. The result is shown below:

| Number of faults per record | 0 | 1 | 2 | 3 | 4 | 5 |
|-----------------------------|---|---|---|---|---|---|
| Number of records | 13 | 13 | 36 | 23 | 9 | 6 |

Calculate the mean number of faults per record.

He has a further 200 records in stock and the mean number of faults on these is $m$. Given that the mean number of faults on his total stock is 2, calculate the value of $m$.   (JMB)

11. What is the mid-value of the class '1 to 5'?

Copy and complete the following table and hence estimate the mean of the distribution.

| Score | Mid-value $x$ | Frequency $f$ | Frequency × mid-value $fx$ |
|-------|---------------|---------------|-----------------------------|
| 1–5 | . . . | 11 | . . . |
| 6–10 | 8 | 12 | . . . |
| 11–15 | . . . | 15 | . . . |
| 16–20 | . . . | 9 | . . . |
| 21–25 | . . . | 3 | . . . |
| | Total | 50 | . . . |

12. The following 45 numbers range from 1 to 25.

2, 24, 13, 2, 25, 14, 23, 22, 16, 14, 13,
12, 16, 24, 13, 4, 3, 16, 15, 3, 8, 16, 14,
14, 16, 4, 3, 17, 5, 14, 13, 18, 7, 6, 15,
4, 13, 7, 14, 9, 23, 17, 14, 6, 15.

Copy and complete the following tally chart, and so group the data into classes 1–5, 6–10 and so on.

| Class | Tally | Frequency |
|-------|-------|-----------|
| 1–5   |       |           |
| 6–10  |       |           |
| 11–15 |       |           |
| 16–20 |       |           |
| 21–25 |       |           |
| Total |       |           |

Following the method of Question 11, calculate an estimate of the mean. Why is your answer only an estimate of the mean?

13. The following are marks scored by 31 students in a maths test:

1, 12, 13, 12, 10, 9, 8, 13, 7, 11, 13, 9, 12, 6, 17, 11,
17, 6, 5, 12, 3, 13, 12, 5, 7, 6, 12, 13, 12, 10, 13

(a) Find the mean, mode and median of the marks.

(b) Group the data into five classes, 1–4 marks, 5–8 marks, etc. Estimate the mean mark from this frequency distribution. Why is your answer different from (a)?

Calculate an estimate of the mean from the following frequency distributions:

14.

| Length (cm) | $0 \leqslant x < 4$ | $4 \leqslant x < 8$ | $8 \leqslant x < 12$ |
|-------------|---------------------|---------------------|----------------------|
| Frequency   | 5                   | 8                   | 17                   |

| Length (cm) | $12 \leqslant x < 16$ | $16 \leqslant x < 20$ |
|-------------|-----------------------|-----------------------|
| Frequency   | 13                    | 7                     |

15.

| Weight (kg) | $0 \leqslant x < 10$ | $10 \leqslant x < 20$ | $20 \leqslant x < 30$ |
|-------------|----------------------|-----------------------|-----------------------|
| Frequency   | 22                   | 12                    | 8                     |

| Weight (kg) | $30 \leqslant x < 40$ | $40 \leqslant x < 50$ |
|-------------|-----------------------|-----------------------|
| Frequency   | 4                     | 4                     |

16.

| Score     | 0–4 | 5–9 | 10–14 | 15–19 | 20–24 |
|-----------|-----|-----|-------|-------|-------|
| Frequency | 3   | 9   | 15    | 10    | 3     |

# 25 STATISTICAL GRAPHS

## PIE CHARTS

The pie chart is an excellent way of showing how a total is broken up into its constituent parts.

**Example** An A-level statistics group of 20 students have the following number of GCSEs at higher level grades:

| Number of GCSEs | 2–4 | 5 | 6 | 7 | 8–12 |
|---|---|---|---|---|---|
| Number of students | 3 | 3 | 6 | 5 | 3 |

As 3 out of 20 people have 2–4 GCSEs, they are $\frac{3}{20}$ of the statistics class. We can convert this fraction to a decimal and so to a percentage:

$$\frac{3}{20} = 0.15 = 0.15 \times 100\% = 15\%$$

and into an angle in a similar fashion:

$$0.15 \times 360° = 54°$$

So $\frac{3}{20}$ of the class with 2–4 GCSEs at higher grades should be shown as 15% of the total or a portion of a pie chart of angle 54°.

Show the *percentages* (*not* the angles) on the pie-chart portions and label them fully or show what they represent by a colour key.

For this example:

| Number of subjects at GCSE | Frequency | % | Angle |
|---|---|---|---|
| 2–4 | 3 | $\frac{3}{20} \times 100 = 15\%$ | $\frac{3}{20} \times 360° = 54°$ |
| 5 | 3 | $\frac{3}{20} \times 100 = 15\%$ | $\frac{3}{20} \times 360° = 54°$ |
| 6 | 6 | $\frac{6}{20} \times 100 = 30\%$ | $\frac{6}{20} \times 360° = 108°$ |
| 7 | 5 | $\frac{5}{20} \times 100 = 25\%$ | $\frac{5}{20} \times 360° = 90°$ |
| 8–12 | 3 | $\frac{3}{20} \times 100 = 15\%$ | $\frac{3}{20} \times 360° = 54°$ |
| Total | 20 | 100% | 360° |

*[handwritten margin notes: "360° ÷ 18° = 1 person", "20", "Make sure that they add up to 360°"]*

396

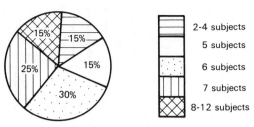

students with GCSE qualifications at higher grades

Fig. 25.1

## PICTOGRAMS

The same data can be illustrated as a pictogram.

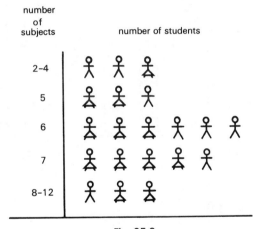

Fig. 25.2

This is (or can be) an eye-catching way of illustrating otherwise dull and uninteresting sets of figures.

## BAR CHARTS

Pie charts are excellent for showing parts of a total, but not a way of comparing *different* totals; a bar chart is used instead.

**Example** All the fifth-formers in a school took maths, English, history and French GCSEs. The totals qualifying with higher level grades in each subject are illustrated in Fig. 25.3. Even a quick glance at the chart is enough to see the relative success of the four departments.

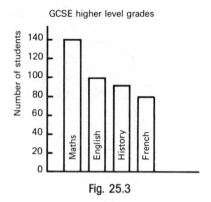

Fig. 25.3

We can split the bars to illustrate the components of each bar or compare results with multiple bars, as in Fig. 25.4.

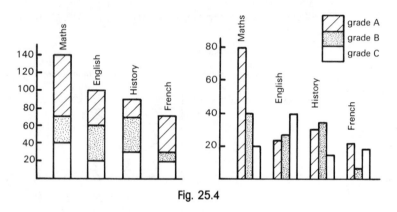

Fig. 25.4

## MISLEADING GRAPHS

Well chosen, well drawn graphs portray information in a way that can be quickly read and understood. Unfortunately, dishonestly drawn graphs can easily mislead.

Often, graphs which convey a false impression depend upon inappropriate and/or broken scales on the $y$-axis. For example, the bar chart in Fig. 25.5 might have been drawn to exaggerate the success of the maths department by breaking the scale.

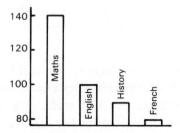

Fig. 25.5

Alternatively, a scale might have been chosen to hide the lack of success of other subjects.

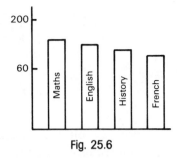

Fig. 25.6

Sometimes pictograms are drawn as a set of enlargements using the correct *linear* scale factor, but with the intention that the areas or volumes will make a more dramatic impression.

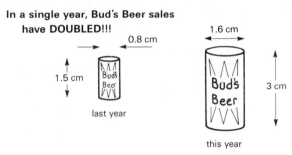

Fig. 25.7

**EXERCISE 25a** 1. (a) From the bar chart in Fig. 25.8, find
(i) the mode,
(ii) the median number of goals scored by Village Rangers.

(b) How many games have the Rangers played? How many goals have they scored? What is their mean number of goals scored per match?

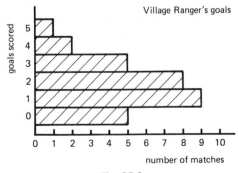

Fig. 25.8

2. The candidates in an examination are awarded grades A, B, C, D, E, F or G. Two classes take the same exam and their results are as listed:

Class 1 (30 students)  A, B, A, B, C, F, C, B, A, B, C, F, B, B, B, D, E, C, B, A, F, B, F, D, E, G, F, B, C, C.

Class 2 (32 students)  A, B, C, C, C, C, F, F, C, F, B, A, B, B, C, D, G, C, C, B, C, C, C, A, C, C, B, C, E, D, E, D, A.

(a) Draw two pie charts, one for each class, to show the proportion of students awarded each grade.

(b) Draw *one* bar chart to compare the performances of the two classes.

3. The pie chart in Fig. 25.9 shows how Whereonearth County divide their education budget between primary, secondary and further education. Find

(a) the *percentage* spent on secondary schools

(b) the *angle* on the chart representing primary school expenditure.

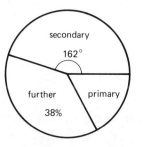

Fig. 25.9

4. The pie chart in Fig. 25.10 shows the allocation of hourly air time between pop music, D.J.'s chat, news and advertisements for a local radio station.

If $P\hat{O}Q = 120°$ and $Q\hat{O}R = 54°$ find the number of minutes of pop music broadcast per hour given that the hourly news bulletin lasts 3 minutes and the headlines (on the half-hour) last another 1 minute.

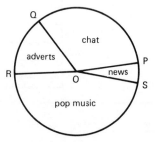

Fig. 25.10

5. The table shows how the assets of an International Commercial Bank were distributed in 1975 and 1980.

| | Percentage of total assets | | | |
|---|---|---|---|---|
| | Europe | Africa | America | The East |
| 1975 | 34 | 41 | 5 | 20 |
| 1980 | 24 | 28 | 24 | 24 |

(a) Draw circular diagrams, each of radius 5 cm, to compare the data for these two years.

(b) The total value of the Bank's assets in 1980 was £13 000 million. Calculate the value of the assets in Africa for that year. (JMB)

6. In a recent by-election 25% of those voting voted for the Liberal/S.D.P. Alliance, 35% voted for Labour and 40% voted for the Conservative Party. 20% of those entitled to vote did not do so.

(a) Find the percentage of those entitled to vote who voted
(i) Alliance (ii) Labour (iii) Conservative.

(b) Use a pie chart to show how the electorate behaved in this election.

7. The pie chart in Fig. 25.11 shows how a charity fund spends each £1 of its income.

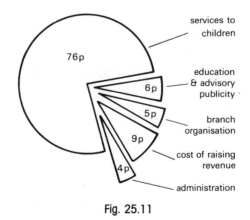

Fig. 25.11

(a) What percentage of income is spent on Administration?

(b) What angle is drawn on the pie chart to represent spending on Branch Organisation?

(c) How much is spent on Services to children when the charity's income is £2 000 000?

(d) What is the ratio of spending on Education and Advisory Publicity to spending on Administration?

(e) How much is spent on Branch Organisation in a year when £20 000 is spent on Administration? (EAEB)

8.      **Rake-off Unit Trust**                    **Get your Money to GROW!**

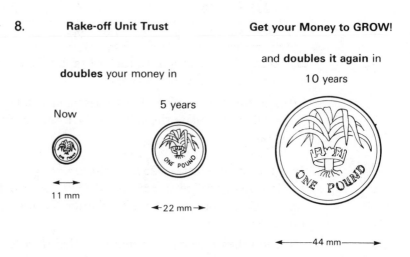

Fig. 25.12

The pictures shown in an advertisement for Rake-off Unit Trust (Fig. 25.12) have been drawn exactly to scale. However, it is not a fair advertisement. Explain.

9. The Managing Director of a manufacturing company is extremely proud of the growth in his company's exports since he took over. He illustrates his figures in the Directors' report to shareholders as follows:

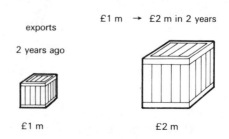

Fig. 25.13

The figures are drawn to scale, but the illustration is non the less misleading. Explain.

10. The Editor of the *Worplesdon World* is claiming a huge increase in the circulation of his newspaper at the expense of one of the rival journals in the town, the *Worplesdon Daily Review*. He uses the following bar chart to illustrate the point.

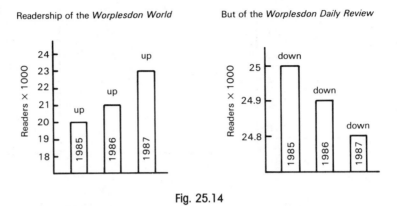

Fig. 25.14

Given that the circulation figures on the chart are actually correct, do you think it fairly represents the truth?

The *Worplesdon Daily Review* decides to respond in kind. Design a bar chart to 'show' that the *Review* is holding its own!

11. A politician on TV one evening claims that the Government has all but beaten inflation and that unemployment is falling sharply. 'We have turned the corner! Look at these graphs.'

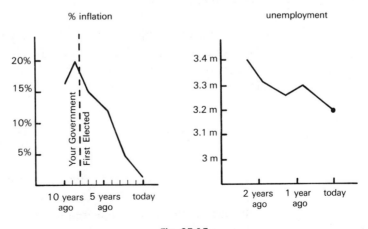

Fig. 25.15

The next day the Opposition refutes the claim. 'The Government says it has beaten price rises — but its policies have had virtually no impact — except, of course massively to increase the number of unemployed. Look at these graphs!'

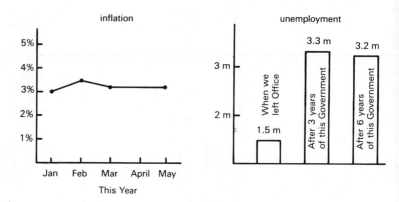

Fig. 25.16

Who is telling the truth?

## HISTOGRAMS

A *histogram* is a special kind of bar chart, drawn with pin-point accuracy on graph paper, with uses beyond simply illustrating data. The features of a histogram are:

(*i*)  the blocks of the chart meet each other,

(*ii*)  the frequency of a class is proportional to the *area* of the corresponding block,

(*iii*)  the widths of the blocks of the chart may vary (as well as the height) according to the widths of the classes. If so, the heights of the blocks represent the *frequency density* (*not* frequency) of each class:

$$\text{frequency density} = \frac{\text{frequency of class}}{\text{class width}}$$

(The *frequency density* indicates how tightly packed a class is; *frequency* measures how many items there are in it. A wide class might have a high frequency but a low frequency density.)

A histogram can be used to estimate the mode. First, find the tallest block representing the most densely packed class (the *modal class*). Draw the 'diagonals' to the neighbouring classes (Fig. 25.17), and read off the mode from the point where the diagonals cross.

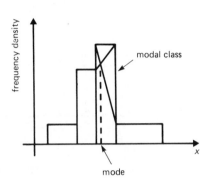

Fig. 25.17

**Example** A survey finds the heights of 150 adult males to be as follows:

| Height (cm) | $160 \leqslant x < 165$ | $165 \leqslant x < 168$ | $168 \leqslant x < 172$ |
|---|---|---|---|
| Frequency | 15 | 27 | 30 |

| Height (cm) | $172 \leqslant x < 175$ | $175 \leqslant x < 180$ | $180 \leqslant x < 190$ |
|---|---|---|---|
| Frequency | 21 | 25 | 32 |

Draw a histogram from this data and estimate the mode.

Setting out the calculation of frequency density:

| Height<br>$x$ cm | Frequency<br>$f$ | Class width<br>$w$ | Frequency density<br>$f \div w$ |
|---|---|---|---|
| $160 \leqslant x < 165$ | 15 | 5 | $15 \div 5 = 3$ |
| $165 \leqslant x < 168$ | 27 | 3 | $27 \div 3 = 9$ |
| $168 \leqslant x < 172$ | 30 | 4 | $30 \div 4 = 7.5$ |
| $172 \leqslant x < 175$ | 21 | 3 | $21 \div 3 = 7$ |
| $175 \leqslant x < 180$ | 25 | 5 | $25 \div 5 = 5$ |
| $180 \leqslant x < 190$ | 32 | 10 | $32 \div 10 = 3.2$ |

The histogram can be plotted, as shown in Fig. 25.18. From the graph, the (estimated) mode is 167.2 cm.

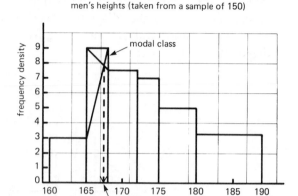

men's heights (taken from a sample of 150)

**Fig. 25.18**

Notice that the class with the highest *frequency* (i.e. 180–190 cm with a frequency of 32) is the widest class. But, because of the width, it has a relatively low frequency density.

**Example**   Returning to the A-level statistics group's GCSE qualifications (page 396).

| Number of subjects at GCSE | Frequency $f$ | Class width $w$ | Frequency density $f \div w$ |
|---|---|---|---|
| 2–4 | 3 | 3* | $3 \div 3 = 1$ |
| 5 | 3 | 1 | $3 \div 1 = 3$ |
| 6 | 6 | 1 | $6 \div 1 = 6$ |
| 7 | 5 | 1 | $5 \div 1 = 5$ |
| 8–12 | 3 | 5* | $3 \div 5 = 0.6$ |

*Notice that the class 2–4 is *three* units wide, as it includes people with 2 subjects, 3 subjects and 4 subjects; similarly the 8–12 class is *five* units wide.

As the classes in this table do not meet (e.g. the 2–4 class does not meet the next class 5) the histogram blocks are extended by one-half in each direction. So the 2–4 class is drawn from $1\frac{1}{2}$ to $4\frac{1}{2}$, the 5 class is drawn from $4\frac{1}{2}$ to $5\frac{1}{2}$, the 6 class is drawn from $5\frac{1}{2}$ to $6\frac{1}{2}$, and so on (see Fig. 25.19). Notice, however, that the block $1\frac{1}{2}$ to $4\frac{1}{2}$ is still *three* units wide — just as it should be since the class 2–4 is three units wide.

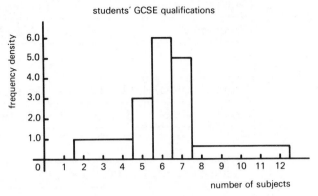

Fig. 25.19

1. Copy the histograms in Fig. 25.20. For each find

(a) the frequency densities of each class,

(b) the frequencies of each class,

(c) the modal class.

Estimate, from your drawing, the value of the mode.

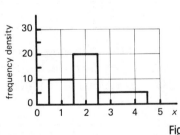 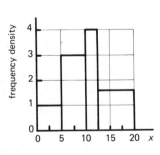

Fig. 25.20

Draw a histogram for each of the following distributions. Remember to divide the frequency of each class by its width to find the frequency density. In each case (a) state the modal class (b) estimate the mode.

2.

| Length ($x$ cm) | $0 \leqslant x < 1$ | $1 \leqslant x < 2$ | $2 \leqslant x < 3$ |
|---|---|---|---|
| Frequency | 6 | 8 | 9 |

| Length ($x$ cm) | $3 \leqslant x < 4$ | $4 \leqslant x < 5$ |
|---|---|---|
| Frequency | 7 | 3 |

407

**3.**

| Number of children per family | 0 | 1 | 2 | 3 | 4 | 5 | 6 | 7 |
|---|---|---|---|---|---|---|---|---|
| Frequency | 4 | 6 | 8 | 4 | 3 | 2 | 0 | 1 |

**4.**

| Score ($x$ points) | 11 | 12 | 13 | 14 | 15 | 16 | 17 | 18 |
|---|---|---|---|---|---|---|---|---|
| Frequency | 3 | 5 | 13 | 15 | 20 | 16 | 12 | 4 |

**5.**

| Volume ($x$ cm³) | $100 \leqslant x < 110$ | $110 \leqslant x < 115$ |
|---|---|---|
| Frequency | 10 | 10 |

| Volume ($x$ cm³) | $115 \leqslant x < 117.5$ | $117.5 \leqslant x < 125$ |
|---|---|---|
| Frequency | 10 | 10 |

**6.**

| Time ($x$ s) | $0 \leqslant x < 5$ | $5 \leqslant x < 10$ |
|---|---|---|
| Frequency | 25 | 42 |

| Time ($x$ s) | $10 \leqslant x < 12$ | $12 \leqslant x < 15$ |
|---|---|---|
| Frequency | 18 | 12 |

Draw a histogram for each of the following distributions. Remember to adjust the blocks so that they meet each other. In each case (a) state the modal class (b) estimate the mode.

**7.**

| Marks | 0–4 | 5–9 | 10–14 | 15–19 | 20–24 |
|---|---|---|---|---|---|
| Frequency | 5 | 8 | 11 | 4 | 2 |

**8.**

| Score | 0–3 | 4 | 5 | 6–8 | 9–12 |
|---|---|---|---|---|---|
| Frequency | 9 | 5 | 7 | 12 | 8 |

**9.**

| Points | 0–9 | 10–19 | 20–39 | 40–59 | 60–99 |
|---|---|---|---|---|---|
| Frequency | 25 | 38 | 52 | 32 | 40 |

# CUMULATIVE FREQUENCY CURVES

The graph of the cumulative frequency is called the *cumulative frequency curve*. It is usually drawn as an S-shaped, smooth curve. (A graph drawn with straight lines is called the *cumulative frequency polygon*.)

The cumulative frequency curve is used to estimate the *median* (the middle item), the *lower* and *upper quartiles* (the values of the items one-quarter and three-quarters through the data), and various *percentiles* (items at given percentage points through the distribution).

*Note* the *interquartile range* = upper quartile − lower quartile and the *semi-interquartile range* = interquartile range ÷ 2.

**Example** 200 students take an exam and their marks are as shown:

| Mark (%) | 20–29 | 30–39 | 40–49 | 50–59 | 60–69 | 70–79 | 80–89 |
|---|---|---|---|---|---|---|---|
| Frequency | 11 | 24 | 48 | 58 | 39 | 13 | 7 |

Draw up a cumulative frequency table, draw the cumulative frequency curve and use it to find (a) the median (b) the upper and lower quartiles and hence the interquartile range (c) the 85th percentile (d) the number of students to score less than 35%.

The cumulative frequency table is as follows:

| Mark | Cumulative frequency c.f. |
|---|---|
| less than 30 | 11 |
| less than 40 | 35 (= 11 + 24) |
| less than 50 | 83 (= 35 + 48) |
| less than 60 | 141 (= 83 + 58) |
| less than 70 | 180 (= 141 + 39) |
| less than 80 | 193 (= 180 + 13) |
| less than 90 | 200 (= 193 + 7) |

Plotting the points $(30, 11)$, $(40, 35)$, $(50, 83)$, and so on, gives the graph shown in Fig. 25.21.

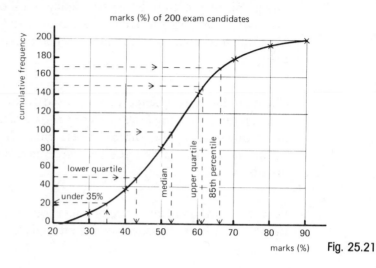

Fig. 25.21

(a) There are 200 students; thus the hundredth student is in the middle and his score is the median mark. Reading across the graph, at cumulative frequency 100, and down to the horizontal axis, we see this mark is $52\frac{1}{2}\%$.

(b) The lower quartile is the mark of the student 50th from bottom. Similarly, as there are 200 students, the three-quarters position is 150th from bottom. Reading across the graph from cumulative frequencies of 50 and 150 down to the horizontal axis, we see that the lower and upper quartiles are 43% and 62% respectively. So the interquartile range is $62 - 43 = 19\%$.

(c) The 85th percentile is the mark gained by the student who is $\frac{85}{100} \times 200 = 170$th. From the graph, his mark is 66%.

(d) To find the number of students who scored less than 35%, read the graph *up* from the horizontal axis at 35% and across to the cumulative frequency axis. We find about 22 students out of the 200 scored less than 35%.

**EXERCISE 25c**   In Questions 1–3:

(a) Draw up a cumulative frequency table from the frequencies given.

(b) Draw the cumulative frequency curve on graph paper.

(c) From your graph, estimate (i) the median (ii) the lower quartile (iii) the upper quartile (iv) the 35th percentile.

(d) Write down the interquartile range.

**1.**

| Men's heights (x cm) | $160 \leqslant x < 165$ | $165 \leqslant x < 170$ | $170 \leqslant x < 175$ |
|---|---|---|---|
| Frequency | 8 | 10 | 22 |

| Men's heights (x cm) | $175 \leqslant x < 176$ | $176 \leqslant x < 178$ | $178 \leqslant x < 188$ |
|---|---|---|---|
| Frequency | 20 | 28 | 42 |

**2.**

| Price (£) | 0–9.99 | 10–19.99 | 20–24.99 |
|---|---|---|---|
| Frequency | 10 | 15 | 24 |

| Price (£) | 25–29.99 | 30–39.99 |
|---|---|---|
| Frequency | 22 | 11 |

**3.**

| Exam score (marks out of 20) | 0–4 | 5–8 | 9–10 | 11 | 12 | 13–20 |
|---|---|---|---|---|---|---|
| Number of students | 4 | 3 | 8 | 7 | 6 | 8 |

**4.** 1000 candidates sit a mathematics examination and the results are distributed as follows:

| Percentage mark | 0–10 | 11–20 | 21–30 | 31–40 |
|---|---|---|---|---|
| Number of candidates | 10 | 40 | 90 | 140 |

| Percentage mark | 41–50 | 51–60 | 61–70 | 71–80 |
|---|---|---|---|---|
| Number of candidates | 240 | 180 | 120 | 100 |

| Percentage mark | 81–90 | 91–100 |
|---|---|---|
| Number of candidates | 60 | 20 |

(a) Draw a cumulative frequency curve to represent these data.

(b) From your curve estimate the median mark.

(c) The top 60% of candidates are to be awarded a 'pass' grade. Estimate the minimum mark required to pass the examination.

(d) The top 30% of candidates are to be awarded a 'merit' grade. Calculate an estimate of the mean mark of those candidates who achieve 'merit' in the examination. (Ox)

5. A sample number of married people were questioned concerning the age at which they were first married. From the answers received the frequency distribution of the ages, in complete years, is given in the following table.

| Age in complete years | 17–21 | 22–26 | 27–31 | 32–36 | 37–41 | 42–56 |
|---|---|---|---|---|---|---|
| Number of people | 42 | 69 | 24 | 19 | 15 | 11 |

Using squared paper, draw a cumulative frequency polygon to illustrate this distribution.

Use your diagram to estimate

(a) the median,

(b) the semi-interquartile range,

(c) the percentage of this sample of people who first married at age 23 to 30 inclusive. (AEB '82)

6. (a) On a particular weekend the mean attendance at the 34 football league matches played on the Saturday was 25 500 and the mean attendance at the 12 matches played on the Sunday was 16 750. Calculate the mean attendance for that weekend, giving your answers to three significant figures.

(b) A manufacturer gives a 'two year' guarantee with a car battery. The lengths of life, in days, of 500 batteries sold by this manufacturer are summarised in the frequency table.

| Length of life ($x$ days) | Frequency |
|---|---|
| $690 \leqslant x < 720$ | 40 |
| $720 \leqslant x < 750$ | 120 |
| $750 \leqslant x < 780$ | 140 |
| $780 \leqslant x < 810$ | 110 |
| $810 \leqslant x < 840$ | 70 |
| $840 \leqslant x < 870$ | 20 |

Draw up a table of cumulative frequencies and draw the cumulative frequency diagram for this distribution.

Use your cumulative frequency diagram to estimate
(i) the median,
(ii) the interquartile range,
(iii) the probability that a battery chosen at random from this group fails before the guarantee expires. (Take 2 years = 730 days.) (JMB)

# ANSWERS

**Exercise 1a**

1. $7, -2$
2. all of them
3. (a) no    (b) yes    (c) yes    (d) yes
4. $\sqrt{2}, \pi$
5. (a) 9    (b) $-3$    (c) 14    (d) 6
   (e) 12    (f) $-16$    (g) $-9$    (h) $-48$
   (i) $-2$    (j) 21    (k) 2    (l) $-6$
6. $20; 75; 10$
7. (a) $-110$    (b) $-1$    (c) $-109$
8. $12, 2$
9. $\sqrt{4} = 2$ which is rational
   (a) 11    (b) 3.48    (c) 1.1
   (d) 0.348    (e) 3.79    (f) 1.2
   (b), (d), (e) are irrational but the written approximations are rational
10. Any written value of $\pi$ is rational since it terminates. No. 0.001 26. 355/113
11. Repeated root of $x \to 1$ for any $x$ unless $x$ is negative when $\sqrt{x}$ does not exist
12. $x^n \to \infty$ if $x > 1$; $x^n \to 0$ if $x < 1$; sign alternates $+, -, +, - \ldots$ if $x < 0$
13. (a) $-3\,^{\circ}C$    (b) $-9\,^{\circ}C$    (c) $6\,^{\circ}C$
    (d) $15\,^{\circ}C$
14. £206.80; £523.20
15. (a) hill walking    (b) 765 m
    (c) 746 m

**Exercise 1b**

1. $1, 2, 3, 4, 6, 9, 12, 18, 36$
2. $1, 2, 3, 4, 6, 9, 12, 18, 27, 36, 54, 108$
3. 36
4. (a) $1, 2, 4, 8, 16$
   (b) $1, 2, 3, 4, 6, 8, 12, 24$
5. 8
6. (a) $1, 13$    (b) $1, 17$; prime numbers
7. $2, 3, 5, 7, 11$
8. yes, 2 is a prime number
9. $2, 3, 5, 7, 11, 13, 17, 19, 23, 29, 31, 37,$
   $41, 43, 47$
10. $1, 2, 4, 7, 21$
11. all prime
12. $127, 131, 137, 139$
13. (a) $2 \times 3^2$    (b) $2 \times 3 \times 11$
    (c) $2^2 \times 3 \times 7$   (d) $2^4 \times 3^2$

14. 210
15. $11; 1089$
16. (a) $2^2 \times 3$    (b) $2^3 \times 3$    (c) $2^2 \times 3^2$
    Include each prime factor to its lowest power
17. (a) $2 \times 3 \times 17; 1 \times 102; 2 \times 51; 3 \times 34;$
    $6 \times 17$
    (b) (i)   $1, 2, 3, 5, 6, 10, 15, 30$
         (ii) $1, 2, 3, 4, 6, 12$
        (iii) $1, 3, 5, 15, 25, 75$
18. $5, 10, 15, 20, 25, 30, 35, 40, 45, 50$
19. (a) $6, 12, 18, 24, 30, 36$
    (b) $15, 30, 45, 60, 75, 90$
20. (a) 30    (b) 30
21. (a) 12    (b) 24    (c) 12
22. LCM $= 15$; HCF $= 1$
23. LCM $= 300$; HCF $= 5$
24. (a) $2 \times 5$    (b) $5^2$    (c) $2^2 \times 3 \times 5$
    LCM is $2^2 \times 3 \times 5^2$
    i.e. include each prime factor to its highest power

**Exercise 1c**

1. (a) $21, 28, 36, 45, 55$
   (b) $36, 49, 64, 81, 100$
   (c) $21, 34, 55, 89, 144$
2.       1   6   15   20   15   6   1
       1   7   21   35   35   21   7   1
     1   8   28   56   70   56   28   8   1
   1   9   36   84   126   126   84   36   9   1
3. $1; 2; 4; 8; 16; 32; 64; 128$
   Each row totals to a power of 2
4. $11^2 = 121; 11^3 = 1331; 11^4 = 14\,641;$
   $11^5$ does not fit since '10s' require carrying
5. (a) $19, 22, 25, 28, 31 \ldots$
   (b) $-5, -9, -13, -17, -21 \ldots$
   (c) $-7, -3, +1, +5, +9 \ldots$
   (d) $24, 31, 39, 48, 58 \ldots$
   (e) $42, 56, 72, 90, 110 \ldots$
   (f) $125, 216, 343, 512, 729 \ldots$
   (g) $98, 128, 162, 200, 242 \ldots$
   (h) $46, 61, 78, 97, 118 \ldots$
   (i) $17, 19, 23, 29, 31 \ldots$
   (j) $10, 25, 8, 27, 6 \ldots$
   (k) $23, -3, 27, -7, 31 \ldots$
   (l) $9, 16, 13, 20, 17 \ldots$

7.

16             25

8.

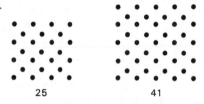

25             41

9.

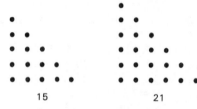

15             21

10. (a) $12^2 = 144$    (b) $6^2 = 36$
    (c) $144 - 36 = 108$ (d) $20^2 - 12^2 = 256$
11. $20^2 = 400$
12. (a) $\dfrac{100 \times 101}{2} = 5050$

    (b) $5050 - \dfrac{49 \times 50}{2} = 3825$

13. yes; no pattern
14. $41^2 + 41 + 41$ necessarily has factor 41
   also $40^2 + 40 + 41$ not prime

## Exercise 1d

1. (a) 809    (b) 4040    (c) 55 050
   (d) 701 107
2. 0.7; 2.2; 3.24; 4.48
3. 1.2; 3.2; 6.5; 8.95
4. 8.76
5. (a) 5392    (b) 7308    (c) 317.8
6. (a) 230    (b) 2300    (c) 230 000
   (d) 230    (e) 2300    (f) 23 000
7. (a) 230    (b) 23    (c) 2.3
   (d) 2.3    (e) 0.2300    (f) 0.000 230 0
8. (a) 34.5    (b) 345    (c) 34 500
   (d) 3450    (e) 345 000
   (f) 345 000 000
9. (a) 34.5    (b) 3.45    (c) 0.0345
   (d) 0.345    (e) 0.003 45
   (f) 0.000 345
10. (a) 0.02    (b) 0.2    (c) 2
   (d) 0.000 2    (e) 0.000 02
   (f) 0.000 002

## Exercise 1e

1. (a) 5.8    (b) 0.73    (c) 2.109
   (d) 2.091
2. (a) 0.046    (b) 0.000 46  (c) 2700
   (d) 27
3. (a) 1.079    (b) 102.1002
   (c) 0.1331    (d) 110 000
4. (a) 0.0012    (b) 4000    (c) 1200
   (d) 30 000
5. (a) 0.000 009    (b) 0.0001
   (c) 1.17    (d) 10 020.01
6. (a) 0.02    (b) 2100    (c) 14
   (d) 9
7. (a) 0.09    (b) 1.1    (c) 1000
   (d) 600
8. (a) 0.1    (b) 0.2    (c) 0.02
   (d) 0.001
9. (a) 0.005    (b) 1.8    (c) 1
   (d) 0.000 25
10. (a) 4    (b) 12    (c) 6
   (d) 3

## Exercise 1f

1. (a) 7.77    (b) 9.79    (c) 10.01
   (d) 10.00    (e) 6.67    (f) 7.29
   (g) 7.30    (h) 7.29
2. (a) 5.05    (b) 12.1    (c) 122
   (d) 10.1    (e) 10.0    (f) 12.1
   (g) 12.0    (h) 101
3. (a) (i) 0.123  (ii) 0.001  (iii) 123.457
   (b) (i) 0.123  (ii) 0.001 23  (iii) 123
4. (a) 3    (b) 4    (c) 3 or 4
   (d) 4    (e) 5    (f) 3
   (g) 3    (h) 1    (i) 1
   (j) 2    (k) 3    (l) 4
5. (a) 40 000    (b) 6000    (c) 1 000 000
   (d) 3000    (e) 0.01    (f) 30
   (g) 0.1    (h) 10    (i) 200
6. (a) 13 325.02    (b) 269.533
   (c) 150.321    (d) 13 890
   (e) 0.577 22    (f) 5.120 88
7. 2.6458; 2.65 (3 s.f.)
8. 0.707 11; 0.577 35
   (a) 0.837    (b) −0.448
9. (a) 0.875 46    (b) 0.305 70
   (c) 0.632 91    (d) 6.4807
   (e) 10.504    (f) 3.1416
10. (a) 1.114; 1.105    (b) 1.244; 1.235
   (c) 1.424; 1.415    (d) 1.544; 1.535
   (e) 1.554; 1.545    (f) 2.244; 2.235
   (g) 2.254; 2.245    (h) 1.004; 0.995

11. (a) 1.2350; 1.2449   (b) 1.2395; 1.2404
12. the girl; 12.30 suggests greater accuracy than 12.3

## Exercise 1g

1. $1000; \frac{1}{1000}$
2. 2 534 000
3. 225 000
4. (a) 60      (b) 3600; 4 500 000
5. (a) 10 000    (b) 1 000 000
6. 6.25
7. (a) 144      (b) 900
8. (a) 25      (b) 80      (c) 2.56
9. (a) 6.356    (b) 2.203
10. (a) $30 \, \text{m}^3$      (b) $3 \times 10^7 \, \text{cm}^3$
     (c) $3 \times 10^4 \, \text{litres}$
11. 60 cm
12. $258.75; 13\frac{1}{3}$ cm
13. 12.1 m; 1210 cm; 533 mm
14. (a) 70      (b) 175      (c) 252
     (d) 55      (e) 400
15. 0.4 p; 90 000; £4500
16. $19\,300 \, \text{kg/m}^3; 51.8 \, \text{cm}^3$
17. $1.76 \times 10^4 \, \text{kg}$
18. $8.77 \times 10^{-5} \, \text{g/cm}^3; 3.5 \, \text{g}$
19. 1.166 litres; 1.2 litres; 336 ml less
20. 15 m/s; 45 ms
21. 86.4 km

## Miscellaneous Exercise 1

1. (a) all      (b) 1, 11, 101
     (c) $-101, 0, 1, 11, 101$
     (d) all except $\sqrt{11}$
2. (a)

     (b) (i) $P$ (ii) $Q$ (iii) $Q, I, N$ (iv) $Q, I$
3. $-4, -3.2, 0.18, 0.2, \sqrt{3}, 2.1$
4. (a) 3, 7      (b) 1, 3, 7      (c) none
     (d) 1, 27, 64
5. (b) 3      (c) 91
     (d) 1, 3, 6, 21, 28
7. (a) 3, 6, 9      (b) 1, 4, 9
     (c) 1, 2, 7
     (d) $7 \times 8 + 6; 6 \times 10 + 2; 6 \times 9 + 8;$ no
8. 840
9. (a) 1      (b) 1
     (c) all numbers      (d) 0
11. 370; 371
12. 35, 51

15. (a)
     (b) 8, 13, 20 red; 8, 12, 16 white
     (c) 29; 40; $n^2 - 4(n - 2)$
     (d) $12 \times 12$; 104 red; 40 white
16. (a) 25      (b) 121      (c) 361
     (d) 841; 1681
17. (a) 256 580 250
     (b) 0.000 256 580 25
     (c) 26.389      (d) 2638.9
18. (a) 3.15      (b) 233.1      (c) 0.0074
     (d) 0.2331      (e) 31.5      (f) 0.315
19. (a) 4460.592      (b) 293.1
     (c) 66.505 94      (d) 2348.6965
     (e) 21 728.571
20. (a) 0.0505      (b) 0.050 51
     (c) 0.1      (d) 0.05
21. (a) 30 m.p.g.      (b) 6
     (c) just about
22. (a) 5 m; 4.8 m; 4.8 m
     (b) 1.1 m; $1.4 \, \text{m}^2$ (1 d.p.)
23. (a) 1 m      (b) $1 \, \text{m} \times 2 \, \text{m}; 1 \, \text{m} \times 3 \, \text{m}$
     (c) 6 m      (d) 6 m      (e) $23 \, \text{m}^2$

## Exercise 2a

1. (a) $\frac{7}{12}$   (b) $\frac{9}{20}$   (c) $1\frac{5}{12}$   (d) $1\frac{7}{20}$
2. (a) $\frac{3}{10}$   (b) $\frac{4}{15}$   (c) $\frac{13}{28}$   (d) $\frac{1}{8}$
3. (a) $\frac{11}{16}$   (b) $\frac{13}{16}$   (c) $1\frac{1}{6}$   (d) $1\frac{11}{40}$
4. (a) $\frac{5}{16}$   (b) $\frac{1}{3}$   (c) $\frac{13}{40}$   (d) $\frac{11}{24}$
5. (a) $\frac{1}{14}$   (b) $\frac{3}{5}$   (c) $\frac{3}{11}$   (d) $\frac{3}{4}$
6. (a) $\frac{1}{6}$   (b) $\frac{1}{27}$   (c) $\frac{3}{8}$   (d) $\frac{5}{16}$
7. (a) $1\frac{1}{4}$   (b) $2\frac{2}{3}$   (c) 9   (d) $\frac{3}{4}$
8. (a) $\frac{5}{7}$   (b) $1\frac{1}{4}$   (c) 4   (d) 10
9. (a) $1\frac{3}{7}$   (b) $\frac{4}{11}$   (c) $1\frac{1}{5}$   (d) $\frac{2}{13}$
10. (a) $1\frac{3}{4}$   (b) $1\frac{4}{7}$   (c) $\frac{4}{5}$   (d) $-1\frac{7}{12}$
11. (a) $3\frac{7}{8}$   (b) $\frac{3}{8}$   (c) $3\frac{23}{32}$   (d) $1\frac{3}{14}$
12. (a) $4\frac{5}{9}$   (b) $1\frac{8}{9}$   (c) $4\frac{8}{27}$   (d) $2\frac{5}{12}$
13. (a) $\frac{1}{5}$   (b) $\frac{3}{4}$   (c) $1\frac{3}{5}$   (d) $\frac{4}{25}$
     (e) $\frac{11}{20}$   (f) $\frac{3}{5}$   (g) $\frac{3}{50}$   (h) $\frac{3}{500}$
     (i) $\frac{9}{20}$   (j) $\frac{18}{25}$   (k) $\frac{1}{20}$   (l) $\frac{12}{25}$
     (m) $\frac{1}{8}$   (n) $\frac{3}{8}$   (o) $\frac{1}{250}$
14. (a) 0.625    (b) 0.35    (c) 0.1875
     (d) 0.24

15. (a) $0.\dot{3}$          (b) $0.8\dot{3}$
   (c) $0.\dot{2}\dot{7}$         (d) $0.\dot{2}85\,71\dot{4}$
16. (a) 0.846   (b) 0.467   (c) 0.529
   (d) 0.0526   (e) 0.0769   (f) 0.793
   (g) 0.762   (h) 0.676
17. (a) $0.\dot{0}\dot{9}$     (b) $0.\dot{1}\dot{8}$     (c) $0.\dot{2}\dot{7}$
   (d) $0.3\dot{6}$
19. $0.\dot{1}42\,85\dot{7}$; $0.\dot{2}85\,71\dot{4}$

## Exercise 2b

1. (a) 31%     (b) 5%      (c) 150%
   (d) $\frac{1}{2}$%     (e) $\frac{1}{10}$%
2. (a) 60%    (b) $66\frac{2}{3}$%    (c) 4%
   (d) $37\frac{1}{2}$%    (e) $10\frac{1}{2}$%
3. (a) 175%    (b) $166\frac{2}{3}$    (c) 280%
   (d) $362\frac{1}{2}$%    (e) $218\frac{1}{2}$%
4. (a) 0.32     (b) 0.89     (c) 0.1
   (d) 0.67     (e) 0.88
   (f) 0.431    (g) 0.834    (h) 0.322
   (i) 1.10     (j) 1.084    (k) 0.585
   (l) 0.835    (m) 0.5125   (n) 0.8575
   (o) 0.744    (p) 0.08    (q) 0.03
   (r) 0.069    (s) 0.085    (t) 0.0125
5. (a) $\frac{3}{4}$   (b) $\frac{3}{5}$   (c) $\frac{8}{25}$   (d) $\frac{3}{10}$
   (e) $\frac{9}{20}$   (f) $\frac{6}{25}$   (g) $\frac{17}{20}$   (h) $\frac{9}{50}$
   (i) $\frac{11}{100}$   (j) $\frac{47}{100}$   (k) $\frac{31}{200}$   (l) $\frac{1}{8}$
   (m) $\frac{1}{30}$   (n) $\frac{21}{400}$   (o) $\frac{1}{6}$
6. (a) 8.5     (b) £9     (c) 75
   (d) £1.30   (e) 78p    (f) £2.88
   (g) 3.196   (h) £3.67   (i) £1.92
   (j) 15.625   (k) £20.50   (l) £53.55
7. 60%; 70%; English
8. 70%      (a) 4%      (b) $13\frac{1}{3}$%
9. 42 m.p.g.; $2\frac{1}{2}$%
10. 2100; 26%
11. 74%; 83%
12. £287.50; 3.17%

## Exercise 2c

1. (a) 75p     (b) £1.28    (c) £1.54
   (d) £2.08   (e) £1.94   (f) £12.68
   (g) £3.26   (h) £4.93
2. (a) $9\frac{1}{2}$%    (b) 30¢; $3.31; $10.50
3. (a) FF1.28   (b) FF12.19   (c) FF36.07
4. (a) £70     (b) £21
5. £29
6. £25.20; £2.52
7. £5900
8. £35.40; 80%

## Exercise 2d

1. (a) £144    (b) £192     (c) £300
   (d) £222
2. (a) £504    (b) £1008    (c) £252
   (d) £5040
3. £8125
4. (a) £2475.30     (b) £2965.90
   (c) £3701.80     (d) 3 yrs 51 days
5. (a) £2475.30     (b) £3049.82
   (c) £4171.02     (d) 2 yrs 308 days
6. compound (£538.62 > £525)
7. (a) £874.74      (b) 1234.76
   (c) £1899.83
   (d) £2681.77
     10 years
8. £14.50; £1702.11; £72.95
9. (a) £5210      (b) £3910
   (c) £2930      (d) £1930
    9 years
10. (a) £143.10      (b) £174.42
   (c) £209.88     (d) £324.50
   (e) £28 800     (f) £295.49
   (g) £20.74      (h) £35 600

## Exercise 2e

1. (a) 21p     (b) 7p     (c) $33\frac{1}{3}$%
2. 56p; 25%
3. (a) 30%      (b) £4      (c) £400
4. £5.00
5. £2.88
6. (a) £5.20    (b) £150.00
7. £30 000; £4500
8. £400

## Miscellaneous Exercise 2

1. (c) 0.5      (d) $\frac{9}{20}$      (e) 0.2
2. $\frac{999}{1000}$
3. £320
4. 55%; English 55%; French 55.6%
5. 45 m
6. £150; 8%
7. (a) $\frac{17}{24}$      (b) $\frac{7}{24}$      (c) 48 miles
8. (a) £1800; £6200
   (b) $T = G - £2000$; $X = 0.3T$
9. 75p; 90p; 60p; 80%
12. 23 and 24
13. (a) £90       (b) £360
   (c) £86.40     (d) £446.40
   (e) £12.40
14. £72; 27.8%; £80; (i) £103.50   (ii) $12\frac{1}{2}$%
15. 20%; $62\frac{1}{2}$p
16. (b) (i) $\frac{1}{2}$   (ii) $\frac{1}{4}$
   (d) C eats $\frac{3}{8}$, B eats $\frac{9}{40}$, A eats $\frac{3}{20}$, $\frac{1}{4}$ left

## Exercise 3a

1. (a) $1:2$    (b) $1:3$    (c) $3:2$
   (d) $1:2:4$    (e) $3:5:6$    (f) $2:3:4:6$
2. (a) $1:100$    (b) $1:1000$    (c) $1:100\,000$
   (d) $1:400\,000$    (e) $1:50$    (f) $3:200$
3. $1:400$; $12\,\text{m}$; $5\,\text{cm}$
4. $1:25\,000$; $8\frac{1}{2}\,\text{km}$
5. (a) $4:8$    (b) $2:4:6$    (c) $1:4:7$
6. (a) $27:18:9$    (b) $18:18:12:6$
   (c) $9:15:12:18$
7. (a) $63:45$    (b) $24:36:48$
   (c) $18:27:27:36$
8. (a) $96:48$    (b) $36:48:60$
   (c) $42:48:54$
9. (a) $121:121$    (b) $44:77:121$
   (c) $22:44:66:110$
10. $\frac{4}{7}$; £2.04
11. £5.40; £3.00
12. £3
13. (a) A £10 000; B £16 000; C £24 000
    (b) £1280
14. (a) $\frac{2}{5}$    (b) 40%    (c) $108\,\text{g}$
15. £14
16. $4:1:2$; $324:81:162$
17. $5\,\text{cm}$; $7\,\text{cm}$
18. $40°, 40°, 100°$
19. $48°$
20. $0.75$; $0.25$
21. $20:28:21$
22. $18:30:35$
23. $10:15:12$
24. $64:40:15$
25. $8:1$
26. $4:63$
27. $21:2$
28. (a) $5.25\,\text{km}$    (b) $40\,\text{cm}$
    (c) $0.2\,\text{km} \times 0.3\,\text{km}$   (d) $60\,000\,\text{m}^2$
29. (a) $4\frac{1}{2}\,\text{km}$
    (b) $100\,\text{m} \times 250\,\text{m}$; $25\,000\,\text{m}^2$
    (c) $1:30\,000$
30. (a) $\frac{1}{2}\,\text{km}$    (b) $48\,\text{cm}$    (c) $5\,\text{km}^2$

## Exercise 3b

1. (a) 6    (b) 40
2. (a) $11\frac{2}{3}$    (b) 5.25
3. (a) 20    (b) 6.25
4. (a) 15    (b) 28
5. (a) 9    (b) 2.5
6. (a) 12    (b) 8
7. (a) 3    (b) 12
8. (a) 9    (b) 6
9. (a) 3    (b) 9

10. (a) 12    (b) 16
11. (a) 2.5    (b) 0.1
12. (a) 9    (b) 12
13. (a) $40\frac{1}{2}$    (b) 6
14. (a) 6    (b) 16
15. $13\frac{1}{2}\,\text{cm}$
16. 6
17. 12
18. (a) $16\,\text{min}$    (b) $10\,\text{min}$    (c) $7\frac{1}{2}\,\text{min}$
19. $90\,\text{N/m}^2$
20. £32; £260
21. $12\frac{1}{2}\,\text{days}$
22. $x = 4.5$; $y = 7.2$; $z = 7.5$
23. (a) $H = KI^2$
    (b) 3388 joules; 4.63 amps
24. (a) $R = \dfrac{K}{d^2}$    (b) $6.1\,\text{ohm}$
    (c) $1.78\,\text{mm}$

## Exercise 4a

1. (a) $2^3$    (b) $3^4$    (c) $4^3$
   (d) $7^6$    (e) $9^7$
2. (a) 16    (b) 27    (c) 49
   (d) 4    (e) 81    (f) 64
   (g) 32    (h) 216    (i) 10 000
   (j) 1 000 000
3. (a) $3 \times 2$, $2^3$, $3^2$, $23$, $32$
   (b) $2 \times 6$, $26$, $6^2$, $62$, $2^6$
   (c) $4 \times 3$, $34$, $43$, $4^3$, $3^4$
4. (a) $2^8$    (b) $3^6$    (c) $2^2$    (d) $3^2$
   (e) $2^{15}$    (f) $3^8$    (g) $10^6$    (h) $10^9$
5. (a) (i) 4   (ii) 16   (iii) 64   (iv) 256
   (b) yes    (c) (i) $\frac{256}{64} = 4\,(= 2^2)$
   (ii) $16 \times 16 = 256\,(= 2^8)$
6. (a) $10^2$    (b) $10^3$    (c) $10^6$
7. (a) $10^5$    (b) $10^8$    (c) $10^9$    (d) $10^{12}$

## Exercise 4b

1. (a) 1    (b) 1    (c) 1    (d) 1
2. (a) $\frac{1}{2}$    (b) $\frac{1}{9}$    (c) $\frac{1}{100}$    (d) $\frac{1}{10\,000}$
3. (a) $\frac{1}{3}$    (b) $\frac{1}{6}$    (c) 1    (d) $\frac{1}{5}$
4. (a) $\frac{1}{4}$    (b) $\frac{1}{6}$    (c) $\frac{1}{25}$    (d) $\frac{1}{27}$
5. (a) $\frac{1}{4}$    (b) 1    (c) $\frac{1}{49}$    (d) $\frac{1}{8}$
6. (a) $2^1$ or 2    (b) $2^1$ or 2    (c) $2^{-2}$ or $\frac{1}{4}$
   (d) $2^3$ or 8    (e) $2^{-6}$ or $\frac{1}{64}$
   (f) $2^{-4}$ or $\frac{1}{16}$   (g) $2^2$ or 4    (h) $2^{-1}$ or $\frac{1}{2}$
   (i) $2^0$ or 1    (j) $2^{-2}$ or $\frac{1}{4}$
   (k) $2^{-2}$ or $\frac{1}{4}$    (l) $2^{-2}$ or $\frac{1}{4}$

8. (a) 2 (b) 9 (c) 6 (d) 3
9. (a) 10 (b) 8 (c) 27 (d) 5
10. (a) 8 (b) 12 (c) 5 (d) 4
11. (a) 4 (b) 7 (c) 3 (d) 5
12. (a) 25 (b) 1000 (c) 216 (d) 4
13. (a) $\frac{1}{7}$ (b) $\frac{1}{3}$ (c) $\frac{1}{10}$ (d) $\frac{1}{1000}$
14. (a) $\frac{1}{6}$ (b) $\frac{1}{7}$ (c) $\frac{1}{4}$ (d) $\frac{1}{5}$
15. (a) 2 (b) 8 (c) $\frac{1}{8}$ (d) 32
16. (a) 1 (b) $-5$ (c) $+25$ (d) $-125$
17. (a) $-8$ (b) 64 (c) 1 (d) $-2$
18. (a) 2 (b) $\frac{1}{2}$ (c) 4 (d) $\frac{1}{4}$
19. (a) $\frac{1}{2}$ (b) $\frac{1}{3}$ (c) 0 (d) $-\frac{1}{2}$
20. (a) 1 (b) $-\frac{1}{3}$ (c) $-\frac{1}{4}$ (d) $-1$
21. 2

24. $3.66 \times 10^{-2}$
25. $5.0113 \times 10^{-2}$
26. $3.88 \times 10^{-1}$
28. $2.5 \times 10^{-7}$
29. $5.25 \times 10^{9}$
30. $1.1 \times 10^{-3}$
31. $5 \times 10^{33}$
32. $2.56 \times 10^{-39}$
33. $4.9\dot{7} \times 10^{-19}$
34. (a) $7.3 \times 10^{9}$; $2.352 \times 10^{13}$; $5.88 \times 10^{12}$
    (b) 4 (c) $2 \times 10^{10}$
35. (a) $2.99 \times 10^{-23}$ (b) $6 \times 10^{-26}$
    (c) $3.3 \times 10^{22}$ (d) 89%
37. $x = 2$, $y = 4$; no

**Exercise 4c**

1. (a) $7.89 \times 10^{1}$ (b) $5.421 \times 10^{2}$
   (c) $3.2 \times 10^{4}$ (d) $3.2 \times 10^{7}$
   (e) $1.1 \times 10^{5}$ (f) $9.3162 \times 10^{2}$
2. (a) $1.34 \times 10^{-2}$ (b) $5.1 \times 10^{-4}$
   (c) $1 \times 10^{-2}$ (d) $1.1 \times 10^{-5}$
   (e) $2 \times 10^{-6}$ (f) $3.10 \times 10^{-3}$
3. (a) $3.456 \times 10^{3}$ (b) $3.456 \times 10^{-1}$
   (c) $3.456 \times 10^{-4}$ (d) $3.456 \times 10^{-8}$
   (e) $3.456 \times 10^{-9}$
4. (a) $5.2 \times 10^{3}$ (b) $5 \times 10^{2}$
   (c) $2.781 \times 10^{8}$ (d) $3.0547 \times 10^{10}$
   (e) $1.21 \times 10^{5}$ (f) $8.136 \times 10^{4}$
5. (a) $3.254 \times 10^{2}$ (b) $7.23 \times 10^{-3}$
   (c) $2.1 \times 10^{-1}$ (d) $2.390\,12 \times 10^{5}$
   (e) $4.2478 \times 10^{1}$ (f) $1.1213 \times 10^{1}$
6. (a) $3.2 \times 10^{4}$ (b) $1.7 \times 10^{7}$
   (c) $5.32 \times 10^{5}$ (d) $3.2021 \times 10^{2}$
   (e) $4.832\,31 \times 10^{2}$ (f) $8.320\,01 \times 10^{8}$
7. $6 \times 10^{9}$
8. $1.25 \times 10^{-4}$
9. $9.24 \times 10^{1}$
10. $3 \times 10^{5}$
11. $2 \times 10^{-9}$
12. $1.2 \times 10^{4}$
13. $4 \times 10^{2}$
14. $4 \times 10$
15. $5 \times 10^{3}$
16. $6 \times 10^{2}$
17. $2 \times 10^{5}$
18. $2 \times 10^{6}$
19. $2 \times 10^{6}$
20. $4 \times 10^{10}$
21. $2.52 \times 10^{3}$
22. $2.08 \times 10^{3}$
23. $3.74 \times 10^{4}$

**Exercise 5a**

1. (a) set $A$ contains set $B$
   (b) 2 is an element of $C$
   (c) $C$ is not a subset of $D$
   (d) $C$ has 10 elements
2. (a) $X \supset Y$ (b) $S \neq \emptyset$ or $n(S) \neq 0$
   (c) $\frac{1}{2} \notin Z$ (d) $n(Z) = 5$ (e) $A \not\subset B$
   (f) $\mathscr{E} = \{1 \leqslant x \leqslant 30\}$
   (g) $n(c) = 3$
3. (a), (b) and (d) are true; (c) is false
4. (a), (c), (d) and (g) are true; (b), (e) and (f) are false
5. (a) $\{5.2\}$ (b) $\{2, 4, 5, 6\}$
   (c) $\{3, 4, 6\}$ (d) $\{1\}$
   (e) 2 (f) 4 (g) 3 (h) 1
6. (a) {London, Edinburgh}
   (b) {Bristol, Manchester, London, Liverpool, Edinburgh, Paris, Bonn, Rome}
   (c) {Bristol, Manchester, Liverpool}
   (d) {Paris, Bonn, Rome}
7. (a) $T = \{3, 6, 9, 12, 15, 18, 21, 24, 27, 30, 33, 36, 39\}$
   (b) $F = \{4, 8, 12, 16, 20, 24, 28, 32, 36, 40\}$

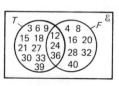

   (c) 12, 24, 36 (d) 12
8. (c), (e), (g) and (h) are true

9.

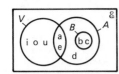

(a), (c), (f), (g), (h) and (i) are true;
(b), (d) and (e) are false; consonants

10.

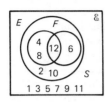

(a) {12}  (b) {2, 10}  (c) ∅
(d) no odd number is a multiple of 6
(e) some even numbers are not multiples of 6
(f) all multiples of 4 are even numbers

11. (a) (i) There are 20 terraced houses in my road
  (ii) There are 30 semi-detached houses in my road
  (iii) There are more than 50 houses in my road
  (iv) Terraced and semi-detached houses are not the only type in my road
  (b) A house in my road that is not terraced or semi-detached
  (c) $T \cap B = \emptyset$
  (d) $B \cap S \neq \emptyset$

12. (a) no  (b) yes  (c) no  (d) yes

13. (a) pupils who bring a packed lunch and come to school by car
  (b) pupils who either come to school by car or who are in the sixth form or both
  (c) pupils who do not come to school by car and who have a school lunch
  (d) pupils who are neither in the sixth form nor have a school lunch;
    $x \in P \cap C'$

**Exercise 5b**

1. (a) 5  (b) 17  (c) 13  (d) 25
   (e) 5  (f) 13
2. (a) 9  (b) true  (c) true
   (d) 12  (e) 10

3.

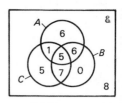

(a) 20  (b) 7  (c) 8
4. (a) 88  (b) 132  (c) 176
5. (a) 3  (b) 5  (c) 16
6. $(54 - x) + x + (47 - x) + 12 = 88$;
   $x = 25$

7.

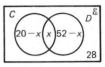

$52 - x$; $(52 - x) + (20 - x) + x + 28 = 88$;
$x = 12$
8. 30
9. 15
10. 4
11. 3
12.

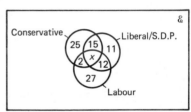

$x = 8$

**Exercise 6a**

1. 20
2. −45
3. 12.8
4. $17\frac{1}{2}$
5. $\frac{13}{16}$
6. 1
7. −1
8. 5.292
9. 13
10. $21\frac{1}{4}$
11. (a) 616  (b) 6.16
12. (a) 113.1  (b) 0.1131
13. 40.5
14. 7
15. 4.4
16. 4.4
17. 0.06

18. $4\frac{4}{9}$
19. $1\frac{1}{2}$
20. $3\frac{3}{7}$

**Exercise 6b**

1. $3a$
2. $7b$
3. $5a$
4. $a^4$
5. $8a + 4b$
6. $6x^2$
7. $2mn$
8. $2m + 2p$
9. $3ab + a + b$
10. $5x + 7y$
11. $5x^3 - 3y$
12. $6 + x - xy$
13. $12p^3q$
14. $30d^3ef$
15. $30p^3q^3$
16. $9m^3n$
17. $3mn$
18. $5st$
19. $3jsf$
20. $\frac{1}{7}$
21. $6mn$
22. $ac^2$
23. → 28. no simplification possible
29. $2a + b$
30. $3p + q$
31. $2b + b^2$
32. $5xy - 2x^2$

**Exercise 6c**

1. $11 + 2x$
2. $5x + x^2$
3. $6ab + 3a$
4. $4xy + 3x + 3y$
5. $3pq + pq^2$
6. $4a + 3b + ab$
7. $8c - 8d$
8. $5mn - 2n^2$
9. $7p + pq - 16q$
10. $2r - 3s + 1$
11. $6 - 3x - y$
12. $2 - u - v$
13. $9 - w - x$
14. $8 - y - z$
15. $11 - 3a + 3b$
16. $3 - 2m + 2n$
17. $13 - 5c + 5d$
18. $1 - 4p + 4q$

19. $u^2 + 8u + 12$
20. $v^2 + 2v - 15$
21. $pn + 2n + p^2 + 2p$
22. $4n^2 + 4mn + m^2$
23. $5c^2 + 28cd + 15d^2$
24. $12e^2 + 25ef + 12f^2$
25. $j^2 - k^2$
26. $m^2 - 2mn - 3n^2$
27. $p^2 - 5pq + 6q^2$
28. $2q^2 - 3qr + r^2$
29. $4x^2 - 14xy + 12y^2$
30. $15u^2 - 44uv + 21v^2$
31. $a^2 + 2ab + b^2$
32. $a^2 + 4ab + 4b^2$
33. $a^2 - 2ab + b^2$
34. $9e^2 - 6ef + f^2$
35. $4e^2 + 12ef + 9f^2$
36. $25g^2 - 20gf + 4f^2$
37. $15 + 4a + 3b$
38. $15 + 8a + a^2 + ab + 3b$
39. $c^2 + 3c + 3d - d^2$
40. $2e + 2f - e^2 - f^2 - 2ef$
41. $c + 3d + dc - d^2$
42. $e + 2f - fe - f^2$

**Exercise 6d**

1. $\dfrac{8a}{15}$
2. $\dfrac{5b}{6}$
3. $\dfrac{7c + 6d}{21}$
4. $\dfrac{3e^2 - 2f}{4}$
5. $\dfrac{3g + 4g^2}{12}$
6. $\dfrac{3g - 4g^2}{12}$
7. $\dfrac{5y}{6}$
8. $\dfrac{x - 2}{6}$
9. $\dfrac{11x + 6}{6}$
10. $\dfrac{7j + 4}{6}$
11. $\dfrac{17k - 8}{12}$

420

12. $\dfrac{19k-3}{6}$

13. $\dfrac{5m+7}{6}$

14. $\dfrac{7n+11}{12}$

15. $\dfrac{p-8}{4}$

16. $\dfrac{5q-r}{6}$

17. $\dfrac{5s-9t-4u}{20}$

18. $\dfrac{k+j}{jk}$

19. $\dfrac{2m-3l}{lm}$

20. $\dfrac{4nq+5p^2}{pq}$

21. $\dfrac{18q^2-2r}{3qr}$

22. $\dfrac{5q^2-2r^2s}{rq}$

23. $\dfrac{8q^2+3r^2}{qr}$

24. $\dfrac{35s}{12t}$

25. $-\dfrac{t}{4u}$

26. $\dfrac{w}{6v}$

27. $\dfrac{x}{10y}$

28. $\dfrac{11u}{9}$

29. $\dfrac{p}{2r}$

30. $\dfrac{s}{2}$

31. $\dfrac{1}{2u}$

32. $\dfrac{3}{5x}$

33. $\dfrac{2}{a^2}$

34. $\dfrac{4u}{v^2}$

35. $12m^2p^2$

36. $\dfrac{3}{5d}$

37. $\dfrac{a^5b}{c^3d}$

38. $\dfrac{a^3}{9}$

39. $\dfrac{1}{xy}$

40. $f^2g$

41. $p^2q$

42. $mn^3$

### Exercise 6e

1. (a) $p^5$    (b) $p^6$    (c) $p^6$    (d) $p^{-6}$
2. (a) $q^{-4}$    (b) $q^{-3}$    (c) $q^2$    (d) 1
3. (a) $x^5y$    (b) $x^4y^2$    (c) $xy^2$    (d) $y^{-1}$
4. (a) $yz$    (b) $y^{-1}z$    (c) $x^{-1}y^3z^{-1}$
      (d) $y^4$
5. (a) $a$    (b) $a^{\frac{1}{2}}$    (c) $ab$    (d) $a^{-\frac{1}{4}}$
6. (a) $a^8$    (b) $a^7$    (c) $a^{-\frac{11}{3}}$    (d) $a^{\frac{5}{4}}$
7. (a) $y^2$    (b) $p^4q^4r$    (c) $m^4n$    (d) $m^2n^4$
8. (a) $p^{-4}$    (b) $y^6$    (c) $q^{-4}$    (d) $x^{-1}$
9. (a) $a^{-1}$    (b) $p^{\frac{1}{2}}q^r$    (c) $p^{-1}q^2$    (d) $t^{\frac{1}{2}}$
10. (a) $abc$    (b) $x^9y^{-4}z^{-1}$
11. (a) $2pqr^{-1}$          (b) $3p^{-3}$

### Exercise 6f

1. $2(3+m)$
2. $3(1+4e)$
3. $3(5+12p)$
4. $5f(1-3g)$
5. $8q(2-r)$
6. $7x(1-3x)$
7. $q(5-q)$
8. $11x(1-11y)$
9. $7mn(3m+4)$
10. $lmn(m-1)$
11. $yz(y+z)$
12. $2a^2(b+3)$
13. $3m(2q-r^2)$
14. $(m+1)(n+2)$
15. $(q+1)(p+2)$
16. $(3+k)(5+l)$

17. $(4-i)(j+2)$
18. $(3+d)(2-c)$
19. $(f+g)(b+i)$
20. $(a+b)(c+d)$
21. $(t+u)(v+2w)$
22. $(e+f)(2g+b)$
23. $(r-s)(u+t)$
24. $(j+k)(2l-m)$
25. $(2w-3y)(x+z)$
26. $(3n-p)(q+r)$
27. $(2a^3-b)(y-z)$
28. $(s^2+t)(u-v)$
29. $(3m^2-2n)(3p-2q)$
30. $(w^2+x)(2y-z)$
31. $(3t+2u)(3w+2v)$
32. $(2a+3b)(4c+d)$
33. $(3x^2-2y)(3x+2z)$
34. $(5e+6f)(2e-b)$
35. $(3j-5)(2m-n)$
36. $(2u-3v)(3w-x)$
37. $b(a+c+d)$
38. $e(3+f^2+g)$
39. $q(2+m+n^2)$
40. $3a^2(1+2b+c^2)$

## Exercise 6g

1. $(x+4)(x+2)$
2. $(x+8)(x+2)$
3. $(x+9)(x+3)$
4. $(x+5)(x+3)$
5. $(x+5)(x+2)$
6. $(x+6)(x-3)$
7. $(x+5)(x-2)$
8. $(x-7)(x-4)$
9. $(x+3)(x+1)$
10. $(x-5)(x-1)$
11. $(3+x)(8+x)$
12. $(5+x)(4+x)$
13. $(y+2)(y+17)$
14. $(y+5)(y+13)$
15. $(z+4)(z-11)$
16. $(x-5)(x+6)$
17. $(n+9)(n-4)$
18. $(p-11q)(p+6q)$
19. $(x-9y)(x-2y)$
20. $(xy-3)(xy-8)$
21. $(2x+3)(x+2)$
22. $(2x+1)(3x+5)$
23. $(2x+1)(x+7)$
24. $(3x+1)(x+2)$
25. $(2x+5)(x+3)$
26. $(3x-2)(x+8)$

27. $(4x-1)(x+5)$
28. $(5x-1)(x-4)$
29. $(7x-2)(x-1)$
30. $(12v-1)(v-12)$
31. $(2c+3)(3c+2)$
32. $(3r-5)(7r+1)$
33. $(2t+1)(5t-7)$
34. $(l-2)(3l-2)$
35. $(5p+3)(2p-7)$
36. $(4s+3)(s+8)$
37. $(2f-9)(f-6)$
38. $(m+5)(3m-2)$
39. $(8e-5)(e+6)$
40. $(d+2)(6d-11)$
41. $(2x+1)(1-3x)$
42. $(2x+3)(2-3x)$
43. $(5x+2)(1-2x)$
44. $(3x+5)(1-4x)$
45. $(2x+1)(1-x)$
46. $(2x+3)(2-x)$
47. $(3x+4)(3-x)$
48. $(5x+1)(7-x)$
49. $(4x-1)(8-x)$
50. $(x-3)(2-11x)$
51. $(3x-7)(2-x)$
52. $(4x-13)(1-x)$
53. $(7g+3)(7-g)$
54. $(5+x)(3-2x)$
55. $(11+3k)(5+2k)$
56. $(5+l)(3-4l)$
57. $(4-9m)(1+4m)$
58. $(m+12n)(m-2n)$
59. $(p-8q)(p+3q)$
60. $(6p+7q)(2p-7q)$

## Exercise 6h

1. $(3-y)(3+y)$
2. $(p-q)(p+q)$
3. $(r-s)(r+s)$
4. $(p-3q)(p+3q)$
5. $(mn-p)(mn+p)$
6. $(uv-3)(uv+3)$
7. $(5-y)(5+y)$
8. $(11-w)(11+w)$
9. $(9-r)(9+r)$
10. $(12-5x)(12+5x)$
11. $(9s-t)(9s+t)$
12. $(6y-x)(6y+x)$
13. $(3t-2u)(3t+2u)$
14. $(11f-7j)(11f+7j)$
15. $(8s-7t)(8s+7t)$
16. $2(3r-s)(3r+s)$

17. $2(2d-e)(2d+e)$
18. $20(a-2b)(a+2b)$
19. $12(d-2e)(d+2e)$
20. $2(5c-7)(5c+7)$
21. $8(5-2z)(5+2z)$
22. 9400
23. 6200
24. 14 600
25. 5900
26. 320
27. 0.000 08
28. 1 028 000
29. 996 000
30. 1 018 000

30. $-1$
31. 3
32. 2
33. $\pm3$
34. $\pm2$
35. 2
36. 2
37. $\pm3$
38. $\pm2$
39. 3
40. $\frac{1}{2}$
41. 16
42. 25
43. 10
44. 8
45. 1
46. $-4$
47. 2
48. 3
49. 3
50. 16
51. 11
52. 3
53. 0.2
54. $11\frac{2}{3}$
55. 2
56. 3
57. 2
58. 3
59. 3
60. 0

## Miscellaneous Exercise 6

4. (a) 19      (b) $\frac{5}{3}$
6. (a) 15      (b) 45      (c) 155
8. (b) 6; 24; 60; 990; 2184

## Exercise 7a

1. 4
2. 3
3. 1
4. 2
5. 3
6. $-5$
7. $\frac{1}{2}$
8. 2
9. 2
10. 3
11. $-\frac{1}{9}$
12. $\frac{2}{3}$
13. 6
14. 8
15. 2.4
16. 5
17. 1
18. $-3$
19. $-3\frac{1}{2}$
20. $\frac{1}{2}$
21. 4
22. 2
23. 9
24. 7
25. $1\frac{1}{2}$
26. 1
27. 4
28. 0
29. 2.4

## Exercise 7b

1. $\dfrac{P}{4}$

2. (a) $\dfrac{V}{r}$      (b) $\dfrac{V}{i}$

3. $\dfrac{F}{a}$

4. $\dfrac{A}{2r}$

5. $\dfrac{E}{mg}$

6. $\dfrac{100I}{Pt}$

7. $\dfrac{2A}{a}$

8. $\dfrac{3V}{ab}$

423

9. $1-p$

10. (a) $at$    (b) $\dfrac{O}{t}$

11. (a) $v-at$    (b) $\dfrac{v-u}{t}$

12. (a) $\dfrac{v^2-u^2}{2s}$    (b) $\sqrt{v^2-2as}$

13. $\dfrac{S-2\pi r}{2\pi}$ or $\dfrac{S}{2\pi}-r$

14. (a) $\dfrac{2E}{m}$    (b) $\sqrt{\dfrac{2E}{m}}$

15. $\sqrt{\dfrac{A}{\pi}}$

16. (a) $y-mx$    (b) $\dfrac{y-c}{m}$

17. $\sqrt[3]{\dfrac{3V}{4\pi}}$

18. (a) $r^2-x^2$    (b) $\sqrt{r^2-x^2}$

19. (a) $\dfrac{mv^2}{P}$    (b) $\sqrt{\dfrac{rP}{m}}$

20. (a) $\dfrac{s-\frac{1}{2}at^2}{t}$    (b) $\dfrac{2(s-ut)}{t^2}$

21. (a) $\dfrac{2A}{a+b}$    (b) $\dfrac{2A}{x}-b$

22. $\dfrac{s^2}{p(1-p)}$

23. (a) $g\left(\dfrac{T}{2\pi}\right)^2$    (b) $l\left(\dfrac{2\pi}{T}\right)^2$

24. (a) $\dfrac{1}{f}-\dfrac{1}{v}$    (b) $\dfrac{vf}{v-f}$

## Exercise 7c

1. (a) 7    (b) 31
2. 5
3. $-2$
4. $13, 14, 15$
5. $n+6$; $10, 12, 14, 16$
6. 2 cm; 12 cm
7. 192 cm$^2$
8. 7 cm
9. $20l$; 81 cm$^2$
10. 6 cm
11. 20
12. 6, 12

13. $9q + 28$; $31$p/kg
14. 21p
15. 5
16. 15, 17, 19
17. 75 000
18. £400
19. £4.32
20. (a) $20 + 2q$; $20 + 5q$; $20 + xq$
     (b) 11
     (c) 7
21. (a) $25 + 5r$; $25 + 8r$;
        $25 + 5r + (x-2)r = 25 + (3+x)r$
     (b) 8     (c) 3

## Exercise 7d

1. $x = 4, y = 1$
2. $x = 3, y = 6$
3. $x = 4, y = 3$
4. $x = 1\frac{1}{2}, y = 2\frac{1}{2}$
5. $a = 5, b = 2$
6. $p = 3, q = 1$
7. $y = 2, z = 3$
8. $p = 19, q = 2$
9. $x = 5, y = 3$
10. $m = 3, n = -2$
11. $p = 7, q = 0$
12. $c = -1, d = 5$
13. $x = 3, y = 2$
14. $x = 1, y = \frac{1}{2}$
15. $x = 1, y = 4$
16. $y = \frac{1}{2}, z = -2$
17. $g = -\frac{1}{2}, b = -1$
18. $e = 1, f = \frac{1}{3}$
19. $m = -\frac{2}{3}, n = \frac{1}{10}$
20. $p = 8\frac{1}{2}, q = 20\frac{1}{2}$
21. $a = 2\frac{1}{2}, b = 1\frac{1}{3}$
22. $x = 1\frac{1}{5}, y = 2\frac{2}{5}$
23. $m = 4, n = 2$
24. $x = 4\frac{4}{5}, y = 1\frac{1}{5}$

## Exercise 7e

1. 9, 6
2. 18, 6
3. 10p; 16p
4. peas 18p; beans 21p
5. child's £1.50; adults £3.00
6. 10
7. $x = 14$; $y = 6$

8. $x = 32, y = 40$
9. $42\,\mathrm{p}$
10. $x = £3; y = £5$
11. $16\,\mathrm{p}; 80\,\mathrm{p}$
12. (a) $m = 5; c = 3$  (b) $n = 2; d = -3$
    (c) $y = 6x - 1$
13. $a = 5; d = 4$
14. $a = 4; u = 5$
15. $a = -2, u = 3$
16. (a) $\frac{3}{5}$  (b) $12\frac{2}{5}$  (c) $3.52$

## Exercise 7f

1. $x = 2$ or $3$
2. $x = -4$ or $3$
3. $p = -3$ or $-2$
4. $x = 0$ or $2$
5. $x = 0$ or $y = 0$
6. $x = 0, 1$ or $2$
7. $x = -3$ or $0$
8. $x = 0$ or $2$
9. $z = 0$ or $4$
10. $z = 0$ or $5$
11. $p = 0$ or $1$
12. $x = 0$ or $\frac{1}{2}$
13. $r = 0$ or $5$
14. $s = 0$ or $3$
15. $r = -3$ or $0$
16. $r = -1$ or $0$
17. $x = -2$ or $-4$
18. $a = -8$ or $2$
19. $b = -3$ or $5$
20. $x = 2$ or $5$
21. $x = \frac{1}{2}$ or $-3$
22. $c = \frac{1}{2}$ or $2\frac{1}{2}$
23. $c = \frac{3}{11}$ or $-1$
24. $x = -\frac{3}{4}$ or $-\frac{1}{3}$
25. $x = -\frac{2}{5}$ or $1$
26. $d = -\frac{7}{5}$ or $1$
27. $x = -\frac{1}{12}$ or $2$
28. $q = -\frac{3}{4}$ or $-4$
29. $x = -9$ or $3$
30. $x = 1$ or $-2$
31. $x = \dfrac{1}{2}$ or $\dfrac{-2}{3}$
32. $x = -5$ or $\frac{1}{3}$
33. $a = 7$ or $4$
34. $x = -4\frac{1}{2}$ or $-2$
35. $x = \frac{1}{2}$ or $-2$
36. $x = \frac{1}{5}$ or $1\frac{1}{2}$

37. $x = -5$ or $\dfrac{-3}{4}$
38. $x = 3$ or $\frac{1}{2}$
39. $b = \dfrac{-2}{7}$ or $\dfrac{4}{3}$
40. $x = \dfrac{-1}{3}$ or $\dfrac{5}{2}$
41. $w = \dfrac{-7}{4}$ or $\dfrac{4}{5}$
42. $x = 3$ or $8$
43. $y = -1\frac{1}{2}$ or $-2$
44. $q = -3$ or $\frac{1}{5}$
45. $-1, 2$
46. $-5, 1$
47. $-2, 5$
48. $-2, 1$
49. $a = 1$ or $-2$
50. $x = -1$ or $3$
51. $b = -1$ or $6$
52. $y = -\frac{1}{2}$ or $1$
53. $c = 1\frac{1}{2}$ or $-5$
54. $z = \dfrac{2}{5}$ or $\dfrac{-2}{3}$

## Exercise 7g

1. $x = -2$ or $-1$
2. $x = -0.5$ or $-2$
3. $x = -\frac{1}{3}$ or $-2$
4. $x = 0.82$ or $-1.82$
5. $x = 1.79$ or $-2.79$
6. $x = 7.32$ or $0.68$
7. $x = 5.45$ or $0.55$
8. $x = 4.83$ or $-0.83$
9. $x = 3.56$ or $-0.56$
10. $x = 1.90$ or $-1.23$
11. $y = -2.85$ or $0.35$
12. $y = 1.45$ or $-3.45$
13. $z = -4.37$ or $1.37$
14. $p = -1.30$ or $2.30$
15. $a = 1.30$ or $-2.30$
16. $a = -0.73$ or $2.73$
17. $m = 1$ or $-3$
18. $z = -0.37$ or $1.37$
19. $b = -0.22$ or $-2.28$
20. $a = -1.77$ or $-0.57$
21. $y = 0.26$ or $-1.26$
22. $x = -0.36$ or $-4.14$
23. $y = 3.41$ or $0.59$
24. $y = 0.78$ or $-1.28$

25. $2.73, -0.73$
26. $0.79, -3.79$
27. $0.43, -0.23$
28. $0.41, -1.08$

## Exercise 7h

1. $-7, 6$
2. $4, -4\frac{1}{2}; -4\frac{1}{2}$
3. $-8, 5; 5$
4. 6 cm
5. 3 cm
6. 2 m
7. 16 ft wide, 19 ft long
8. 17 ft, 12 ft
9. 2.5
10. $1\frac{1}{2}$ m wide, 3 m long
11. 20 cm
12. 14 ft × 12 ft
13. 7 m × 14 m
14. (a) 14 or $-15$
    (b) 10 or $-11$
15. (b) $12; 14$
16. (b) 15
17. (a) 9 m     (b) 4.5 s
18. (a) 5     (b) 9, 12, 15
    (c) 20, 21, 29

## Miscellaneous Exercise 7

1. (a) (i) 14 (ii) 8    (b) (i) 470 (ii) 3
2. (a) (i) $6p^2 - pq - 15q^2$ (ii) $\dfrac{a-1}{6}$
   (b) (i) $5ab(3b - a + 5)$ (ii) $(4-y)(x-y)$
   (iii) $3ab(b - 2a)$ (iv) $(x-5)(x-1)$
3. (a) $x = 1, y = 5$    (b) $x = 2, y = 3$
   (c) $x = 4, y = -3$
4. (a) $2x(3y + 1)$    (b) $x^2(3 + 2xy)$
   (c) $4xy(3xy + 1)$    (d) $(m + p)(n + 2m)$
   (e) $(2r - s)(t - v^2)$    (f) $(x + 7)(x - 2)$
   (g) $(2x + 7)(x - 3)$
5. (a) $x = -4$ or $-5$    (b) $x = 3$ or $-2$
   (c) $x = -\frac{2}{3}$ or 1
   (d) $x = 1.47$ or $-1.14$
   (e) $x = 1.71$ or $-3.21$
   (f) $x = 3.79$ or $-0.791$
6. (b) $p = 2A + 2$ (i) 28 (ii) 19
   (c) (i) 12.5 (ii) $p = 18, d = 11, A = 19$
   (iii) 7 (iv) 16 (v) $p = 2A - 2d + 2$
7. (a) $-7\frac{1}{2}$    (b) $-3$ or $\frac{1}{2}$    (c) $-5$
8. (a) $\mathcal{E}$    (b) $\{2\}$    (c) $\emptyset$
   (d) $\{0, 8\}; -4$

**426**

9. (a) (i) 7 (ii) $\frac{1}{3}$    (b) $\dfrac{1-x}{2}$
   (d) $p = 0.57$ or $-0.73$
10. (a) $55\,°F$    (b) 100 chirps per minute
    (c) $40\,°F$    (d) $C = \dfrac{40}{9} + \dfrac{5N}{36}$
11. (a) $nx$    (b) $\dfrac{nx}{y}$
12. (a) (i) 68 p (ii) $8y + 12$ (iii) $6x + 12$
    (iv) $8a + bx + 12$
    (b) $\dfrac{y - 12}{8}$
13. (a) $\dfrac{ny}{x}$ grams;    (b) $£\dfrac{xz}{n}$
14. (a) $£(189 - x)$    (b) $2x$
    (c) $2x = 189 - x$    (d) $£126$
15. $x = 2, y = 1$
16. $b = £2.50, c = £3.50$
17. (a) $x(x - 3)\,\text{cm}^2$
    (b) 18 cm     (d) 13 cm by 16 cm
18. (a) $(x - 1)$ cm    (b) $\dfrac{x}{1}; \dfrac{1}{x-1}$
    (c) 1.62 cm

## Exercise 8a

1. (a) 2    (b) 6    (c) 8    (d) $\frac{2}{3}$
   (e) 0    (f) $-10$    (g) $-\frac{1}{2}$
2. (a) 3    (b) 19    (c) $-5$    (d) 5
   (e) 1    (f) 6    (g) 0
3. (a) 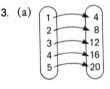    (b)
   (c)     (d)
   (e) 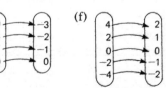    (f)

4. (a) 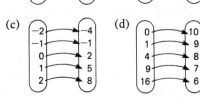 (b)

   (c) (d)

5. (a) $\frac{1}{2}$    (b) $\frac{1}{3}$    (c) 1    (d) $-\frac{1}{2}$
   (e) $-1$    (f) 2    (g) 3    (h) 4
   (i) $-2$    (j) $-3$

6. (a) 0    (b) 5    (c) 25    (d) $-5$
   (e) $-15$

7. (a) 1    (b) 3    (c) 5    (d) $-3$
   (e) $-5$

8. (a) 0    (b) 1    (c) 8    (d) $-1$
   (e) $-8$

9. (a) 6    (b) 12    (c) 6    (d) 12
   (e) 22    (f) 4    (g) $4\frac{1}{2}$    (h) $4\frac{1}{8}$
   (i) $4\frac{1}{2}$    (j) $4\frac{1}{8}$

10. (a) 2    (b) 5    (c) $-1$    (d) $\frac{1}{3}$
    (e) $\frac{1}{2}$    (f) $-\frac{3}{8}$

11. (a) 0    (b) 3    (c) 12    (d) $-4$
    (e) $-1\frac{1}{2}$    (f) $\frac{1}{2}$

12. (a) 0    (b) $-\frac{3}{2}$    (c) $-4$    (d) $-\frac{5}{2}$
    (e) 14    (f) 26    (g) $-1$    (h) $-\frac{1}{4}$
    (i) $-1\frac{3}{4}$

13. (a) 4    (b) $\frac{1}{2}$    (c) 0    (d) $-1\frac{1}{2}$
    (e) 5    (f) 3    (g) $-2$    (h) $-2\frac{1}{2}$
    (i) $-3$

14. (a) $2\frac{1}{2}$    (b) $1\frac{2}{3}$    (c) $2\frac{1}{3}$    (d) 4
    (e) $1\frac{3}{4}$    (f) 1

15. (a) $-\frac{1}{2}$    (b) $\pm 4$    (c) $-4, 2$

16. (a) $-2, 4$    (b) $\frac{1}{4}, 1$    (c) $0, \frac{2}{3}$

## Exercise 8b

1. (a) 5    (b) 3    (c) 10    (d) 5
   (e) 11    (f) 15    (g) 21    (h) 25

2. (a) $\frac{1}{2}$    (b) 4    (c) $\frac{1}{3}$    (d) 9
   (e) $\frac{1}{4}$    (f) $\frac{1}{9}$    (g) $\frac{1}{4}$    (h) $\frac{1}{9}$

3. (a) 9    (b) 2    (c) 6    (d) 8
   (e) 8    (f) 6    (g) $-1$
   (h) $-3$; $fg(x) = 3x - 3$

4. (a) 4    (b) 3    (c) 12
   (d) 6; $jh(x) = 4x + 2$

5. (a) $-2$    (b) $-2$    (c) 10    (d) 6
   (e) $-5$    (f) 3

6. (a) 0    (b) 2    (c) 16    (d) 4
   (e) 0    (f) $(x-2)^2$    (g) $x^4$
   (h) $x$

7. (a) 2    (b) 4    (c) 3    (d) 7; $x$

8. (a) $fg: x \to (x-3)^2$
   (b) $gf: x \to x^2 - 3$
   (c) $fh: x \to \frac{1}{4}x^2$
   (d) $hf: x \to \frac{1}{2}x^2$
   (e) $gh: x \to \frac{1}{2}x - 3$
   (f) $hg: x \to \frac{1}{2}x - 1\frac{1}{2}$

9. (a) $fg: x \to x^{12}$    (b) $gf: x \to x^{12}$

## Exercise 8c

1. $f^{-1}: x \to \dfrac{x-4}{2}$

2. (a) $f^{-1}: x \to 3(x+1)$
   (b) $g^{-1}: x \to \dfrac{4x-2}{3}$

3. $f^{-1}: x \to \frac{1}{2}x$;    (a) 8    (b) 4

4. $f^{-1}: x \to \frac{1}{4}x$;    (a) 16    (b) 4

5. $f^{-1}: x \to \dfrac{x-6}{5}$;    (a) 26    (b) 4

6. $f^{-1}: x \to \dfrac{x-5}{3}$;    (a) 17    (b) 4

7. $f^{-1}: x \to \dfrac{x+2}{6}$;    (a) 22    (b) 4

8. $f^{-1}: x \to 2(x-1)$;    (a) 3    (b) 4

9. $f^{-1}: x \to 4(x+2)$;    (a) $-1$    (b) 4

10. $f^{-1}: x \to 3x - 2$;    (a) 2    (b) 4

11. $f^{-1}: x \to 2x + 5$;    (a) $-\frac{1}{2}$    (b) 4

12. $f^{-1}: x \to 8x + 4$;    (a) 0    (b) 4

13. $f^{-1}: x \to \dfrac{1}{x}$;    (a) $\frac{1}{4}$    (b) 4

14. $f^{-1}: x \to \dfrac{4}{x}$;    (a) 1    (b) 4

15. $f^{-1}: x \to -x$    (a) $-4$    (b) 4

16. $f^{-1}: x \to \sqrt{x+1}$;    (a) 15    (b) 4

17. $f^{-1}: x \to \sqrt{\dfrac{x-1}{2}}$;    (a) 33    (b) 4

18. $f^{-1}: x \to \sqrt{\dfrac{x-2}{3}}$;    (a) 50    (b) 4

19. $f^{-1}: x \to \sqrt{x} + 1$;    (a) 9    (b) 4

20. $f^{-1}: x \to \dfrac{x^2-1}{2}$;    (a) 3    (b) 4

21. (a) $g^{-1}: x \to \dfrac{x-1}{3}$  (b) 7  (c) 2

22. (a) $p^{-1}: x \to \dfrac{5-x}{2}$  (b) 7  (c) $-1$

23. (a) $j^{-1}: x \to 3 - 3x$  (b) $-1$  (c) 6
24. (a) $s^{-1}: x \to 1 - 2x$  (b) $\frac{1}{2}$  (c) $\frac{1}{4}$
25. (a) $f^{-1}: x \to 2 - 8x$  (b) 3  (c) $-\frac{1}{8}$

### Miscellaneous Exercise 8

1. (a) A, B, C  (b) A, E  (c) A
   (d) B, D  (e) B

2.
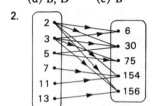

3. (a) {negative odd numbers}
   (b) {positive even numbers}
   (c) {positive even numbers}
4. (a) {positive integers}
   (b) {positive integers}
   (c) {positive rational numbers}
5. (a) $\{\frac{1}{4}\}$  (b) $\{-2\frac{1}{2}\}$  (c) $\{0\}$
   (d) $\emptyset$  (e) $\{2\}$  (f) $\{0, 1\}$
   (g) $\{0, 2\}$  (h) $\{-1, 2\}$
6. (a) $1\frac{2}{3}$ or $2\frac{1}{3}$
   (b) $(x-2)(x-7)$; 2 or 7
   (c) 5.24 or 0.76
7. $g: x \to 2x$; $h: x \to x + 1$
8. (a) 0; 4  (b) $i$
   (c) $h: x \to 4 - x$; $i: x \to x^2$
   (d) $ih$
9. (b) $g^{-1}: x \to \dfrac{x}{3}$

   (c) (i) $f^{-1}g^{-1}: x \to \dfrac{x+3}{6}$
   
   (ii) $gf: x \to 3(2x - 1)$
   
   (iii) $(gf)^{-1}: x \to \dfrac{x+3}{6}$
10. (a) 14  (b) 20  (c) 13
11. (a) 4  (b) 9  (c) 11  (d) 12
    (e) $\emptyset$  (f) 18
12. (a) 10; 5; 6  (b) 14; 16 or 7
    (c) {even numbers}; {odd numbers}
    (d) $ff$ must halve
    (e) prints 2, 1, 2, 1, ...

13. (b) $-5$  (e) $\dfrac{x}{x-1}$

### Exercise 9a

1. Points are all on the line $y = 2x + 1$; yes; no
2. $(4, 4)$
3. no; three points

4. (a)

| x | y |
|---|---|
| 0 | 5 |
| 5 | 0 |
| 1 | 4 |

(b)

| x | y |
|---|---|
| 0 | 3 |
| $-3$ | 0 |
| 1 | 4 |

(c)

| x | y |
|---|---|
| 0 | $-1$ |
| 1 | 0 |
| 2 | 1 |

(a) and (b) intersect at $(1, 4)$; (b) and (c) are parallel — they do not intersect

5. (a)

| x | y |
|---|---|
| 0 | 3 |
| $-3$ | 0 |
| 3 | 6 |

(b)

| x | y |
|---|---|
| 0 | 3 |
| $-\frac{3}{2}$ | 0 |
| 3 | 9 |

(c)

| x | y |
|---|---|
| 0 | 3 |
| $-1$ | 0 |
| 3 | 12 |

Same intercept, different slopes

6. (a)

| x | y |
|---|---|
| 0 | 0 |
| 1 | 1 |
| 5 | 5 |

(b)

| x | y |
|---|---|
| 0 | 4 |
| $-4$ | 0 |
| 5 | 9 |

(c)

| x | y |
|---|---|
| 0 | $-4$ |
| 4 | 0 |
| 5 | 1 |

Same slope, different intercepts

7. all except (e) and (f)

8. (a)

| $x$ | $y$ |
|---|---|
| 0 | 7 |
| $3\frac{1}{2}$ | 0 |
| 1 | 5 |

(b)

| $x$ | $y$ |
|---|---|
| 0 | $-1$ |
| $\frac{1}{2}$ | 0 |
| 1 | 1 |

(a) and (b) intersect at $(2, 3)$; $x = 2$, $y = 3$ is the solution to the equations of the lines solved simultaneously

9. (a) $x = 4, y = 1$    (b) $x = 3, y = 6$
   (c) $x = 4, y = 3$    (d) $x = 1\frac{1}{2}, y = 2\frac{1}{2}$
   (e) $x = 1, y = 4$    (f) $x = 3, y = 2$

10. (a) (i) 21   (ii) 53.2
   (b) (i) 10   (ii) 27.14

11. (a) (i) 6.5 m   (ii) 8.25 cm
   (b) (i) 5 kg   (ii) 5 cm

## Exercise 9b

1. (a) (i) 4 (ii) 3    (b) (i) $-1$ (ii) 2
   (c) (i) $-4$ (ii) 5    (d) (i) 5 (ii) 4
   (e) (i) 1 (ii) 3    (f) (i) $-\frac{2}{3}$ (ii) $\frac{4}{3}$

2. $y = \dfrac{-5x+3}{4}; \dfrac{-5}{4}; \dfrac{3}{4}$

3. $y = \dfrac{2x-5}{6}; \dfrac{1}{3}; \dfrac{-5}{6}$

4. (a) (i) $-\frac{7}{2}$ (ii) $\frac{5}{2}$    (b) (i) $-\frac{1}{3}$ (ii) $\frac{5}{9}$
   (c) (i) $-\frac{5}{9}$ (ii) $\frac{8}{9}$    (d) (i) $\frac{3}{2}$ (ii) 1
   (e) (i) 1 (ii) 0    (f) (i) $-2$ (ii) $\frac{5}{2}$

5. (a), (c) and (e)
6. (d), (f), (g) and (i) are true

7. (a) $y = \dfrac{x}{3} + 1$    (b) $y = \dfrac{3x}{4}$

   (c) $y = \dfrac{x}{6} + 3$    (d) $y = -x + 5$

   (e) $y = \dfrac{x}{6}$    (f) $y = \dfrac{7x}{2} + \dfrac{1}{2}$

   (g) $y = -x + 6$    (h) $y = \dfrac{3x}{2} + \dfrac{1}{2}$

   (i) $y = 3$    (j) $y = \dfrac{2x}{3} + \dfrac{4}{3}$

   (k) $y = -5x + 16$    (l) $y = \dfrac{3x}{4} + \dfrac{1}{2}$

8. (a) 1    (b) 1    (c) $-1$    (d) $\frac{3}{5}$
   (e) $-1$    (f) $1\frac{1}{2}$    (g) 0    (h) $-1$

9. (a) $y = x + 1$    (b) $y = -\dfrac{x}{2} + 7$
   (c) $y = -x + 9$    (d) $y = -x + 5$
   (e) $y = \frac{2}{3}x$    (f) $y = 7$
   (g) $y = -\frac{5}{2}x + \frac{1}{2}$    (h) $y = 2x - 7$

10. (i) (d)   (ii) (a)   (iii) (e)   (iv) (f)   (v) (c)
   (vi) (b)

11. 18 square units

## Miscellaneous Exercise 9

1.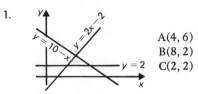
A(4, 6)
B(8, 2)
C(2, 2)

Area of $\triangle$ABC $= 12$ square units

2. (a) 1    (b) $-1\frac{1}{2}$    (c) 0    (d) 2
   (e) $-2$    (f) $\frac{1}{5}$    (g) $-\frac{1}{5}$    (h) $-5$

3. P(2, 4); R(8, 6); S(6, 2)
   $y = -\frac{1}{2}x + 10; y = 2x - 10$

4. (a) $A(0, 3); D(0, 12); AD = 9$ units
   (b) $F(4, 6)$
   (c) 18 square units; 30 square units

5.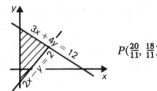
$P(\frac{20}{11}, \frac{18}{11})$

6. $\{2, 5\}$

7. $y = x + 1; y = \frac{1}{2}x + 2\frac{1}{2}$
   D(2, 1); $\frac{1}{2}$; 1

8. (a) $4.4^{\circ}$C    (b) $15.6^{\circ}$C    (c) $22^{\circ}$C
   (d) $59^{\circ}$F    (e) $89.6^{\circ}$F    (f) $20^{\circ}$F

9. 

| | | |
|---|---|---|
| Sales | £2000 | £6000 |
| Commission | £300 | £900 |
| Salary | £2500 | £2500 |
| Income | £2800 | £3400 |

   (a) £2860    (b) £3334    (c) £5000

10. gradient 2; intercept 3; $y = 2x + 3$
11. $I = 0.1775 V$

12. $V = \dfrac{-5t}{2} + 30$

## Exercise 10a

1. (a) $1 \leqslant x \leqslant 5$    (b) $-2 \leqslant x < 2$
   (c) $-2 < x < 2$    (d) $-1 < x \leqslant 2$
   (e) $102 < x < 104$

**2.** (a) [number line: filled from −3 to 2, marks −4 −3 −2 −1 0 1 2]

(b) [number line: open from 4 to 6, marks 0 1 2 3 4 5 6]

(c) [number line: open at 3 to filled 5, marks 0 1 2 3 4 5 6]

(d) [number line: open at 5, marks 0 1 2 3 4 5 6 7]

(e) [number line: filled 0 to 2, marks −4 −2 0 2 4]

(f) [number line: filled at 0, marks −5 −3 −1 0 1]

**3.** [number line: marks −4 −2 0 2 4]

[number line: open at 4, marks −4 −2 0 2 4]

(a) [number line] $0 < x < 2$ [marks −2 0 2]

(b) [number line] $-4 \leqslant x < 4$ [marks −4 −2 0 2 4]

(c) [number line] $x < -3\ x > 2$ [marks −4 −2 0 2 4]

(d) [number line] $2 < x < 4$ [marks −4 −2 0 2 4]

**4.** (a) $1 < x < 3$ [number line, marks −2 0 2 4]

(b) $-2 < x < 5$ [number line, marks −2 0 2 4]

**5.** [number line: marks −2 −1 0 1 2 3]

**6.** (a) $2 < x \leqslant 4$   (b) $-1 < x \leqslant 6$
**7.** (a) $-2 < x \leqslant 1$   (b) $x > 3$
**8.** (a) $-3 < x < 3$   (b) $-3 \leqslant x \leqslant 5$
**9.** $x < 5$
**10.** $x \geqslant 2$
**11.** $x \geqslant 1\frac{2}{3}$
**12.** $x < 24$
**13.** $x > \frac{1}{2}$
**14.** $x < -\frac{10}{3}$
**15.** $x \leqslant -3$
**16.** $x \geqslant 16$
**17.** $x < 7$
**18.** $x > 8$
**19.** $x < -\frac{5}{2}$

**20.** $x > 0$
**21.** $x < 15$
**22.** $x > 5$
**23.** $x > 23$
**24.** $x \leqslant 1$
**25.** $x \leqslant -13$
**26.** $x < 0$
**27.** $x < -\frac{3}{2}$
**28.** $x \leqslant \frac{2}{7}$
**29.** $x > \frac{3}{4}$
**30.** $x \leqslant -\frac{3}{2}$
**31.** (a) $\{3\}$          (b) $\{1, 2\}$
         (c) $\{1, 2\}$        (d) $\{1, 2\}$
**32.** $\{1, 2\}$
**33.** $\{x \geqslant 2\}$
**34.** (a) $\{1, 2, 7, 8\}$ (b) $\emptyset$              (c) $\{1, 2\}$
**35.** (a) $\{-2, -1, 0, 1\}$  (b) $\{-2, -1, 1, 2\}$
         (c) $\{-2, 2\}$
**36.** (a) $\{-4, -3\}$          (b) $\{0, 1, 2\}$
         (c) $\{-4, -3, -2, 2\}$

## Exercise 10b

**1.** (a) $x \leqslant 2$                (b) $y < 4$
     (c) $x + y \leqslant 6$          (d) $y < 3x$
**2.** (a)                 (b)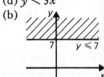

(c) 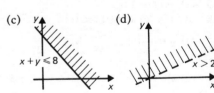          (d)

**3.** C
**4.** A
**5.** C

**6.**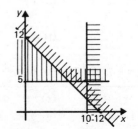

430

**7.**

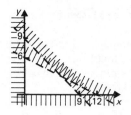

**8.**

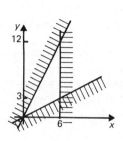

**9.**

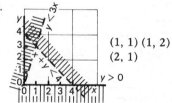

(1, 1) (1, 2)
(2, 1)

$y > 0$

**10.**

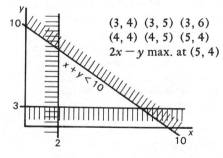

(3, 4) (3, 5) (3, 6)
(4, 4) (4, 5) (5, 4)
$2x - y$ max. at (5, 4)

**11.**

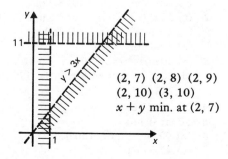

(2, 7) (2, 8) (2, 9)
(2, 10) (3, 10)
$x + y$ min. at (2, 7)

**12.**

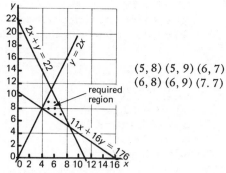

(5, 8) (5, 9) (6, 7)
(6, 8) (6, 9) (7. 7)

   (a) (6, 9)     (b) (6, 7)

**13.** 4 points: (3, 2) (3, 3) (3, 4) (4, 2)
   Max. income at (3, 4), £1450

**14.** (a) (7, 4) £470; (7, 5) £500; (7, 6) £530;
      (7, 7) £560; (7, 8) £590; (8, 4) £520
   (b) £590

**15.** (5, 1) £78; (5, 2) £96; (6, 1) £90;
   (6, 2) £108; (7, 1) £102; (8, 1) £114
   Max. profit £114

**16.** (a) $x > 2$; $y \geqslant 1$     (c) more small jars
   (f) 37

**Miscellaneous Exercise 11**

**1.**

| $x$ | $-4$ | $-3$ | $-2$ | $-1$ | 0 | 1 | 2 | 3 | 4 |
|---|---|---|---|---|---|---|---|---|---|
| $x^2$ | 16 | 9 | 4 | 1 | 0 | 1 | 4 | 9 | 16 |
| $-4$ | $-4$ | $-4$ | $-4$ | $-4$ | $-4$ | $-4$ | $-4$ | $-4$ | $-4$ |
| $y$ | 12 | 5 | 0 | $-3$ | $-4$ | $-3$ | 0 | 5 | 12 |

(a) $-2$ and 2     (b) $-4$
(c) (i) $\pm 2.8$  (ii) $\pm 3.2$
(d) $x = 4$, $x = -1$
(e) $y = 2x - 1$ intersects at $x = -1$ and 3
(f) 4

**2.**

| $x$ | $-4$ | $-3$ | $-2$ | $-1$ | 0 | 1 | 2 | 3 | 4 | 5 |
|---|---|---|---|---|---|---|---|---|---|---|
| $x^2$ | $+16$ | $+9$ | $+4$ | $+1$ | 0 | 1 | 4 | 9 | 16 | 25 |
| $-x$ | $+4$ | $+3$ | $+2$ | $+1$ | 0 | $-1$ | $-2$ | $-3$ | $-4$ | $-5$ |
| $-6$ | $-6$ | $-6$ | $-6$ | $-6$ | $-6$ | $-6$ | $-6$ | $-6$ | $-6$ | $-6$ |
| $y$ | 14 | 6 | 0 | $-4$ | $-6$ | $-6$ | $-4$ | 0 | 6 | 14 |

(a) $-2$ and 3
(b) (i) $-3.4$  (ii) $-5.8$  (iii) $-2.6$
(c) (i) 4.5 or $-3.5$  (ii) $-0.64$ or 1.64
    (iii) $-3.3$ or 4.3
(d) (i) $-2 < x < 3$  (ii) $-3.3 \leqslant x \leqslant 4.3$
(e) (i) $x < -3.4$; $x > 4.4$
    (ii) $x < -1.6$; $x > 2.6$

(f) $-3; +3$

(g) $y = 3-x$ intersects at $x = \pm 3$

(h) $y = 2x-2$ intersects at $x = 4$ and $-1$

3.
| $x$ | $-5$ | $-4$ | $-3$ | $-2$ | $-1$ | 0 | 1 | 2 | 3 | 4 | 5 |
|---|---|---|---|---|---|---|---|---|---|---|---|
| $y$ | $-16$ | $-7$ | 0 | 5 | 8 | 9 | 8 | 5 | 0 | $-7$ | $-16$ |

(a) $-3$ and $3$

(b) (i) 1.2   (ii) $-4.7$

(c) (i) $\pm 2.6$   (ii) $\pm 2.1$

(d) $-3 < x < 3$

(e) (i) $x < -2.4$; $x > 2.4$

  (ii) $x < -3.2$; $x > 3.2$

(f) $2; -4$

(g) $y = 5$ intersects at $x = \pm 2$

(h) $y = 2x + 1$ intersects at $x = -4$ and $2$

  $x < -4.85$, $x > 1.85$

4.
| $x$ | $-3$ | $-2.5$ | $-2$ | $-1.5$ | $-1$ | $-0.5$ |
|---|---|---|---|---|---|---|
| $y$ | 6 | $-1.875$ | $-6$ | $-7.125$ | $-6$ | $-3.375$ |

| $x$ | 0 | 0.5 | 1 | 1.5 | 2 | 2.5 | 3 |
|---|---|---|---|---|---|---|---|
| $y$ | 0 | 3.375 | 6 | 7.125 | 6 | 1.875 | $-6$ |

$0.6 < x < 2.3$; $y = x$ intersects at $x = 0$ and $\pm 2.45$

5.
| $x$ | $-1$ | $-0.5$ | 0 | 0.5 | 1 | 1.5 | 2 | 2.5 |
|---|---|---|---|---|---|---|---|---|
| $y$ | 21 | 5.125 | 0 | 4.875 | 19 | 41.625 | 72 | 109.575 |

(a) $-0.49, 0.51$   (b) $-0.98, 1.03$

(c) 0

6. (b) $0.27; 3.73$

  (c) $\dfrac{1}{x} = 4-x$; $x^2 - 4x + 1 = 0$

7. (a)
| $x$ | 1 | 1.5 | 2 | 3 | 4 | 5 | 6 |
|---|---|---|---|---|---|---|---|
| $y$ | 6 | 3.17 | 2 | 1.33 | 1.5 | 2 | 2.67 |

  (c) $1.75 < x < 5.75$

  (e) 2.3

8. (a)
| $x$ | 0 | 1 | 2 | 3 | 4 | 5 | 6 |
|---|---|---|---|---|---|---|---|
| $y$ | 1 | 2 | 4 | 8 | 16 | 32 | 64 |

  (c) 4.3   (d) $7\frac{1}{2}$   (e) 10

10. (a) $(0, 0), (1, 1)$   (b) $g(x) = f^{-1}(x)$

  (c) Reflection in $y = x$

## Exercise 12a

1. (a) 33.3 m/s   (b) 120 km/h

2. (a) (i) 4500 m/s

  (ii) 16 200 km/h; 18 min 31 s

3. 112 km/h; 31.25 m/h

4. 24 m/h

5. (a) 7 hours   (b) $3\frac{1}{2}$ hours

  (c) 14.5 hours

6. (a) 22 km/h   (b) $16\frac{1}{3}$ s

  (c) 33 km/h

7. $7\frac{1}{2}$ m.p.h.

8. 15 m.p.h.; no

9. (a) $3.84 \times 10^8$ m

  (b) 500 s

10. (a) 21 miles   (b) 48 min

  (c) 38.4 m.p.h.

  (d) (i) 105 miles  (ii) 134  (iii) 47 m.p.h.

11. (a) (i) 442 km  (ii) 172 km

  (b) (i) 344 km  (ii) 43 km/h

  (c) (i) 330  (ii) 3 h 18 min

  (d) 100 miles

## Exercise 12b

1. 40 km

2. 105 min

3. 9.40 a.m.

4. 10.17 a.m.; 48 km from Ayton

5. (a) 3 km/h   (b) $5\frac{1}{2}$ km/h; 11 km

  (c) 3 km/h

6. (a) BC   (b) DE

  (c) (i) 40 miles  (ii) 110 miles

7. (a) 16 km/h   (b) 14.4 km/h

  (c) 18 km/h; 11.43 a.m. and 12.15 p.m.

8. (c) (i) 3.40 p.m.  (ii) 30 m.p.h.

  (iii) 40 m.p.h.  (iv) 3.15 p.m.

9. (a) (ii) 12.46 p.m.

  (b) (ii) 2.06 p.m. (iii) 1.26 p.m.;

    67 miles from $A$

10. (f)

11. (i) (b)   (ii) (e)   (iii) (c)

12. (b)

## Exercise 12c

1. (a) 15 m/s   (b) 4 m/s$^2$

  (c) 124.5 m   (d) 8.9 m/s

2. (a) 18 m/s   (b) 3.5 m/s$^2$

  (c) 4.5 m/s$^2$   (d) 260 m

  (e) 10.8 m/s

3. (a) 30 m/s   (b) 10.03   (c) 40 s

  (d) 80 s   (e) 2400 m   (f) 3900 m

  (g) $21\frac{2}{3}$ m

4. $10v$ m; 20 m/s

5. 50 m; 30 m/s

6. (a) 90 m   (b) 720 m

  (c) 22.5 m/s

7. 10 m/s; 325 m
8. 830 m
9. (a) 15.6 m/s    (b) 1.6 s    (c) 1.11 m/s$^2$
   (d) 160 m
10. $-2$; 40;
    (a) 0.65 s or 3.85 s
    (b) 2.25 s    (c) 15 m/s$^2$

## Exercise 13a

1. (a) right angle    (b) acute angle
   (c) reflex angle    (d) obtuse angle
2. (a) opposite    (b) alternate
   (c) corresponding    (d) alternate
   (e) corresponding
3. (a) $70°$    (b) $40°$    (c) $120°$
   (d) $70°$    (e) $100°$    (f) $45°$
5. $a = b = e = g = 32°$;
   $c = d = f = 148°$
6. $x = 25°$
7. $a = 55°$; $b = 55°$; $c = 45°$; $d = 80°$
8. $a = c = 75°$; $b = d = e = 105°$
9. $a = 100°$; $b = 80°$; $c = 100°$;
   $d = 60°$; $e = 120°$; $f = 60°$
10. $a = 55°$; $b = 70°$; $c = 110°$; $d = 55°$
11. $x = 20°$
12. $x = 63°$
13. $x = 85°$; $y = 113°$
14. $p = 82°$; $q = 56°$; $r = 42°$; $s = 82°$;
    $t = 56°$
15. $x = 30°$; $y = 40°$; $z = 110°$
16. $x = 70°$; $y = 35°$; $z = 35°$
17. $a = 30°$; $b = 50°$; $c = 100°$; $d = 80°$
18. $a = 130°$; $b = 50°$; $c = 80°$; $d = 100°$

## Exercise 13c

1. (a) $026°$    (b) $018°$    (c) $351°$
   (d) $255°$    (e) $168°$    (f) $107°$
   (g) $240°$    (h) $292°$    (i) $165°$
   (j) $147°$
2. (a) $40°$    (b) $5°$    (c) $325°$
   (d) $264°$    (e) $228°$    (f) $117°$
   (g) $355°$    (h) $261°$    (i) $219°$
   (j) $168°$
3. (a) $035°$    (b) $325°$    (c) $145°$
   (d) $215°$
4. (a) $180°$    (b) $135°$    (c) $225°$
   (d) $315°$    (e) $337.5°$

5. ① Rouen $302°$
   ② Caen $254°$
   ③ Le Mans $162°$
   ④ Orleans $108°$
   ⑤ Paris $038°$
6. (a) Portsmouth    (b) Carlisle
   (c) 750 km    (d) Nottingham
   (e) $020°$, 420 km
7. $138°$
8. $327°$
9. $229°$
10. $054°$
11. $219°$
12. $135°$
13. (a) $108°$    (b) $173°$
14. (a) 23 km    (b) $245°$
15. 161 km; $056°$
16. $242°$; 1.4 km; $8\frac{1}{2}$ min
17. $300°$; 64 km; 19 h

## Exercise 14a

1. (a) $x = 70°$    (b) $x = 60°$, $y = 60°$
   (c) $x = 140°$    (d) $x = 35°$, $y = 55°$
   (e) $x = 30°$    (f) $x = 60°$, $y = 40°$
   (g) $x = 75°$, $y = 30°$
   (h) $x = 100°$, $y = 40°$
   (i) $x = 88°$, $y = 46°$
   (j) $x = 29°$, $y = 73°$
   (k) $x = 46°$, $y = 68°$, $z = 88°$
   (l) $x = 48°$, $y = 48°$, $z = 68°$
2. 10 cm$^2$
3. 12 cm
4. 8 cm
5. AP = 12 cm; AC = 18 cm
6. 10 cm
7. 8 cm
8. $x = 113°$, $y = 44°$

## Exercise 14b

1. $\frac{3}{2}$; $x = 4\frac{1}{2}$, $y = 2\frac{2}{3}$
2. $\frac{2}{1}$; $x = 1.8$, $y = 1.5$
3. $\frac{3}{2}$; $x = 6$, $y = 4\frac{1}{2}$
4. $\frac{2}{1}$; $x = 13$, $y = 24$
5. $\frac{5}{4}$; $x = 7\frac{1}{2}$, $y = 8\frac{3}{4}$
6. $\frac{4}{3}$; $x = 4\frac{1}{2}$, $y = 4$
7. $\frac{2}{3}$; $x = 9.45$, $y = 6.3$
8. $\frac{2.1}{1}$; $x = 3.36$, $y = 3.78$
9. $\frac{5}{7}$; $x = 7.5$, $y = 5.6$

10. $\frac{3}{5}$; $x = 5.4$, $y = 4.5$
11. $\frac{3}{2}$; $x = 15$, $y = 22\frac{1}{2}$
12. $\frac{5}{4}$; $x = 2\frac{1}{2}$, $y = 3\frac{1}{8}$
13. $\frac{3}{2}$; $x = 8$, $y = 5\frac{1}{3}$
14. $\frac{3}{2}$; $x = 2.5$, $y = 3.75$
15. (b) 10      (c) 7.5      (d) 4 : 5
16. 1 : 9
17. 4 : 3
18. LN = 6, ST = $6\frac{2}{3}$; 32 square units
19. 2 cm; 5.5 cm; $24\frac{3}{4}$ cm$^2$
20. 2 cm; $2\frac{1}{2}$ cm
21. 9 cm; 18 cm; 40 cm$^2$; 130 cm$^2$

## Exercise 14c

1. (a) RHS      (b) SAS      (c) ASA
   (d) SSS      (e) SAS      (f) ASA

## Miscellaneous Exercise 14

1. $u = 70°$; $v = 35°$; $w = 35°$; $x = 35°$;
   $y = 75°$
2. $A\widehat{B}F = 120°$; $B\widehat{C}F = 30°$;
   $C\widehat{F}G = 30°$; $B\widehat{F}C = 90°$
3. $u = 62°$; $v = 72°$; $w = 53°$; $x = 55°$;
   $y = 9°$; $z = 63°$
4. (a) 16 : 12 : 15      (b) 256 : 144 : 225
5. (a) 32      (b) 8      (c) 4
6. (a) $\frac{1}{4}$      (b) $\frac{1}{8}$      (c) $\frac{1}{16}$
   (d) $\frac{3}{16}$
7. AD = 18 cm; DC = 32 cm
12. (a) $\frac{4}{9}$      (b) $\frac{2}{5}$      (c) $\frac{21}{25}$      (d) $\frac{2}{5}$
13. (c) $\frac{1}{2}$      (d) $\frac{1}{4}$
14. (b) 2400 cm$^2$, $20\frac{1}{4}$ cm

## Exercise 15a

1. $x = 35°$; $y = 145°$
2. $x = 106°$; $y = 74°$
3. $x = 110°$; $y = 70°$
4. $x = 150°$; $y = 90°$
5. $x = 90°$; $y = 63°$
6. $x = 30°$; $y = 80°$
7. $x = 45°$; $y = 70°$
8. $x = 40°$; $y = 140°$
9. $x = 90°$; $y = 40°$
10. 

| parallelogram |
| --- |
| rectangle |
| rhombus |
| square |

11. (a) 21 cm$^2$      (b) 15 cm$^2$
    (c) 1.86 cm$^2$      (d) 24 cm$^2$
12. 3 cm; no
13. kite; 18 square units
14. 84.5 m$^2$
21. (a) rectangle
    (b) kite or isosceles trapezium
    (c) kite or trapezium

22. 204
23. (a) D      (b) C

## Exercise 15b

1. 107°
2. (a) 45°, 135°      (b) 40°, 140°
   (c) 36°, 144°; $\dfrac{360}{n}$; $180° - \dfrac{360}{n}$
3. 180°; 540°
4. 4; 720°
5. 900°; 128.6°
6. 1080°; 135°
7. a square
8. (a) 4      (b) 5
9. 60°, 80°, 100°, 140°, 160°
10. (a) 144°, 108°, 72°, 144°, 108°, 144°
    (b) 1 : 2 : 3 : 1 : 2 : 1
11. 13
12. 15
13. 30°

## Miscellaneous Exercise 16

1. (a)       (b)

   (c)      (d)

   (e)       (f)

434

(g)

(h)

(i)

(j)

(k)

(l)

2. c, 4; d, 6; f, 3; g, 2; h, 2; i, 2; l, 2
3. c, d, g, h, i and l
4. kite, isosceles trapezium
5. rectangle, rhombus
6. parallelogram
7. rectangle
8.

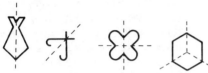

9. (i) (a)

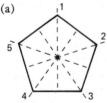

(b)

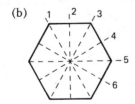

(c)

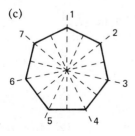

(d)

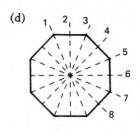

(ii) 5, 5, 5    6, 6, 6    7, 7, 7    8, 8, 8
(iii) (b) and (d)
(iv) (b)

10. (a) (i) X, A, T  (ii) EXC  (iii) X
(b)

11. (a) A, M, U   (b) B, C, E   (c) N
12. (a) rectangle
    (b) square, isosceles trapezium or kite
    (c) parallelogram
    (d) rectangle or square
    (e) rectangle
13. (a) 9        (b) 3         (c) infinite number
19. (a), (b), (e), (f)
20. All equilateral triangles, squares, and regular hexagons tessellate
21. (a) yes    (b) no


**Exercise 17a**
1. (a) 10      (b) 25      (c) 61      (d) 3.9
   (e) 84      (f) 15      (g) 12.0    (h) 5.0
   (i) 1.6     (j) 14.5    (k) 22      (l) 51.3
   (m) 18.0    (n) 5.39    (o) 6.18    (p) 84
   (q) 3.6     (r) 48      (s) 40      (t) 290
   (u) 9.7
2. 10.5 cm
3. 7.07 cm
4. 6 cm
5. 7.75 cm; 15.5 cm$^2$
6. 13 cm$^2$
7. 112 cm
8. 116.6 cm
9. (a) 6        (b) 8       PQ = 10
10. (a) 5       (b) 13      (c) 17      (d) 25
    (e) 29      (f) 17
11. 13
13. $x = 33.5$ cm; $y = 36.7$ cm; $z = 39.7$ cm
14. 19.48 m

**435**

**15.**

| $p$ | $q$ | $p^2 - q^2$ | $2pq$ | $p^2 + q^2$ |
|---|---|---|---|---|
| 2 | 1 | 3 | 4 | 5 |
| 3 | 1 | 8 | 6 | 10 |
| 3 | 2 | 5 | 12 | 13 |
| 4 | 1 | 15 | 8 | 17 |
| 4 | 2 | 12 | 16 | 20 |
| 4 | 3 | 7 | 24 | 25 |
| 5 | 1 | 24 | 10 | 26 |
| 5 | 2 | 21 | 20 | 29 |
| 5 | 3 | 16 | 30 | 34 |
| 5 | 4 | 9 | 40 | 41 |
| 6 | 1 | 35 | 12 | 37 |
| 6 | 2 | 32 | 24 | 40 |
| 6 | 3 | 27 | 36 | 45 |
| 6 | 4 | 20 | 48 | 52 |
| 6 | 5 | 11 | 60 | 61 |
| 7 | 1 | 48 | 14 | 50 |
| 7 | 2 | 45 | 28 | 53 |
| 7 | 3 | 40 | 42 | 58 |
| 7 | 4 | 33 | 56 | 65 |
| 7 | 5 | 24 | 70 | 74 |
| 7 | 6 | 13 | 84 | 85 |
| 8 | 1 | 63 | 16 | 65 |
| 8 | 2 | 60 | 32 | 68 |
| 8 | 3 | 55 | 48 | 73 |
| 8 | 4 | 48 | 64 | 80 |
| 8 | 5 | 39 | 80 | 89 |
| 8 | 6 | 28 | 96 | 100 |
| 8 | 7 | 15 | 112 | 113 |
| 9 | 1 | 80 | 18 | 82 |
| 9 | 2 | 77 | 36 | 85 |
| 9 | 3 | 72 | 54 | 90 |
| 9 | 4 | 65 | 72 | 97 |
| 9 | 5 | 56 | 90 | 106 |

(e) $x = 51.3°$, $y = 38.7°$, $z = 6.24$ cm
(f) $x = 56.9°$, $y = 33.1°$, $z = 9.22$ cm
(g) $x = 56.3°$, $y = 33.7°$, $z = 10.8$ cm
(h) $x = 50.8°$, $y = 39.2°$, $z = 7.6$ cm
(i) $x = 64.3°$, $y = 25.7°$, $z = 11.0$ cm

4. 13.1 cm, 11.0 cm
5. (a) 9.14 cm     (b) 33.2°
6. $b = 11.3$ cm, 56.6 cm$^2$
7. 29.4 cm$^2$
8. 3.02 cm, 16.9 cm$^2$
9. (a) 22.6°   (b) 67.4°   (c) 1.25 m
    (d) 53 cm$^2$
10. (a) 1.9 m   (b) 6.8 m   (c) 53.1°
11. 18.2 m
12. 46.3 m
13. 76.1°; 4.85 m

**Exercise 17c**

1. (a) $x = 6.69$ cm, $y = 7.04$ cm
   (b) $x = 0.52$ cm, $y = 0.56$ cm
   (c) $x = 8.8$ cm, $y = 4.7$ cm, $z = 6.4$ cm
   (d) $x = 18$ cm, $y = 8.8$ cm, $z = 3.82$ cm
   (e) $x = 5.4$ cm, $y = 12.8$ cm
   (f) $x = 11.3$ cm, $y = 16.1$ cm
   (g) $x = 4.2$ cm, $y = 4.3$ cm
   (h) $x = 6.2$ cm, $y = 11.2$ cm
   (i) 30.1 cm
   (j) 45.6 cm
   (k) 7.4 cm
   (l) 16.1 cm
   (m) $x = 9.64$ cm, $y = 3.51$ cm,
      $z = 7.98$ cm
   (n) $x = 3.51$ cm, $y = 2.02$ cm, $z = 5.17$ cm
   (o) $x = 7.71$ cm, $y = 6.39$ cm
   (p) $x = 16.26$, $y = 7.58$ cm, $z = 8.68$ cm
2. 10.9 cm; 49.0 cm$^2$
3. 2.76 m; 1.46 m$^2$
4. 13.6 m$^2$
5. 2.97 cm; 8.92 cm$^2$

**Exercise 17d**

1. 39 cm; 40.8 cm; 17.1°
2. 1.41 m; 4.24 m; 70.5°
3. (a) 4.24 m      (b) 45°
   (c) 35.3°      (d) 70.5°
4. 51.3°; 77.4°
5. (a) 87.5 m      (b) 306°
   (c) 1.72 km     (d) 2.91°
6. (a) 7.07 cm     (b) 11.2 cm; 70.5°

**Exercise 17b**

1. (a) 13.76 cm      (b) 10 cm
   (c) 11.5 cm       (d) 1.09 cm
   (e) 7.14 cm       (f) 8.07 cm
   (g) 4.02 cm       (h) 15.4 cm
   (i) 19.2 cm       (j) 8 cm
   (k) 28.6 cm      (l) 2.55 cm
2. (a) 45°    (b) 30°    (c) 23.6°
   (d) 55.8°   (e) 65.4°   (f) 51.1°
   (g) 38.7°   (h) 31.8°   (i) 64.6°
   (j) 42.6°   (k) 28°     (l) 36.8°
3. (a) $x = 4.10$ cm, $y = 2.87$ cm
   (b) $x = 6.69$ cm, $y = 7.43$ cm
   (c) $x = 23.2$ cm, $y = 24.6$ cm
   (d) $x = 67.4°$, $y = 26$ cm

## Exercise 17e

1. (a) (i) 0.97  (ii) −0.57
   (c) (i) +1, −1  (ii) $37°$, $143°$
   (iii) $134°$, $226°$  (iv) $180° < x < 360°$
   (v) $90° < x < 270°$  (vi) $45°$, $225°$
2. (a) $38.7°$  (b) $51.7°$  (c) $28.3°$
   (d) 6.39 m  (e) 3.05 cm  (f) $65.8°$
3. (a) 28.6 mm  (b) 41.8 cm
   (c) 37.3 cm  (d) 7.70 cm
   (e) 10.0 cm
4. (a) $79.5°$, $56.1°$, $44.4°$
   (b) $41.4°$, $55.8°$, $82.8°$
   (c) $125.0°$, $42.1°$, $12.9°$
   (d) $110.5°$, $41.3°$, $28.1°$
5. (a) $\widehat{A} = 64.9°$; $\widehat{B} = 50.1°$; CB = 13.0 cm
   (b) $\widehat{B} = 73.0°$; $\widehat{C} = 59.0°$; AC = 16.7 cm
   (c) $\widehat{X} = 33.9°$; $\widehat{Z} = 43.1°$; XZ = 17.1 cm
   (d) $\widehat{P} = 48.1°$; $\widehat{R} = 21.9°$; PR = 42.9 mm
   (e) $\widehat{R} = 56.1°$; $\widehat{S} = 87.4°$; $\widehat{T} = 36.5°$
   (f) $\widehat{M} = 47.9°$; $\widehat{N} = 96.4°$; $\widehat{O} = 35.7°$

## Miscellaneous Exercise 17

2. (a) 10 km E; 17.32 km N
   (b) (i) 42.32 km  (ii) 40 km E
   (c) 58.23  (d) $043.4°$
3. (a) 11.8 km  (b) 19.7 km  (c) 20.3 km
   (d) 23.5 km  (e) $239.7°$
4. (b) (i) 14 miles  (ii) $328°$
   (c) (i) 17.3 miles  (ii) 6.43 miles
       (iii) 10.9 miles
5. (a) $68.0°$  (b) 1.35 cm  (c) 2.91 cm
6. (b) (i) 40 m  (ii) 28 m  (iii) $35°$
7. (a) $54.0°$  (b) 35.0 m  (c) 35.2 m
   (d) 431 m$^2$  (e) $21.6°$
8. (a) (i) $60°$  (ii) $60°$  (iii) 5.20 cm
   (b) (i) 12 cm  (ii) 22.4 cm
9. (a) 94.3 m  (b) $122°$  (c) 26 m
   (d) $27.5°$
10. (a) 78.5 m$^2$  (b) (i) 26 m  (ii) $67.4°$
    (c) (i) 23.3 m  (ii) $59°$
11. (a) 6 cm  (b) 13 cm  (c) $\frac{5}{12}$
12. 3608 m; $028.4°$; 1948 m; 18 s

## Exercise 18a

1. (a) 9.14 cm$^2$; 12.3 cm
   (b) 14.1 cm$^2$; 21.4 cm
   (c) 8.05 cm$^2$; 14.1 cm
   (d) 2.86 cm$^2$; 12.3 cm

(e) 39.7 cm$^2$  (f) 33.6 cm$^2$
(g) 44.6 cm$^2$  (h) 27.9 cm$^2$
2. (a) 21.5 cm$^2$  (b) 62.8 cm$^2$
   (c) 6.28 cm$^2$  (d) 75.4 cm$^2$
   (e) 1.38 cm$^2$  (f) 0.88 cm$^2$
   (g) 24.9 cm$^2$  (h) 201.06 mm$^2$
3. (a) 6.28 cm; 15.7 cm$^2$
   (b) 18.8 cm; 75.4 cm$^2$
   (c) 40.8 cm; 306 cm$^2$
4. (a) 2.5 cm  (b) 27 cm  (c) 12.5 cm
   (d) 5.94 cm  (e) 6.33 cm
   (f) 6.80 cm
5. (a) 5 cm  (b) 15 cm  (c) 200 cm
   (d) 3.16 cm  (e) 5.97 cm  (f) 4.80 cm
6. 201 m; 497
7. 21 cm
8. 491 cm$^2$
9. (a) 50 cm$^2$  (b) 78.5 cm$^2$
   (c) 28.5 cm$^2$
10. (a) 9.06 cm$^2$  (b) 6.72 cm$^2$
11. 74.8 cm$^2$

## Exercise 18b

1. $30°$
2. $50°$
3. $90°$
4. $65°$
5. $133°$
6. $40°$
7. $130°$
8. $140°$
9. $20°$
10. $90°$
11. $35°$
12. $52°$
13. $90°$
14. $110°$
15. $25°$
16. $34°$
17. $x = 90°$; $y = 90°$; $z = 58°$
18. $x = 40°$; $y = 100°$; $z = 50°$
19. $x = 116°$; $y = 64°$; $z = 116°$
20. $x = 95°$; $y = 85°$; $z = 85°$
21. $x = 90°$; $y = 42°$; $z = 48°$
22. $x = 42°$; $y = 90°$; $z = 48°$
23. $x = 88°$; $y = 22°$; $z = 136°$
24. $x = 26°$; $y = 26°$; $z = 64°$
25. $x = 250°$; $y = 125°$; $z = 55°$
26. $x = 90°$; $y = 48°$; $z = 42°$
27. $x = 28°$; $y = 51°$; $z = 28°$

28. $x = 40°; y = 40°; z = 25°$
29. $x = 33°; y = 33°; z = 123°$
30. $x = 42°; y = 30°; z = 42°$
31. $x = 60°; y = 120°; z = 20°$
32. $x = 30°; y = 60°; z = 78°$
35. (a) 4 cm (b) 12.5 cm (c) 14 cm
36. (a) 12 cm (b) 10 cm (c) 16.5 cm

## Exercise 18c

1. $55°$
2. $60°$
3. $63°$
4. $60°$
5. $x = 70°; y = 55°; z = 55°$
6. $x = 48°; y = 84°; z = 48°$
7. $x = 60°; y = 60°; z = 120°$
8. $x = 32°; y = 48°; z = 42°$
9. $x = 53°; y = 53°; z = 74°$
10. $x = 62°; y = 110°; z = 35°$
11. $x = 90°; y = 31°; z = 59°$
12. $x = 42°; y = 28°; z = 110°$
13. $x = 55°; y = 35°; z = 65°$

## Miscellaneous Exercise 18

1. (a) trapezium (b) 10 cm
   (c) 5.37 cm² (d) 17.9 cm
   (e) 7.07 cm
2. 1580 mm²
3. (a) (i) 8 cm (ii) 6 cm (iii) 10 cm
   (iv) 6 cm
   (b) (i) 4 cm (ii) 9.17 cm (iii) 264 cm²
   (iv) 260 cm²
4. 51 cm²
5. (a) 3.14 cm (b) 33.7 cm (c) 42.4 cm²
   (d) 10.7 cm
6. 40π km
7. 50 cm²
9. (a) 25° (b) 65° (c) 65° (d) 50°
10. (a) 20° (b) 110°
11. (a) 50° (b) 100° (c) 25°
12. (a) 54° (b) 18° (c) 126°
13. $f = 50°; g = 100°; h = 130°; i = 80°;$
    $j = 40°; k = 40°; l = 50°$
14. 90°; 90°; 58°; 32°; 90°; 58°; 29°; 119°

## Exercise 19a

1.

|  | F | V | E | F + V |
|---|---|---|---|---|
| Cube | 6 | 8 | 12 | 14 |
| Triangular prism | 5 | 6 | 9 | 11 |
| Tetrahedron | 4 | 4 | 6 | 8 |
| Square based pyramid | 5 | 5 | 8 | 10 |
| Cuboid | 6 | 8 | 12 | 14 |
| Pentagonal prism | 7 | 10 | 15 | 17 |
| Hexagonal pyramid | 7 | 7 | 12 | 14 |

$F + V - 2 = E$

2.

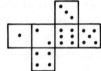

3. (a) triangular prism
   (b) cuboid
   (c) hexagonal prism
   (d) hexagonal pyramid
6. (a) 8 (b) 34 (c) 54

## Exercise 19b

1. 1131 m³; 377 m²
2. 8 m³; 24 m²
3. 101 cm³; 7.21 cm; 141 cm²
4. 83.3 cm³
5. 4189 cm³; 1257 cm²
6. 4021 cm³; 1407 cm²
7. 3 m³; 13 m²
8. 60 cm³; 132 cm²
9. 14.4 cm³
10. sphere (33.5 cm³ > 27 cm³)
    cube (54 cm² > 50.3 cm²)
12. 1.73 m³
13. 1.5 m²
14. 16 m²; 96 m³
15. 1.16 m²; 2.32 m³
16. 2.356 cm²; 235.6 cm³
17. 220 cm²; 0.088 m³
18. 94.2 cm³
19. 9.42 cm³; 9.42 cm³/s
20. 0.0126 m³/s; 64 min
21. $3.14 \times 10^{-5}$ m³/s

**Exercise 19c**

1. (a) 6 cm$^2$, 24 cm$^2$, 54 cm$^2$
   (b) 1 cm$^3$, 8 cm$^3$, 27 cm$^3$    (c) $1:2:3$
   (d) $1:4:9$        (e) $1:8:27$

2. (a) $4\pi$ cm$^2$, $16\pi$ cm$^2$, $36\pi$ cm$^2$
   (b) $\dfrac{4\pi}{3}$ cm$^3$, $\dfrac{32\pi}{3}$ cm$^3$, $36\pi$ cm$^3$
   (c) $1:2:3$      (d) $1:4:9$
   (e) $1:8:27$

3. $\dfrac{2\pi}{3}$ cm$^3$, $\dfrac{16\pi}{3}$ cm$^3$, $18\pi$ cm$^3$; $1:8:27$

4. 3

5. 960

6. 293

7. 32

8. 25

9. 113.1 cm$^3$; 113.1 cm$^2$; 113 100 cm$^3$;
   11 310 cm$^2$

10. 75 cm$^3$; 4800 cm$^3$

11. 40 litres

12. 220 ml

13. (a) 18 cm      (b) 382 cm$^3$
    (c) 113 cm$^3$     (d) 269 cm$^3$

14. 2.88 m; 1.25 cm × 0.875 cm

15. (a) $p = 8$ cm, $q = 7\frac{1}{2}$ cm, $r = 9$ cm,
    $s = 15$ cm
    (b) (i) 250 cm$^2$, (ii) 360 cm$^2$
    (c) (i) 437.5 cm$^3$ (ii) 224 cm$^3$

**Miscellaneous Exercise 19**

1. (a) 0    (b) 8    (c) 12    (d) 6
   (e) 1

2. (a) (i) 0 (ii) 8 (iii) 24 (iv) 24 (v) 8
   (b) (i) 0 (ii) 8 (iii) 36 (iv) 54 (v) 27
   (c) (i) 0 (ii) 8 (iii) $12(n-2)$
        (iv) $6(n-2)^2$ (v) $(n-2)^3$

3. (a) 120     (b) 288     (c) $4n^2 + 4n$

4. (a) (i) 6 (ii) 8 (iii) 12
   (b) 2

5. (a) (i) 4950 cm$^3$ (ii) 75 cm$^3$ (iii) 66
   (b) 63    (c) (i) 615 g (ii) 40.6 kg

6. (a) 18.8 cm      (b) 4524 cm$^2$
   (c) 63.7         (d) 467 cm$^3$

7. (a) 2 m         (b) 251 m$^3$
   (c) 12.6 m$^3$     (d) 264 m$^3$
   (e) 24 m       (f) 0.785 m$^3$
   (g) 336

8. (a) 5 cm; 11 cm    (b) 102 cm$^2$
   (c) 10 200 cm$^3$    (d) 23.5 kg

9. (a) 37.8 m$^2$       (b) 454 m$^3$
   (c) 3.9 m        (d) 277 m$^2$

10. (a) 14 m$^2$        (b) 34.6 m$^2$
    (c) 19 800 kg

11. (a) 635 cm$^2$     (b) 251 g
    (c) 62.8 g

12. (a) 71.5 cm$^3$    (b) 248 cm$^2$
    (c) 11

**Exercise 20a**

1. (a) $1 \times 3$    (b) $2 \times 2$    (c) $1 \times 2$
   (d) $2 \times 1$    (e) $3 \times 2$    (f) $3 \times 1$
   (a) and (c) are row matrices,
   (d) and (f) are column matrices

2. (a) $\begin{pmatrix} 6 & 4 \\ 3 & 10 \end{pmatrix}$     (b) $\begin{pmatrix} -2 & 2 \\ -1 & -6 \end{pmatrix}$
   (c) $\begin{pmatrix} 14 & 26 \\ 8 & 17 \end{pmatrix}$    (d) $\begin{pmatrix} 9 & 14 \\ 12 & 22 \end{pmatrix}$

3. (a) not possible    (b) $\begin{pmatrix} 10 \\ 12 \end{pmatrix}$
   (c) $(11 \ \ 4 \ \ 1)$
   (d) $\begin{pmatrix} 7 & 10 \\ 15 & 22 \end{pmatrix}$

4. (a) $\begin{pmatrix} 5 & 1 \\ 4 & 2 \end{pmatrix}$   (b) $\begin{pmatrix} 3 & 1 \\ 0 & 0 \end{pmatrix}$   (c) $\begin{pmatrix} 8 & 2 \\ 4 & 2 \end{pmatrix}$
   (d) $\begin{pmatrix} 7 & 2 \\ 2 & 1 \end{pmatrix}$   (e) $\begin{pmatrix} 18 & 4 \\ 12 & 6 \end{pmatrix}$   (f) $\begin{pmatrix} 43 & 10 \\ 26 & 13 \end{pmatrix}$
   (g) $\begin{pmatrix} 2 & \frac{1}{2} \\ 1 & \frac{1}{2} \end{pmatrix}$   (h) $\begin{pmatrix} -8 & -2 \\ -4 & -2 \end{pmatrix}$
   (i) $\begin{pmatrix} \frac{1}{4} & 0 \\ \frac{1}{2} & \frac{1}{4} \end{pmatrix}$   (j) $\begin{pmatrix} \frac{3}{4} & 0 \\ 1\frac{1}{2} & \frac{3}{4} \end{pmatrix}$   (k) $\begin{pmatrix} 2\frac{1}{4} & \frac{1}{2} \\ 1\frac{1}{2} & \frac{3}{4} \end{pmatrix}$
   (l) $\begin{pmatrix} -7\frac{1}{4} & -2 \\ -2\frac{1}{2} & -1\frac{1}{4} \end{pmatrix}$
   (m) $\begin{pmatrix} 6 & 1 \\ 4 & 1 \end{pmatrix}$   (n) $\begin{pmatrix} 4 & 1 \\ 10 & 3 \end{pmatrix}$   (o) $\begin{pmatrix} 18 & 5 \\ 10 & 3 \end{pmatrix}$
   (p) $\begin{pmatrix} 1 & 0 \\ 4 & 1 \end{pmatrix}$   (q) $\begin{pmatrix} 6 & 1 \\ 16 & 3 \end{pmatrix}$   (r) $\begin{pmatrix} 26 & 7 \\ 18 & 5 \end{pmatrix}$
   (s) $\begin{pmatrix} 26 & 7 \\ 70 & 19 \end{pmatrix}$ (t) $\begin{pmatrix} 40 & 7 \\ 28 & 5 \end{pmatrix}$

5. (a) $\begin{pmatrix} 3 & 0 \\ 6 & 3 \\ 3 & 6 \end{pmatrix}$    (b) $\begin{pmatrix} 4 & 2 & 4 \\ 6 & 4 & 2 \end{pmatrix}$

(c) not possible

(d) $\begin{pmatrix} 6 & 5 \\ 8 & 4 \end{pmatrix}$ (e) $\begin{pmatrix} 2 & 1 & 2 \\ 7 & 4 & 5 \\ 8 & 5 & 4 \end{pmatrix}$

(f) $\begin{pmatrix} 1 & 0 \\ \frac{1}{2} & 1 \end{pmatrix}$ (g) $\begin{pmatrix} 4 & 0 \\ 4 & 4 \end{pmatrix}$ (h) $\begin{pmatrix} 20 \\ 22 \end{pmatrix}$

(i) $\begin{pmatrix} 2 & 0 \\ 5 & 2 \\ 4 & 4 \end{pmatrix}$ (j) $\begin{pmatrix} 12 & 10 \\ 16 & 8 \end{pmatrix}$

(k) $\begin{pmatrix} 12 & 10 \\ 16 & 8 \end{pmatrix}$ (l) not possible

(m) $(0 \ -4)$ (n) $(5)$

(o) $\begin{pmatrix} 1 & -2 \\ -2 & 4 \end{pmatrix}$

(p) $\begin{pmatrix} 1 \\ 0 \\ -3 \end{pmatrix}$ (q) $(-4 \ -3 \ 0)$

(r) $\begin{pmatrix} 2 \\ -3 \end{pmatrix}$ (s) $\begin{pmatrix} 12 \\ -18 \end{pmatrix}$ (t) $\begin{pmatrix} 12 \\ -18 \end{pmatrix}$

(u) $\begin{pmatrix} 2 & 0 \\ 5 & 2 \\ 4 & 4 \end{pmatrix}$ (v) $\begin{pmatrix} 4 & 2 & 4 \\ 8 & 5 & 4 \end{pmatrix}$ (w) $(8)$

(x) $\begin{pmatrix} 2 & -4 \\ -3 & 6 \end{pmatrix}$

6. $a = 3, b = 2$
7. $x = 3, y = -1$
8. $a = 1, b = -1, c = 2, d = -8$
9. $a = 1, b = -2$
10. $x = 2, y = 4$
11. $x = 1, y = 3$
12. $x = 3, y = 0$

**Exercise 20b**

1. $\begin{pmatrix} 1 & 0 \\ 0 & 1 \end{pmatrix}$; $\begin{pmatrix} -7 & 4 \\ 2 & -1 \end{pmatrix}$

2. $\begin{pmatrix} 1 & 0 \\ 0 & 1 \end{pmatrix}$; $\begin{pmatrix} \frac{1}{2} & -\frac{1}{4} \\ -\frac{1}{2} & \frac{3}{4} \end{pmatrix}$

3. (a) (i) 1 (ii) $\begin{pmatrix} 7 & -2 \\ -3 & 1 \end{pmatrix}$

(b) (i) 1 (ii) $\begin{pmatrix} 3 & -1 \\ -11 & 4 \end{pmatrix}$

(c) (i) $-1$ (ii) $\begin{pmatrix} -3 & 2 \\ 5 & -3 \end{pmatrix}$

(d) (i) 3 (ii) $\frac{1}{3}\begin{pmatrix} 3 & -5 \\ -3 & 6 \end{pmatrix}$

(e) (i) 2 (ii) $\frac{1}{2}\begin{pmatrix} 2 & -2 \\ -3 & 4 \end{pmatrix}$

(f) (i) 2 (ii) $\frac{1}{2}\begin{pmatrix} 5 & -2 \\ -9 & 4 \end{pmatrix}$

(g) (i) 9 (ii) $\frac{1}{9}\begin{pmatrix} 1 & 0 \\ -1 & 9 \end{pmatrix}$

(h) (i) 2 (ii) $\frac{1}{2}\begin{pmatrix} 4 & -6 \\ -3 & 5 \end{pmatrix}$

(i) (i) 6 (ii) $\frac{1}{6}\begin{pmatrix} 2 & -2 \\ -1 & 4 \end{pmatrix}$

(j) (i) $-2$ (ii) $\frac{1}{2}\begin{pmatrix} -4 & 6 \\ 3 & -4 \end{pmatrix}$

(k) (i) 2 (ii) $\frac{1}{2}\begin{pmatrix} 3 & -4 \\ -4 & 6 \end{pmatrix}$

(l) (i) $-2$ (ii) $\frac{1}{2}\begin{pmatrix} -4 & 3 \\ 6 & -4 \end{pmatrix}$

4. (a) $-1$ (b) 18 (c) $\begin{pmatrix} -5 & 3 \\ 2 & -1 \end{pmatrix}$

(d) $\frac{1}{18}\begin{pmatrix} 5 & -8 \\ 1 & 2 \end{pmatrix}$

5. (a) $-5$ (b) $\frac{1}{3}\begin{pmatrix} 3 & -6 \\ -2 & 5 \end{pmatrix}$

(c) 6 (d) 4 (e) $\frac{1}{4}\begin{pmatrix} 2 & -1 \\ -2 & 3 \end{pmatrix}$

(f) $\begin{pmatrix} -\frac{1}{5} & \frac{4}{5} \\ \frac{2}{5} & -\frac{3}{5} \end{pmatrix}$

6. (a) $\begin{pmatrix} 1 & -2 \\ -1 & 3 \end{pmatrix}$ (b) $\frac{1}{4}\begin{pmatrix} 3 & -2 \\ -1 & 2 \end{pmatrix}$

(c) $\begin{pmatrix} 8 & 12 \\ 3 & 5 \end{pmatrix}$ (d) $\frac{1}{4}\begin{pmatrix} 5 & -12 \\ -3 & 8 \end{pmatrix}$

(e) $\begin{pmatrix} 8 & 6 \\ 6 & 5 \end{pmatrix}$      (f) $\frac{1}{4}\begin{pmatrix} 5 & -6 \\ -6 & 8 \end{pmatrix}$

(g) $\frac{1}{4}\begin{pmatrix} 5 & -6 \\ -6 & 8 \end{pmatrix}$      (h) $\frac{1}{4}\begin{pmatrix} 5 & -12 \\ -3 & 8 \end{pmatrix}$

7. 0; all of them

## Exercise 20c

1. $x = 6, y = -1$
2. $x = 4, y = 2$
3. $M = \begin{pmatrix} 2 & 3 \\ 1 & 1 \end{pmatrix}$; $M^{-1} = \begin{pmatrix} -1 & 3 \\ 1 & -2 \end{pmatrix}$;

   $x = 2, y = 1$

4. $\begin{pmatrix} 2 & -3 \\ -3 & 5 \end{pmatrix}$;

   (a) $x = 3, y = -2$    (b) $a = -1, b = 3$
5. $x = -1, y = 2$
6. $x = 10, y = -7$
7. $x = 1\frac{1}{2}, y = 1\frac{1}{2}$
8. $x = 3, y = 5$
9. $a = 5\frac{1}{2}, b = -2$
10. $p = 4.3, q = 2.1$
11. $x = 2, y = \frac{1}{2}$
12. $x = 2, y = 2$
13. $x = 6\frac{2}{3}, y = -2\frac{1}{3}$
14. $x = 2\frac{3}{4}, y = \frac{1}{2}$
15. $x = -s, y = -s$
16. $x = \frac{7}{5}, y = \frac{11}{2}$
17. $x = \frac{1}{3}, y = -6$
18. $x = \frac{1}{2}, y = \frac{1}{2}$

## Exercise 20d

1. (a) $\begin{pmatrix} 6 & 2 & 2 \\ 4 & 4 & 2 \\ 3 & 1 & 5 \end{pmatrix}$

(b) $\begin{pmatrix} 10 \\ 10 \\ 9 \end{pmatrix}$ = games played

(c) $\begin{pmatrix} 2 \\ 1 \\ 0 \end{pmatrix}$; $\begin{pmatrix} 14 \\ 12 \\ 7 \end{pmatrix}$

2. (a) $\begin{pmatrix} 2 & 1 & 2 \\ 3 & 2 & 1 \end{pmatrix}$    (b) $\begin{pmatrix} 30 \\ 70 \\ 80 \end{pmatrix}$; $\begin{pmatrix} 290 \\ 310 \end{pmatrix}$

(c) $(600)$ = total spent

3. (a) $\begin{pmatrix} 800 & 900 & 500 \\ 1000 & 1200 & 200 \end{pmatrix}$

(b) $(5800 \ 6900 \ 1500)$ = units used

(c) $\begin{pmatrix} 0.5 \\ 0.3 \\ 0.1 \end{pmatrix}$    (d) $(5120)$

4. $\begin{pmatrix} 3000 & 420 & 1320 & 150 \\ 3100 & 425 & 1320 & 140 \end{pmatrix}\begin{pmatrix} 0.24 \\ 0.40 \\ 1.00 \\ 2.00 \end{pmatrix}$;

$\begin{pmatrix} 2508 \\ 2514 \end{pmatrix}$; $(1 \ 1)$; $(5022)$

5.      P  Q  R

$\begin{matrix} A \\ B \end{matrix}\begin{pmatrix} 2 & 0 & 1 \\ 1 & 2 & 2 \end{pmatrix}$

     X  Y  Z

$\begin{matrix} A \\ B \end{matrix}\begin{pmatrix} 4 & 5 & 1 \\ 4 & 11 & 4 \end{pmatrix}$

6. (a)   N  P  Q

$\begin{matrix} A \\ B \end{matrix}\begin{pmatrix} 2 & 2 & 0 \\ 1 & 1 & 2 \end{pmatrix}$

(b)      X  Y  Z

$\begin{matrix} N \\ P \\ Q \end{matrix}\begin{pmatrix} 1 & 0 & 0 \\ 1 & 1 & 0 \\ 0 & 1 & 1 \end{pmatrix}$

(c)   X  Y  Z

$\begin{matrix} A \\ B \end{matrix}\begin{pmatrix} 4 & 2 & 0 \\ 2 & 3 & 2 \end{pmatrix}$

7. (a) (i) 1  (ii) 1

(b)   X  Y

$\begin{matrix} P \\ Q \end{matrix}\begin{pmatrix} 3 & 1 \\ 0 & 2 \end{pmatrix}$

(c)   X  Y

$\begin{matrix} A \\ B \\ C \end{matrix}\begin{pmatrix} 3 & 5 \\ 3 & 1 \\ 6 & 4 \end{pmatrix}$

**Miscellaneous Exercise 20**

1. $a = 1, b = 4$

2. (a) $\begin{pmatrix} -4 & 4 \\ -7 & 6 \end{pmatrix}$; $\begin{pmatrix} 4 & 3 \\ -4 & -2 \end{pmatrix}$; $\begin{pmatrix} 7 & 4 \\ 12 & 7 \end{pmatrix}$; $\begin{pmatrix} 2 & -1 \\ -3 & 2 \end{pmatrix}$

   (b) $m = 4, n = -1$   (c) $\begin{pmatrix} -1\frac{1}{2} & -1 \\ \frac{1}{4} & 0 \end{pmatrix}$

3. (a) $a = 4, b = -2$

   (b) $\begin{pmatrix} 2 & -1\frac{1}{2} \\ -1 & 1 \end{pmatrix}$; $\begin{pmatrix} -2\frac{1}{2} & -3 \\ 2 & 2 \end{pmatrix}$

   (c) $\begin{pmatrix} -6 & 2 \\ -15 & 5 \end{pmatrix}$; $(-1)$

4. (a) $\begin{pmatrix} 5 & -6 \\ -4 & 5 \end{pmatrix}$   (b) $\begin{pmatrix} 7 \\ -3 \end{pmatrix}$

   (c) $\begin{pmatrix} -1 & -2 \\ 0 & 2 \end{pmatrix}$

5. (a) $\begin{pmatrix} 2 & -1 \\ 1 & 0 \end{pmatrix}$; $\begin{pmatrix} 1 & -1 \\ \frac{1}{2} & 0 \end{pmatrix}$; $\begin{pmatrix} 1\frac{1}{2} & -2 \\ 1 & -1 \end{pmatrix}$

   (b) $\begin{pmatrix} -1 & 2 \\ -2 & 2 \end{pmatrix}$; $\begin{pmatrix} -2 & 4 \\ -2 & 3 \end{pmatrix}$

   (c) $\begin{pmatrix} 1 & -1 \\ 1 & -\frac{1}{2} \end{pmatrix}$; $\begin{pmatrix} 1\frac{1}{2} & -2 \\ 1 & -1 \end{pmatrix}$

6. (a) $\begin{pmatrix} 2 & 4 & 1 \\ 3 & 1 & 2 \end{pmatrix}$

   (b) $\begin{pmatrix} 30 \\ 22 \end{pmatrix}$ = weekly spending

   (c) $(1 \ 1)$

7. (a) $\begin{pmatrix} 63 \\ 26 \\ 57 \end{pmatrix}$ = each child's money

   (b) $\begin{pmatrix} 1 \\ 1 \\ 1 \\ 1 \\ 1 \end{pmatrix}$

   (c) $(4 \ 1 \ 2 \ 3 \ 2)$ = number of coins of each value

   (d) $(1 \ 1 \ 1) \ Q \begin{pmatrix} 1 \\ 2 \\ 5 \\ 10 \\ 50 \end{pmatrix}$

8. (a) $\begin{array}{c} P \\ R \\ H \\ D \\ L \\ C \end{array} \begin{pmatrix} 24 \\ 23 \\ 22 \\ 20 \\ 19 \\ 17 \end{pmatrix}$

   (b) (i)

| | W | D | L |
|---|---|---|---|
| P | 11 | 2 | 2 |
| R | 11 | 3 | 1 |
| H | 8 | 7 | 0 |
| D | 11 | 0 | 4 |
| L | 8 | 3 | 4 |
| C | 6 | 6 | 3 |

   (ii) $\begin{array}{c} P \\ R \\ H \\ D \\ L \\ C \end{array} \begin{pmatrix} 24 \\ 25 \\ 23 \\ 22 \\ 19 \\ 18 \end{pmatrix}$

   (c) P won; R lost; H draw; D draw; L won; C lost

9. (a)

| | X | Y | Z |
|---|---|---|---|
| R | 1 | 1 | 0 |
| S | 0 | 1 | 1 |
| T | 1 | 0 | 1 |

   (c)

| | A | B |
|---|---|---|
| R | 3 | 2 |
| S | 3 | 1 |
| T | 2 | 3 |

10. (a) Diagonals indicate the route from a town to itself

   (b)

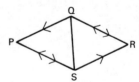

**Exercise 21a**

1. $(5, 4), (6, 6), (4, 5)$; $\begin{pmatrix} -3 \\ -2 \end{pmatrix}$

2. (a) $\begin{pmatrix} 3 \\ -3 \end{pmatrix}$   (b) $\begin{pmatrix} 3 \\ 0 \end{pmatrix}$   (c) $\begin{pmatrix} -1 \\ 1 \end{pmatrix}$

   (d) $\begin{pmatrix} -3 \\ 0 \end{pmatrix}$   (e) $\begin{pmatrix} -5 \\ -6 \end{pmatrix}$   (f) $\begin{pmatrix} 14 \\ -17 \end{pmatrix}$

3. $\begin{pmatrix} 3 \\ 5 \end{pmatrix}$

4. $\begin{pmatrix} 4 \\ -4 \end{pmatrix}$; $(6, -1)$

5. (a) $\begin{pmatrix} -2 \\ -1 \end{pmatrix}$    (b) $\begin{pmatrix} 1 \\ -2 \end{pmatrix}$    (c) $\begin{pmatrix} -3 \\ 1 \end{pmatrix}$

   (d) $\begin{pmatrix} -5 \\ -3 \end{pmatrix}$    (e) $\begin{pmatrix} -4 \\ 2 \end{pmatrix}$

6. $\begin{pmatrix} 4 \\ -4 \end{pmatrix}$

8. (a) $\begin{pmatrix} 3 \\ 1 \end{pmatrix}$    (b) $\begin{pmatrix} -5 \\ -5 \end{pmatrix}$    (c) $\begin{pmatrix} -8 \\ -6 \end{pmatrix}$

   (d) $\begin{pmatrix} 8 \\ 6 \end{pmatrix}$    (d) is the inverse of (c)

## Exercise 21b

1. (a)     (b)

   (c)    (d)

2. $A'(1, -1)$; $B'(5, -1)$; $C'(4, -3)$; $D'(2, -3)$
3. reflection in $y = -x$ equivalent to

$$\begin{pmatrix} 0 & -1 \\ -1 & 0 \end{pmatrix}$$

4. $x = 3$
5. $x = 1$
7. $y = x$; $(3, 2)$
10. reflections in $y = x$ and $y = -x$

$$A^{-1} = \begin{pmatrix} 0 & 1 \\ 1 & 0 \end{pmatrix} \qquad B^{-1} = \begin{pmatrix} 0 & -1 \\ -1 & 0 \end{pmatrix}$$

## Exercise 21c

1. (a)     (b)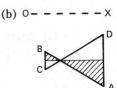

   (c)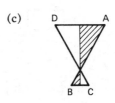

   (d)

2. $A'(-1, 1)$; $B'(-1, 5)$; $C'(-3, 4)$; $D'(-3, 2)$
3. rotation by $180°$; $\begin{pmatrix} -1 & 0 \\ 0 & -1 \end{pmatrix}$
4. $(6, 1)$; $270°$
5. (a) $(1, 1)$    (b) $(3, 2)$
6. $90°$
7. $(5, 5)$
8. rotation by $180°$
10. (a) identity    (b) rotation by $90°$
   (c) rotation by $180°$
12. (a) $\begin{pmatrix} 0 & -1 \\ 1 & 0 \end{pmatrix}$    (b) $\begin{pmatrix} 0 & 1 \\ -1 & 0 \end{pmatrix}$
   (c) $\begin{pmatrix} -1 & 0 \\ 0 & -1 \end{pmatrix}$
14. (a) $R_{90°}$    (b) no

## Exercise 21d

4. (a) $A'(2, 2)$; $B'(10, 2)$; $C'(8, 6)$; $D'(4, 6)$
   (b) 24 square units
5. $1\frac{1}{2}$ square units

6. (a) $-1\frac{1}{2}$; $(0,0)$　　(b) $\begin{pmatrix} -1\frac{1}{2} & 0 \\ 0 & -1\frac{1}{2} \end{pmatrix}$

(c) $13\frac{1}{2}$ square units

(d) $2\frac{1}{4} = (-1\frac{1}{2})^2$

7. (c) $\frac{9}{1}$　　(e) $\frac{1}{3}$; $(1,4)$

8. (c) 4　　(e) $(2,0)$; $\frac{1}{2}$

9. (d) $(3,0)$; $-2$

10. (a) $\begin{pmatrix} \frac{1}{2} & 0 \\ 0 & \frac{1}{2} \end{pmatrix}$　　(b) $\begin{pmatrix} 4 & 0 \\ 0 & 4 \end{pmatrix}$

(c) $\begin{pmatrix} 8 & 0 \\ 0 & 8 \end{pmatrix}$; $\begin{pmatrix} 0 & -2 \\ -2 & 0 \end{pmatrix}$

11. (a) $\frac{2}{1}$　　(b) $\frac{3}{1}$　　(c) $\frac{2}{1}$　　(d) $\frac{3}{1}$

(e) $\frac{1}{2}$

12. (a) $A'(2,1)$; $B'(10,1)$; $C'(8,3)$; $D'(4,3)$

(b) $\begin{pmatrix} \frac{1}{2} & 0 \\ 0 & 1 \end{pmatrix}$; $x$-stretch　　(c) ABCD

13. (b) $y$-stretch　　(c) enlargement $\begin{pmatrix} 2 & 0 \\ 0 & 2 \end{pmatrix}$

14. (a) $\begin{pmatrix} \dfrac{1}{k} & 0 \\ 0 & \dfrac{1}{k} \end{pmatrix}$　　(b) $\begin{pmatrix} \dfrac{1}{k} & 0 \\ 0 & 1 \end{pmatrix}$

(c) $\begin{pmatrix} 1 & 0 \\ 0 & \dfrac{1}{k} \end{pmatrix}$

## Miscellaneous Exercise 21

1. (b) (i) C　(ii) E　(iii) A　(iv) C　(v) A
2. (d) $-90°$ rotation, centre $(4,0)$
   (e) (iii) enlargement, scale factor $\frac{1}{2}$
3. (d) (ii) $270°$ rotation, centre $(0,0)$
4. (c) Reflection in $y$-axis
   (d) (ii) $180°$ rotation about origin
   (e) (ii) $B \cdot A = C$ (also $A \cdot B = C$)
5. (c) rotation of $180°$, centre $(-1,2)$
   (f) $y = x - 2$
6. (a) rotation about the origin of $120°$, $360°$, $300°$
   (b) $LM = R^2$; $ML = R^4$
   (c) $LMN$ is a reflection in $m$; $LML$ is a reflection in $n$
7. reflection in $x = -1\frac{1}{2}$
8. (a) (ii) rotation of $240°$
   (b) (ii) reflection in $m$
9. $(0,2)$, $90°$; $P'(-3,6)$, $Q'(-3,10)$, $R'(-5,6)$

## Exercise 22a

2. (a) $\begin{pmatrix} 4 \\ 5 \end{pmatrix}$　(b) $\begin{pmatrix} 1 \\ 7 \end{pmatrix}$　(c) $\begin{pmatrix} 6 \\ 0 \end{pmatrix}$　(d) $\begin{pmatrix} 3 \\ -6 \end{pmatrix}$

(e) $\begin{pmatrix} 0 \\ -6 \end{pmatrix}$　(f) $\begin{pmatrix} -2 \\ -7 \end{pmatrix}$

3.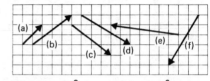

4. (a) $2.83$, $45°$　　(b) $5$, $37°$
   (c) $5$, $323°$　　(d) $5.83$, $329°$
   (e) $7.07$, $172°$　　(f) $5.83$, $239°$
5. (a) $13$, $67.4°$　　(b) $13$, $112.6°$
   (c) $13$, $247.4°$　　(d) $13$, $292.6°$
   (e) $13$, $22.6°$　　(f) $13$, $202.6°$
6. (a) $\begin{pmatrix} -3 \\ -2 \end{pmatrix}$　　(b) $3.61$　　(c) $3.61$

7. (a) $6.4$, $128.7°$　　(b) $12.8$, $128.7°$
   (c) $16.01$, $128.7°$; the vectors are parallel
8. $\mathbf{c} \parallel \mathbf{e}$

## Exercise 22b

3. $12.8$; $19.2$; $3.2$; $16.0$

4. $\begin{pmatrix} 4 \\ 3 \end{pmatrix}$

5. $\begin{pmatrix} -2 \\ 5 \end{pmatrix}$

6. $\begin{pmatrix} 2 \\ 8 \end{pmatrix}$

7. $\begin{pmatrix} 4 \\ 9 \end{pmatrix}$

8. $\begin{pmatrix} -4 \\ 5 \end{pmatrix}$

9. $\begin{pmatrix} 5 \\ 1 \end{pmatrix}$

10. $\begin{pmatrix} 2\frac{1}{2} \\ \frac{1}{2} \end{pmatrix}$

11. $\begin{pmatrix} -9 \\ -3 \end{pmatrix}$

12. $\begin{pmatrix} -7 \\ -18 \end{pmatrix}$

13. $\begin{pmatrix} 4 \\ \frac{1}{2} \end{pmatrix}$

14. $\begin{pmatrix} 21 \\ -2 \end{pmatrix}$

15. $\begin{pmatrix} -9 \\ 10 \end{pmatrix}$

16. 1
17. 3
18. $-2$ or 3
19. 2
20. $m = 0, n = 2$
21. $p = -2, q = 2$
22. $a = 2, b = 2$
23. $x = 3, y = 7$
24. $m = 3, n = 4$
25. $p = 1\frac{1}{2}, q = \frac{1}{4}$
26. $r = 0, s = 2$
27. $c = -2$
28. $x = 5$

### Exercise 22c

1. (a) $-a$    (b) $b-a$    (c) $a-b$
   (d) $2a+b$

2. (a) $b$    (b) $a$    (c) $a+b$
   (d) $b-a$    (e) $-b$    (f) $-a$
   (g) $-a-b$    (h) $a-b$

3. (a) $b-a$    (b) $d-b$    (c) $c-b$
   (d) $d-a$    (e) $a-d$    (f) $b-d$
   (g) $c-d$    (h) $-d$

4. (a) $b-a$    (b) $b-a$    (c) $-a$
   (d) $\frac{1}{2}b$    (e) $-\frac{1}{2}b$    (f) $\frac{1}{2}b-a$
   (g) $a-\frac{1}{2}b$

5. (a) $c$    (b) $a+c$    (c) $c-a$
   (d) $-a$    (e) $-c$    (f) $a-c$
   (g) $2(a-c)$    (h) $2a-c$    (i) $a-2c$
   (j) $a+c$

6. (a) $q-p$    (b) $\frac{3}{4}(q-p)$
   (c) $\frac{3}{4}q+\frac{1}{4}p$

7. (a) $2a$    (b) $2a+b$    (c) $b-a$
   (d) $a+b$; $\overrightarrow{OP}=\frac{1}{3}(2a+b)$; $1:2$

8. (a) $b$    (b) $b-2a$    (c) $\frac{2}{3}(b-2a)$
   (d) $\frac{2}{3}(a+b)$    (e) $2b-2a$    (f) $b-a$
   (g) $a+b$
   $2:1$; $\overrightarrow{OL}=a$; $\overrightarrow{BL}=a-2b$; $\overrightarrow{BA}=2a-2b$
   $\overrightarrow{BG}=\frac{2}{3}(a-2b)=\frac{2}{3}BL$

9. $\overrightarrow{AB}=b-a$; $\overrightarrow{MN}=3(b-a)$;
   $\overrightarrow{AX}=\frac{1}{4}(3b-a)$; $\overrightarrow{BX}=\frac{1}{4}(3a-b)$;
   $\overrightarrow{BM}=3a-b$

10. (a) $2v$    (b) $2v+z$    (c) $z-v$
    (d) $\frac{1}{3}(z-v)$
    (e) $v+\frac{1}{3}(z-v)=\frac{1}{3}(2v+z)=\frac{1}{3}\overrightarrow{OW}$

12. (a) $\overrightarrow{PQ}=a+2b$; $\overrightarrow{PR}=6a+12b$
    (c) PR and XZ are parallel; their ratio
    is $1:6$

### Miscellaneous Exercise 22

1. (a) 5    (b) 5    (c) 7.1; no
   (d) 3.5    (e) 5    (f) 13.0

2. (a) (i) $\begin{pmatrix} 16 \\ -12 \end{pmatrix}$ (ii) $\begin{pmatrix} -5 \\ 5\frac{1}{2} \end{pmatrix}$ (iii) $b=7, k=2$
   (b) $\overrightarrow{PQ}=q-p$; $\overrightarrow{OM}=\frac{1}{2}(p+q)$

3. (a) (ii) 6 cm
   (b) (i) $b+a$ (ii) $\frac{1}{3}(b+a)$ (iii) $b-a$
   (iv) $\frac{2}{3}a-\frac{1}{3}b$ (v) $\frac{4}{3}a-\frac{2}{3}b$

4. (a) $b-a$
   (b) (i) $2a$ (ii) $2b$ (iii) $2(b-a)$ (iv) $2:1$

5. (a) (i) $b-a$ (ii) $\frac{1}{2}a$ (iii) $b-\frac{1}{2}a$
   (iv) $\frac{1}{3}b$
   (c) $\frac{2}{3}a+\frac{1}{3}b$
   (d) $\frac{2}{3}b-\frac{2}{3}a$; $\frac{1}{3}a+\frac{2}{3}b$
   (e) $\frac{1}{3}a$    (f) $3:2:1$

6. (a) (i) $-p$ (ii) $p+q$ (iii) $p-q$
   $OU=\frac{1}{2}(p-q)$; $OV=\frac{1}{4}(p+q)$
   (b) $OS=u-v=\frac{1}{4}p-\frac{3}{4}q$
   (c) $p=u+2v$; $q=2v-u$; $OA=2u+v$
   $V$ . . . $A$
     . . .
   $O$   $U$

7. (a) (i) $b-a$ (ii) $\frac{3}{4}(b-a)$ (iii) $\frac{1}{4}(3b+a)$
   (iv) $2(b-a)$
   (b) (i) $40°$ (ii) $2\frac{1}{2}$

8. (a) $OB=a+c$; $OP=\frac{3}{4}(a+c)$;
   $AP=\frac{3}{4}c-\frac{1}{4}a$
   (b) $OQ=(1-\frac{1}{4}x)a+\frac{3}{4}xc$
   (c) $OQ=c+ya$
   (d) $x=1\frac{1}{3}$; $y=\frac{2}{3}$
   (e) $\frac{2}{1}$

9. (a) (i) $\mathbf{b}-\mathbf{a}$ (ii) $\frac{1}{4}(\mathbf{b}-\mathbf{a})$ (iii) $\frac{3}{4}\mathbf{a}+\frac{1}{4}\mathbf{b}$

   (b) (i) $\begin{pmatrix} 3 \\ 4 \end{pmatrix}$ (ii) $\sqrt{5}$ (iii) $(2,-1)$

     $5l+m=8; 3l+m=2; l=3, m=-7$

10. (a) $\mathbf{a}$                 (b) $\mathbf{a}-\mathbf{b}$
   (c) $2\mathbf{a}-\mathbf{b}; -\mathbf{b}+k\mathbf{a}; 3\mathbf{a}-\mathbf{b}$

8. (a) $\frac{35}{117}$   (b) $\frac{22}{117}$   (c) $\frac{19}{39}$

9. (a) $\frac{25}{81}$   (b) $\frac{16}{81}$   (c) $\frac{41}{81}$

10. (a) $\frac{2}{9}$   (b) $\frac{1}{6}$   (c) $\frac{1}{3}$

11. (a) $\frac{1}{4}$   (b) $\frac{3}{20}$   (c) $\frac{3}{10}$

12. (a) $\frac{20}{539}$   (b) $\frac{120}{539}$

## Exercise 23a

1. (a) $\frac{1}{6}$   (b) $\frac{1}{6}$   (c) $\frac{1}{2}$
2. $\frac{1}{5}$
3. (a) $\frac{1}{52}$   (b) $\frac{1}{13}$   (c) $\frac{1}{4}$
4. $\frac{1}{491}$
5. yes; $p(3 \text{ heads})$ must be less than 1
6. 1
7. 0
8. $\frac{17}{20}$
9. 0.9
10. 0.2
11. 0.05
12. $\frac{99}{100}$

## Exercise 23d

1. (a) $\frac{1}{36}$   (b) $\frac{5}{18}$   (c) $\frac{25}{36}$   (d) $\frac{11}{36}$
2. (a) $\frac{1}{4}$   (b) $\frac{1}{2}$   (c) $\frac{3}{4}$
3. (a) $\frac{1}{8}$   (b) $\frac{7}{8}$
4. $\frac{7}{16}$
5. $0.328; 0.672$
6. $\frac{64}{729}; \frac{665}{729}$
7. 0.65
8. $\frac{1}{2}; \frac{5}{9}; \frac{7}{9}$
9. $\frac{55}{62};$     (a) $\frac{55}{62}$   (b) $\frac{367}{620}$
10. (a) $\frac{47}{85}$   (b) $\frac{15}{17}$   (c) $\frac{997}{1700}$

## Exercise 23b

1. (a) $\frac{1}{2}$   (b) $\frac{2}{13}$
2. (a) $\frac{1}{3}$   (b) $\frac{1}{2}$
3. (a) $\frac{7}{12}$   (b) $\frac{7}{12}$   (c) $\frac{5}{6}$
4. $\frac{2}{5}$
5. $\frac{4}{25}$
6. (a) $\frac{1}{5}$   (b) $\frac{29}{100}$
7. $\frac{1}{2}$
8. $\frac{7}{12}$
9. $\frac{12}{35}; \frac{23}{35}$
10. $\frac{17}{24}$

## Exercise 23e

1.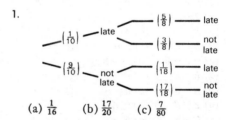

  (a) $\frac{1}{16}$   (b) $\frac{17}{20}$   (c) $\frac{7}{80}$

2.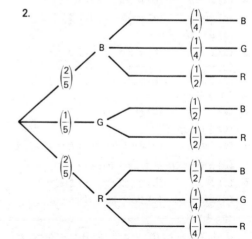

  (a) $\frac{2}{5}$   (b) $\frac{4}{5}$

## Exercise 23c

1. (a) $\frac{1}{36}$   (b) $\frac{1}{18}$
2. (a) $\frac{4}{663}$   (b) $\frac{8}{663}$
3. (a) $\frac{1}{8}$   (b) $\frac{3}{8}$
4. $\frac{8}{729}$
5. (a) $\frac{3}{64}$   (b) $\frac{9}{64}$
6. (a) $\frac{1}{36}$   (b) $\frac{1}{36}$
  (c) $\frac{1}{18}$; $5+4, 4+5, 6+3, 3+6; \frac{1}{9}$
7. (a) $\frac{1}{216}$   (b) $\frac{1}{216}$   (c) $\frac{5}{216}$   (d) $\frac{1}{72}$
  (e) $\frac{5}{72}$

**3.**

1st draw    2nd draw    3rd draw

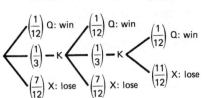

$\frac{13}{108}$

**4.**

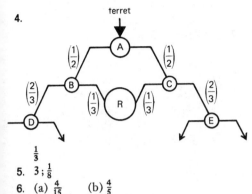

$\frac{1}{3}$

5. $3;\frac{1}{8}$
6. (a) $\frac{4}{15}$  (b) $\frac{4}{5}$

## Miscellaneous Exercise 23

1. (a) (ii) $\frac{2}{5}$  (b) 54
   (d) (i) $\frac{6}{25}$  (ii) $\frac{16}{25}$
   (e) $\frac{27}{125}$
2. (a) $\frac{1}{6}$  (b) $\frac{1}{6}$  (c) $\frac{1}{3}$  (d) $\frac{1}{3}$
   (e) $\frac{1}{36}$  (f) $\frac{1}{216}$
3. (a) KLM, LMK, MKL, MLK, LKM, KML
   (b) (i) $\frac{1}{6}$  (ii) $\frac{1}{3}$
4. (b) (i) $\frac{1}{5}$  (ii) $\frac{12}{25}$  (iii) 0
   (c) $\frac{1}{25}$  (d) $\frac{16}{25}$
5. (a) $1;\frac{1}{36}$  (b) $2;\frac{1}{18}$  (c) 7
6. (a) $\frac{1}{36}$  (b) $\frac{11}{36}$  (c) $\frac{1}{9}$  (d) $\frac{1}{1296}$
   (e) $\frac{7}{432}$
7. (a) $\frac{5}{36}$  (b) $\frac{1}{12}$  (c) $\frac{1}{6}$
8. (a) (i) $\frac{4}{5}$  (ii) $\frac{1}{60}$  (iii) $\frac{2}{5}$  (iv) $\frac{3}{5}$
   (b)

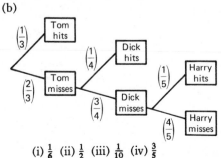

   (i) $\frac{1}{6}$  (ii) $\frac{1}{2}$  (iii) $\frac{1}{10}$  (iv) $\frac{3}{5}$

9. $\frac{2}{3}$  (a) $\frac{4}{9}$  (b) $\frac{5}{9}$  (c) $\frac{1}{40}$
   (d) $\frac{11}{40}$; 203
10. (a) $\frac{3}{8}$  (b) $\frac{1}{4}$  (c) $\frac{5}{8}$  (d) $\frac{3}{64}$
    (e) $3;\frac{1}{64}$

## Exercise 24a

1. (i) 4 (ii) 2 and 4 (iii) 4
2. (i) 5 (ii) 3 (iii) 4
3. (i) 8 (ii) 9 (iii) 9
4. (i) 2 (ii) no mode (iii) 1
5. (i) 53.2 (ii) no mode (iii) 53.1
6. (i) 105 (ii) 104 (iii) $104\frac{1}{2}$
7. $57\frac{1}{2}\%$
8. The workers are using the mode; the boss is using the mean
9. 12
10. 7.6
11. 3, 3, 5, 7
12. 6
13. 11
14. 4
15. 2
16. 135; 96; 7.7
17. 10.2
18. 54
19. $19\frac{2}{3}$
20. 11
21. (i) 195 (ii) 19
22. 0
23. 17 years and 7 months

## Exercise 24b

1. (a) 0 and 3  (b) 5  (c) 4.42
2. (a) 5  (b) 5  (c) 4.73
3. (a) 3.5  (b) 3  (c) 3
4. (a) 5  (b) 5  (c) 5
5. (a) $1\frac{1}{3}$  (b) 0  (c) 1
6. (a) 1  (b) 2  (c) 1.98
7. (a) 6  (b) 7  (c) 7.6
8.

| Score | 0 | 1 | 2 | 3 | 4 | 5 |
|---|---|---|---|---|---|---|
| $f$ | 14 | 13 | 13 | 9 | 3 | 2 |

mode = 0
9. (a) 3  (b) 4  (c) 3.7  (d) 3.6
10. $2.2; m = 1.9$

11. Mid-point 3

| $x$ | $f$ | $fx$ |
|----|----|-----|
| 3 | 11 | 33 |
| 8 | 12 | 96 |
| 13 | 15 | 195 |
| 18 | 9 | 162 |
| 23 | 3 | 69 |
| | 50 | 555 |

mean = 11.1

12. 12.56
13. (a) 10; 12; 11

(b)

| Marks | $f$ |
|-------|-----|
| 1–4 | 2 |
| 5–8 | 8 |
| 9–12 | 13 |
| 13–16 | 6 |
| 17–20 | 2 |

mean = 10.24

14. 10.7
15. 16.2
16. 12.1

## Exercise 25a

1. (a) (i) 1    (ii) 2    (b) 30; 53; 1.77
3. 45%; 61.2°
4. 27 min
5. £3640 m
6. (a) (i) 20%  (ii) 28%  (iii) 32%
7. (a) 4%    (b) 18°    (c) £1 520 000
   (d) 3:2    (e) £25 000

8. area ratios $1:2^2:4^2$ i.e. $1:4:16$
9. volume ratios $1:2^3$ i.e. $1:8$
10. neither; distorted scales chosen to give wrong impression

## Exercise 25b

1. (i) (a) 10, 20, 5    (b) 10, 20, 10
   (c) 2; mode = 1.9
   (ii) (a) 1, 3, 4, 1.6    (b) 5, 15, 10, 12
   (c) 10–12.5; mode = 10.75
2. (a) $2 \leqslant x < 3$    (b) 2.3
3. (a) 2    (b) 1.7
4. (a) 15    (b) 15.1
5. (a) 115–117.5    (b) 116
6. (a) 10–12    (b) 10.25
7. (a) 10–14    (b) 11.2
8. (a) 5    (b) 4.95
9. (a) 10–19    (b) 14.5

## Exercise 25c

1. (c) (i) 176  (ii) $174\frac{1}{2}$  (iii) 179  (iv) 175
   (d) $4\frac{1}{2}$
2. (c) (i) 24  (ii) 18  (iii) 28  (iv) 21
   (d) 10
3. (c) (i) $10\frac{1}{2}$  (ii) $8\frac{1}{2}$  (iii) 12  (iv) $9\frac{1}{2}$
   (d) $3\frac{1}{2}$
4. (b) 49    (c) 45    (d) 74
5. (a) 25    (b) 5, 44
6. (a) 23 200
   (b) (i) 770  (ii) 56  (iii) $\frac{7}{50}$

# INDEX

KIZILKAZ